TO: Terr[...]

God Bless youl

Charles Wahamon
Whitt

LEGACY

LEGACY

THE DAYS OF DAVID CROCKETT WHITT

BY

COLONEL CHARLES DAHNMON WHITT

JESSE STUART FOUNDATION
ASHLAND, KENTUCKY
2008

Dedicated to

My late Father Marvin Bertran Whitt,
who always had faith in my abilities, and instilled in me
the need to follow the Lord Jesus Christ.

My Wife Sharon Cogan Whitt,
who has always believed in me and supported my efforts.

My Brother Larry Paxton Whitt,
who advised, encouraged, and edited for me.

FIRST EDITION

Copyright © 2008 by Col. Charles Dahnmon Whitt

Published By:
Jesse Stuart Foundation
1645 Winchester Avenue
Ashland, KY 41101
(606) 326-1667 • JSFBOOKS.com

CONTENTS

PREFACE

One day, in the hills of Montgomery County Virginia, a baby was born. This day was December 13, 1836, the same year that the Alamo fell. Some famous American died at the battle of the Alamo. Jonas and Susannah Whitt, the Father and Mother of this new baby were well aware of this famous American. They would name their baby after the brave man who died at the Alamo. This new little person will be known from then on as David Crockett Whitt.

This collection of information will be about David Crockett Whitt and his family, his travels, his hard times, and his adventures. I will be as accurate as possible, but I will add my thoughts to fill in missing information. This will be History with a little fiction mingled in to keep you awake.

Chapter 1

In the Beginning

The middle of December, in Montgomery County is cold and windy. Not a problem for these hardy people. In these days there was no indoor plumbing; Cabins were heated with wood that was cut to fit the grates in the open fire places. All the cooking and baking was done around the fire. This was also a special place for the family to gather on those cold days. Jonas and his older sons John Bunyon, and James Griffith Whitt had stored in plenty of fire wood for this winter.

Susannah had been a mother six times before, but every birth in these days was hard.

Jonas was a house builder and also a millwright. Also he as did all the early people of the region, raise large gardens, raise hogs, chickens, and cattle.

This day was different than most days, Susannah knew it was time. She had felt the stinging pain of labor begin.

"Jonas, Jonas, would you send John to get the midwife," Susannah requested?

She expressed that she wanted everybody out of the house except Rachel and Rhoda the 16 year old twins. They are practically grown women; they should be able to help when Martha gets here.

She told Jonas to go about your work, it will be some time before the baby gets here, and you will just be in the way. So the men folk went to their duties, each a little apprehensive as to what was taking place on this day.

When would the baby come, would it be a boy or a girl?

The twins fixed up the bed just the way Susannah prescribed. They put an oil cloth under the thin blanket, and provided several prop up pillows. Then they got another thin quilt to put over Susannah for warmth and privacy. Next they gathered clean rags that had been saved just for this day. They also got a bucket of water and poured it in the boiling pot on the fire. Two other items would be provided if they were needed, a jug of corn liquor and a nice smooth piece of wood to bite on.

Next day December 14th 1836 was also a different kind of a day, but with worry subsided. Susannah was a mother again, a happy woman, but very worn and weak. She was in a freshly cleaned bed with a little boy at her breast.

The children were all glad that they could gather around mother and new born. Susannah would spend the bigger part of a week in this bed. It was the custom in those days for a new mother to have a weeks rest after giving birth.

The twins, Rhoda and Rachel would be in charge of cooking and taking care of the household. This would be good training and a confidence builder for the girls.

Jonas has been hunting and also doing a little carpenter work for a neighbor.

John Bunyon and James Griffith Whitt were taking care of the normal chores such as feeding the animals, bringing in the fire wood, and also doing some hunting.

The family would have a good Christmas this year and a lot to be thankful for. There was plenty of food laid up. They had killed a corn fed hog, they had corn, pickled beans, pickled beets; also they had holed up yams, potatoes, and a few apples. They also had pumpkins and squash.

Along with all of this bounty the men folk had brought in some rabbits, squirrels, and a good shot by young James Griffith brought down a nice Tom Turkey.

They had a small but warm cabin. But the most important thing they had to be thankful for was Susannah and little David Crockett Whitt were both healthy and doing fine.

The smell of smoke and food cooking filled the families little cabin home. This was a delight

The country was still young at this time; it had gone through Indian wars, two wars with the mother country Great Britain. Still there were great differences between Virginia and some of the Northern States.

Virginia as did other Southern States thought of them selves as small countries. It is true all the states pulled together and defeated the most powerful nation on Earth. Virginia held tight to the idea of self government, and states rights.

Even Hezekiah and the Reverend Richard Whitt had fought for this state and country. These two men are the father and grand father of Jonas Whitt. Grand Paw Hezekiah had received a land grant from the State of Virginia for his service in the war of Independence. The grant of land was west many miles from Montgomery County. It was in a very large county called Russell. It was on a creek called Indian, which fed the upper Clinch River.

This area was a wild and wonderful land. It was big valleys of rolling hills nestled between great majestic mountains. At this time in history there was still some wild animals such as wolves, bears, a few panthers, deer, turkey, wild cats, all types of small game and in the Clinch were catfish, small mouth bass, sunfish, and horny heads. In the mountain streams like Clear Fork and Wolf Creek rainbow and brook trout could be caught. This is one of the most beautiful areas in Virginia and really in the whole United States.

The Jonas Whitt family would spend some time here in Montgomery County, but would pull up roots and follow Hezekiah to the Promised Land, the land Hezekiah had earned as a soldier in the Virginia Militia.

Here it is the middle of March and the field is not plowed, they had a lot of snow and rain this year. Looks like the ground will dry enough to plow soon. Potatoes should be planted by Saint Patrick Day, to have a good crop. Also a lettuce bed needed to be made ready. Onions sets can be set out in about a month. The cash crop will have to have attention also. A tobacco bed will have to be prepared, so the seeds can be planted. Corn, beans, and most other seed will have to wait until the tenth of May to be planted.

The cows will be calving any time. The chickens should start laying eggs again after taking off the winter. The Jonas Whitt family has plans and plenty to do.

Tazewell County, the new county established from Russell county, was their new promised land.

Crops will be harvested as quick as possible and the Jonas Whitt family will go to the Promised Land. Hezekiah has land in this beautiful part of western Virginia, which he will sell some to his sons for the price of one dollar.

By late summer little Crockett and Susannah will be able to travel. Excitement is in the air, even though the trip is a few months off. Jonas will work on some mills and do some house building to get traveling money. The boys will do most of the farm work while Jonas works in his trade. Grist mill work is needed for the expanding Virginia.

Hopefully there will be mills to build and also houses should be needed. Jonas should have plenty of good work in Tazewell County. There is a nice little town getting started there called Jeffersonville.

I mentioned Archibald Whitt. He is the brother to Hezekiah; I believe he ended up staying around Montgomery County even though some of his children would move west to the Clinch valley. Archibald married his wife Hannah D. Brewster in Montgomery County.

The Reverend Richard P. Whitt Sr. preformed the marriage ceremony as of most in the county of Montgomery. The Reverend Richard was the farther of both Hezekiah and Archibald. The children of Archibald were Abijah Whitt born 1791, Susannah Whitt born 1794, A son named Hezekiah born 1796, James Whitt born 1792, Hannah Jane Whitt, born 1806, Milburn Whitt born 1805, Rachel Whitt born 1785, Rhoda Whitt born 1787, and John Floyd Whitt born in 1816. One thing I have noticed is the Whitt's like naming their children after relatives. If you read this entire book you will see what I mean.

By doing Genealogy you find out all kinds of things about your family. One thing I discovered is shocking in today's world. In my family as well as in many other families a lot of cousins were wed.

I might as well let out the big secret, Jonas Whitt married his first cousin Susannah Whitt the daughter of Archibald. Oh my, are the kids alright? Not a dummy among them, and all have ten fingers and ten toes. I have seen this in many early marriages and in many families.

I guess Jonas loved Susannah and Susannah loved Jonas. After all the only people around in the sparse settled country in the early years of the nineteenth century were kin folks.

When there were two families living near by each other, the men of one family would marry the ladies of the other family and Vice Versa. This sometimes created double cousins.

All right, back to the farm. Spring has come and gone, summer is almost over. All kinds of preparation are going on. Things to do, get in the crops in as soon as possible, line up buyers for the corn, tobacco, almost all the animals, house, farm, furniture.

The tobacco may have to be sold in the field. Only the bare necessities will be taken to the new and exciting home in the Clinch valley.

The Whitt family needed to turn everything into cash, traveling and getting set up in a new land will take cash.

They will have to travel horse back, or walk the whole long way. Only trails and paths lead to the western part of Virginia. There are some mountains in Tazewell county that exceed 4000 feet in elevation. Hopefully gaps can be found. There will be homes and stations along the way. Hopefully people will be kind to the travelers, giving advice, and directions. Also lodging and food can be available along the way but not always when you would like it.

Also in western Virginia there can be dangers, robbers and outlaws sometimes take advantage of travelers. Wild animals can cause havoc. Accidents could take life or limb.

Doctors and law officers are far and few between. Travelers had to have a savvy of nature and good common sense. They will be at the mercy of outlaws, storms, and Mother Nature. They learned to survive by wit and a faith in God. Most of the early people in this era had a deep faith in their Creator. After all The Whitt Matriarch, John Witt (Whitt) came to this country in 1659 as a Huguenot. He was looking for a place to Worship God in freedom.

CHAPTER 2

THE JOURNEY BEGINS

The time of preparation is almost gone. It will take about four or five weeks on the trail to get to Hezekiah's home in Tazewell County. The time has come and the Whitt's head south west toward Wythe the first leg of the journey.

The mules are loaded down, the horses will carry the younger children and of course Susannah and young David Crockett Whitt. The older boys and the twins will help drive the live stock, along with Jack the family dog. Jonas and the boys John Bunyon, and James Griffith all carry their Brown Betsey Muskets.

A great adventure awaits the Whitt family. Everything Jonas and his family own is on the trial, and a prayer has been prayed before the first step was taken. The Whitt's are God fearing people of the Baptist faith.

Jonas' Grand Father and Great Grand Father were both Baptist Ministers. Even John Witt, Jones' Great Great Grand Father was a man of God who sailed to America to enjoy freedom of religion.

He was a French Huguenot, before coming to Charles City, Virginia in 1659. Some people spelled his name Witt, others spelled it Whitt. Johns father Robert's name was spelled Whytt.

It is sort of a gloomy day to start the trip, but spirits are high as the Whitt's move along the trail.

They only have to go through one county to reach Tazewell County. This statement is misleading .The counties boundaries have changed greatly in the last one hundred years. Montgomery County was large, the next county was Wythe also very large. Next was Russell and Washington in the year 1792.

By 1800 Tazewell, Grayson, and Lee counties had been carved out of the other counties. By 1820 Giles and Scott counties were taken from the bigger counties. The trip the Whitt's were taking would go through land that would have later been called Pulaski County. The entire Trip would be about 140 rugged mountain miles.

Later the Counties of Tazewell and Russell would give up land to form Wise, Buchanan, McDowell, and Dickinson Counties. Also Carroll was formed from Grayson County.

Many thoughts went into the planning of this trip; every thing was packed in a way that the most used items would be easy to access. Oiled skins were on hand to keep out the rain when it would surely come. Also an oiled piece of hide was on hand to cover the flint and strike pan of the Muskets.

The lean-to canvas, cooking pots, and food were packed to be handy. Dried jerked beef, parched corn, and fruit were some food that could be eaten as the Whitt Family moved along.

Jonas led the little party along through the high weeds, and small bushes that continually try to reclaim the sparse trails. They wound up and down and followed the game trails and the man made trails. Many of these trails had been used for years by the Native Americans on hunting trips or by war parties the Indians carved out.

Thank God the Indians were mostly peaceable or had moved to the far west by this time. Gods beautiful art work and creation could be seen all about them.

As they traveled along many birds and animals showed them selves for a very short time up ahead, sometimes on the side and if you looked back you may get a glimpse of a woodland creature.

A fresh source of meat was always at hand for a sure shot Whitt. Usually small game was taken, such as squirrel, rabbit, possom, coon, turkey, grouse, or even a ground hog.

Late summer even presented berries, fruits, and nuts. Yesterday they camped by a large creek which provided some fine food. They set throw lines at bed time and this morning they had a large catfish, two big red eyes, and a small mouth bass.

Fish were always welcome as a needed change of diet. The Boys grubbed out a few worms and uncovered some bugs for bait. James Griffith had a big surprise when he flipped over a big flat rock; out rolled a very big copperhead snake.

A couple well aimed fist sized rocks done in Mr. Snake. A bite from this fellow could very well do you in. Mountain diamond backs had to be avoided also. Some of these large poisonous snakes could be seven feet long and about eight inches in diameter. It's good that they were not a daily occurrence.

Last night just after everyone had bedded down, a scream sounded from the near by woods. It sounded almost like a woman screamed. The goose bumps jumped up on all in the camp.

Jonas said, "don't worry it is only a Panther on the prowl." He told the family that his father Hezekiah told many stories about the big cats. As long as we have a fire and stay together there is nothing to worry about.

Another large fellow that roams these mountains is the muscular black bear. Bears are not usually a threat unless they have cubs, or are injured in some way. Jonas always said that any creature that is cornered will fight and can be very dangerous.

Even though in the year of 1837 some of the native animals of the western woodland of Virginia have vanished to the far west, every now and then you hear of some elk, or even a woods buffalo. The mountains were home to many white tail deer.

As the Whitt's traveled along toward Wythe, Ol 'Jack started barking, as they came up on three rough looking men headed east.

Jonas was on alert, but the men meant no harm. The men had been coming down the Ohio river when their boat was overturned in a fierce wind storm. They had lost almost all of their supplies and nearly gave up their lives, they told Jonas. The Whitt's shared supper with them and gave them a few meager supplies.

Jonas couldn't help but ask about the mighty Ohio River.

"Is it a mile wide like so many have said?" Jonas asked.

"Naw it aint that big, but she's mighty wide," said one of the three.

"How did you fellows wind up here in this area?" asked Jonas.

"Wells we figgered, walk toward the rising sun and east bound to get back to a town sommers." one replied.

"Wheres you-uns headed fer; go-un west?" another one asked.

Jonas explained they were to meet up with his father and other family near a new town called Jeffersonville.

"We uns not heard of that place, seems like all we do is climb up and down these here mountains," said one of the three.

"If wees didn't know bout sit-un snars and knows bout fish-un, wees would have starved plum to death," one declared.

"Good thing its summer, fer if it had a been winner we sure woulda froze," Another one said.

"We believe in the Creator and we talks to him regular; Thanks to God wees be here today," they confessed.

Jonas said, "we also believe in God and we put our faith in Him to take care of us."

"You boys sleep here by our fire tonight and we will part in the morning," Jonas said.

"My son John will keep watch so the rest of us can get a good nights rest," Jonas said.

"A few days journey and you will start seeing towns and get back to where ever you want to go," Jonas added.

"Wees sure glad we uns run into you Whitt's; we uns might make it yet," one said.

"We started out from the hills of Penns-a-vania, and were aiming to go out twards one of them western place's, maybe Texas," one said.

"We all three are brothers, our Paw and Maw both died on us," one said.

"Gran Paw came over from the old country; I think about Germany," one said.

"We uns never learned to talk that fern stuff; we uns natural born mericans," said another. Our name is Hession or something like that so we jest goes by Hess.

The morning sun was rising fast; John built up the fire, and woke everyone. He laid back down to snooze for about an hour, while breakfast was cooking and the family prepared to travel.

The Hess men ate with the Whitt's and Jonas gave them a good farewell. They headed east.

Jonas got John up, and John ate a quick breakfast.

The Whitts were moving down the trail again, talking as they went.

"Jonas did you hear them Hess brothers ask James Griffith where our slaves were?" asked Susannah.

"No I didn't hear that, why did they think we had slaves?" asked Jonas.

"Them Hess fellows said they thought all the folks down south were rich and had plenty of slaves to do the work," answered Susannah.

"Well those boys have plenty to learn about Virginia, don't they Susannah?" asked Jonas.

"How's little Crockett fairing, haven't heard a peep out of that young fellow this morning?" asked Jonas.

"He's doing fine; you can almost see him grow," Susannah answered.

"We should be getting close to the berg of Wytheville," Jonas said.

"We should be able to get a few supplies there before we head north toward Rocky Gap," Jonas added.

"I hope we can stay over night at an Inn," Susannah said, "a bath for every one, especially the women folks will be most welcome."

"A night's sleep in a bed might feel pretty good too," replied Jonas.

"I hope they can accommodate us," was the answer from Susannah.

After two more days traveling, Jonas said as he topped the hill; "I can see smoke from the town."

Every one had a grin on their face when they heard these words.

It wasn't really a big town; it was a wide place in the trail with a few scattered cabins and some more modern buildings, a little church, a stable, a general store, post office and a court house. Yes there was an Inn and tavern. The Inn was up stairs over the tavern. This place was the center of every thing in Wythe County. The little church served also as a school. Wytheville was the county seat and had a nice court house, for all county business.

As the Whitt party came in to town a couple of the towns people came out on the street to meet them. It was a big thing to get visitors in western Virginia.

An older gentleman by the name of Elkins was the first to speak to the travelers.

"Welcome folks, How you doing? Been on the trail long? Where you coming from? Where you heading?"

"Whoa there mister, One question at a time," Jonas responded.

"We are the Whitt's from Montgomery County," Jonas said.

"We are a little worn, point us to the Inn, please," Jonas

continued.

"Paw, I see stable and corral over there," John Bunyon said.

The other man that came over with Mr. Elkins was a Mullins.

Mr. Mullins spoke up and said, "I run the Store over there; can I help you folks with any thing?" he asked.

Jonas replied, "we may need a few things before we leave."

Mr. Mullins spoke once again, "I mean can I help you get settled in for the night, help with the animals or unpacking?"

"Thanks Mr. Mullins, we will be fine," answered Jonas.

"Mr. Elkins, What do you do around here?" Jonas said to the older man.

Mr. Elkins spoke up laughing, "I am the official greeter in Wytheville."

"I do a little blacksmithing and leather work" he added.

He pointed and said," I'm set up over there behind the stable in that old shed."

"Thank you gentlemen; for the welcome, now pardon me for a minute so I can get a room at the Inn so the women can get settled, little Crockett is a bit worn too," Jonas said.

"It seems that babies can handle joshling on a horse back better than grown folks." added Jonas.

"Let me introduce you to the inn keeper, and I will let you folks get settled," replied Mister Elkins.

"His name is Tanner, He is a good fellow, but some folks think he is not real friendly," replied Mister Elkins.

"He does keep order in his Tavern and Inn," He added.

"That will be fine," Jonas said, "let's go in and meet Mr. Tanner."

Mr. Tanner was a big burly man with a full beard and barrel chest.

Elkins spoke up first, "this is Mr. Whitt from Montgomery County, and they need some rooms."

Mr. Tanner looked at Jonas and said, "welcome sir to Wytheville."

"Thank you Mr. Tanner," replied Jonas.

"Now about them rooms, do you have two rooms, and can you provide baths for the lady folks?" Jonas asked.

"Yes I do have two rooms and we can start heating up the bath water right away," replied Mister Tanner.

"After you get settled in you are welcome to come back in the tavern for a drink and conversation," Mister Tanner said.

"I might just do that," Jonas replied.

Mr. Elkins spoke up again, "Can I take you over to the stable and get your animals settled in also?"

"Yes, Just as soon as I can get the ladies in their room," replied Jonas.

Mr. Tanner spoke up once again, "We have pretty good fare here for supper if you all want to eat later."

Things were shaping up pretty good for a good visit and rest in Wytheville.

After all the animals were fed, watered, and tended to, Jonas was next for a bath.

Susannah, Rhoda, Rachel, Elizabeth and Emma, were refreshed and were happy for a bath, a bed, and some relief from the trail.

Jonas said, "my bath was nice also, first one I had for about a month, an all over bath that is," added Jonas.

Even the Boys got one, they were not too impressed!

The whole family went down to eat supper. Brown beans, fried potatoes, corn on the cob, and a piece of fried pork made a dandy meal. Butter milk and coffee was the drink. For desert an apple cobbler was served.

"This is a meal fit for a king," exclaimed Susannah.

It was really nice not to cook on the trail, with all the packing and un-packing. After all were full, the family all but Jonas went up to the room to get ready for bed.

Jonas went over to a table where some gentlemen were sitting.

"Have a seat and join us for drink," replied one of them.

Jonas joined the men, and fired up his pipe.

He ordered a whiskey and said, "this is the life."

"I only regret it will be short lived," Jonas said.

"We got to get back on the trail in the morning," Jonas added.

"Where you headed for Mr. Whitt?" one of the men asked.

"We are moving to the new County of Tazewell," Jonas answered.

One of the men said, "been through there back years ago, scouting for Indians."

"Nice country, big mountains with rolling hills in between," he said.

"The Clinch River starts out there," he added.

"Two forks, one close to Jeffersonville, the other fork called Little River comes right out of the ground at Maiden Springs," he said.

"How is the ground there?" asked Jonas.

"What do you mean?" he asked.

"Is it rich and good for crops?" asked Jonas.

"Oh yes, one place south east of Jeffersonville, in the Clinch Valley the land is so rich, they even call it that," he continued.

"Call it what?" asked Jonas.

"Rich-lands," was his reply.

"It sounds like almost heaven to me," said Jonas.

"Are you a farmer, or do you have a trade also?" one of the men asked.

"Well I farm some, but I am a house builder, and a millwright," replied Jonas..

"Millwright you say?" he asked.

"Yes I build and work on Grist Mills," Jonas said.

"That is very interesting, how on earth do you get all those moving parts to work, anyway?" one man asked.

"It's not all that bad, once you learn about it," said Jonas.

"I hope I can find some work in Tazewell County," Jonas added.

"They will need a fellow like you, always a need for houses, and mills," one man added.

"You got any kin over that way Whitt?" he asked.

"Yes I do, my father Hezekiah Whitt lives there," said Jonas.

"Hezekiah, I heard about him; I heard he was way up in the county government," he said.

"Heard he helped set up Tazewell County, Governor Henry appointed him and eight other fellows to organize the county," he continued.

"Well you Whitts will have a good start there with your father being Hezekiah," he said.

"We are not looking for a hand out mister," Jonas said strongly.

"Didn't mean it quite that way, all I'm saying is it doesn't hurt to know people in high places," he said.

"Well I guess I can agree with that," said Jonas.

"Well gentlemen, we have talked about me, now what do you do around here," Jonas asked?

Jim White spoke up, "I got a farm bout two miles from here, I come in about once a week for supplies and some conversation."

"Like to know the news, you know! "said Jim White.

William Whitten spoke up next, "I got a piece of ground too, I like coming to town to get a drink and listen to the folks talk."

Whitten said, "Jonas, my name just about the same name as Whitt."

"Yelp, we are probable kin way back in the old country, guess we will never know," replied Jonas.

The third man spoke up, "I'm Jim Kiser, I got a farm also bout three miles out, I too come in so I can to hear whats going on."

"Mister Whitt what is the news back your way?" asked Jim.

"Don't know much news," Jonas said.

"I heard that the North is fixxin to add tax to what ever we Southerners send out of the country, but not what they send," Jonas added.

"That is not right," replied Jim.

"Not only that, they are some folks up north trying to stir up a mess about slaves," added Jonas.

"I ain't got any but some folks in the south do," Jonas said.

"Some folks up north has them too," replied William.

"It ain't no Yankee's business what we southern people do," argued Jonas.

"Well I agree with you Jonas," said Jim Whitten.

"I got a few, but they are just like part of my family," Jim added.

"Well some folks are always butting in where they don't belong, I guess," said Jonas.

"I also heard that they want to build canals all over the country, so we can ship goods every where," Jonas said.

"That's about all I heard," Jonas added.

"Oh I did run into three Hess men on the trail a few days back, they were about starved, said they lost their supplies in a boat accident on the Ohio River and been traveling east ever since," Jonas said.

"Why did they come out this way?" asked William.

"They said if they went east they were bound to find people sometime," Jonas replied.

"Where they from, and what were were they up to?" William asked.

"Pennsylvania is where they started from, said they were heading west, maybe all the way to Texas," Jonas told them.

"People do strange things when they have trouble," William said.

"Gentlemen, I have enjoyed your company, but I guess I had better get up to my room," Jonas said.

"I do have one question before I go, have you been up the trail to Rocky Gap?" asked Jonas.

"Sure, there is even a road part of the way," William said."

"Its rough but it is still the best way to go," William added.

"It is near impossible to take a family straight across some of our mountains, always go for a gap when you are in the mountains," added William.

"Keep an eye out up there close to the Gap, I hear some outlaws hang out there and pounce on un-suspecting folks," William instructed.

"Folks came here back in the spring from there, they reported being robbed and roughed up some what," Jim said.

"The sheriff took some men up there but never found even a sign of them," Jim added.

"We will be watching for trouble," said Jonas.

"Thanks men for everything," Jonas added.

"Thank you Jonas, for the news; good night," William said.

As Jonas came into their room, Susannah said, "Jonas look at little Crockett, he is standing up here holding on to the bed."

"Trying to walk kinda early; ain't he?" asked Jonas.

"I guess he's tired of me holding him so much as we travel," Susannah said.

"Probably makes him sore, I know it does me," she added.

"Well I'm ready for a good night's sleep," Jonas replied.

"Susannah how is the bed, seen any bugs yet?" Jonas asked.

"No but the ropes need tightened a little," Susannah said.

"Well if we can stand it I'm not going to tighten up the bed this time of evening," replied Jonas.

"I will just say this, sleep tight, and don't let the bed bugs bite," said Susannah.

Morning came quickly to the tired Whitt family, Jonas slept extra hard, the shot of whiskey and the good bed aided his rest.

When He put his feet on the floor, his first words were, "It doesn't take long to stay all night in Wytheville".

"I know what you mean, even the children slept like logs," Susannah said with a laugh.

"We better get moving, day lights a wasting, we got a long way to go today," added Susannah.

Jonas and the boys jumped into their clothes and headed for the stable.

Mr. Elkins greeted them, "how did you folks sleep?"

"Real good Mister Elkins," Jonas answered.

"Now we got to get ready for the trail, got to pack the animals and be ready to move as soon as we eat breakfast," added Jonas.

"You heading toward Rocky Gap, I guess?" asked Mister Elkins.

"Yes that seems the best way to avoid crossing straight over the mountains," Jonas said.

"You are right about that, I just wanted to give you a little warning about it," said Mister Elkins.

"What's that Mister Elkins?" Jonas asked.

"Some times bandits hang around the gap, waiting to way lay unsuspecting folks," warned Mister Elkins.

"I have heard that, we will be ready for them if they try," replied Jonas.

"We have three Brown Betsy's, and a six shot cap and ball pistol; any body wanting to hurt my family will have a cap busted on their ass," Jonas said strongly!

"Good for you, Mister Whitt, I am glad you are prepared," replied Mister Elkins.

"Take the Lord with you," added Mister Elkins.

"We always do, we pray every morning before we start out," Jonas said.

"That is wonderful," said Mister Elkins.

By now the women were dressed and packed. Rachel and Rhoda carried the bags to the stable so Jonas could get them on the pack animals.

"Is your Maw bout ready for breakfast?" Jonas asked.

"Yes she is, she is feeding little Crockett and will meet us at the tavern for breakfast," answered Rhoda.

"Alright boys, that is about all we can do until we get started," Jonas said

"Animal's fed, watered, packed, Jonas added.

"The cows, pigs, and sheep are ready to get out of the corral, and I am ready to eat," replied John Bunyon Whitt.

"Let's go eat," Jonas replied.

"The Whitt's gathered around one of the big family sized tables, ready to eat.

Mister Tanner came up.

"Mister Whitt you all ready for breakfast?" asked Mister Tanner?

"Yes sir, Mister Tanner, what's for breakfast," Jonas asked?

"We have coffee and fresh milk to drink, and cat head biscuits, fried taters, gravy, salt bacon, fresh eggs, and a big red tomato if you would like," said Mister Tanner.

"Also I got fresh honey and some of Mrs. Tanners black berry jam," he added.

"Sounds good, bring it on Mister Tanner, we are ready," replied Jonas.

The smell of the food cooking had already tantalized the appetites and all were ready for the treat of kitchen prepared food. Everyone ate to the pleasure of fullness.

"We better get going before we all want to take a nap," said Susannah.

"You all head for the stable, I will settle up with Mister Tanner, and be right behind you," replied Jonas.

Finally the little Whitt party was heading north toward Rocky Gap, every step bringing them closer to Jeffersonville and their new home.

"In a few days we will pass through the gap," Jonas said to the Boys.

"Start paying attention for trouble," Jonas added.

"Trouble Paw?" asked John.

"Yes John, the two legged kind, don't worry the women folk, just be ready this week for any thing," instructed Jonas.

"I'm not worried Paw," said James Griffith, "we prayed and I know the Lord will deliver us from the wicked."

"Yes you are right, but God still wants us to be ready for any trouble," Jonas replied.

"Oh! I know," answered James.

"Wonder how it will be in Tazewell county?" asked James.

"Wonder how Grand Paw Hezekiah is doing?" asked John.

"It won't be too awful long, before you can see for yourself," said Jonas.

"Keep them pigs up with the cows, and pay attention to what is going on around you," Jonas instructed.

Jonas moved to the head of the party, James Griffith was in the middle pushing the live stock, and his brother John Bunyon stayed at the rear as a rear guard. Rachel and Rhoda helped drive the stock with James Griffith.

First day went by good with out any problems or concerns.

Rhoda kept saying, " Paw we have been going up hill since we left Wytheville."

"Well little girl, we have to climb this mountain until we hit Rocky Gap," Jonas said.

"Be glad we don't have to cross straight over the mountain," Jonas added.

Even though the family got rest at Wytheville they were tiring fast with the steady climb toward Rocky Gap. They stoped beside a good mountain spring for the night.

Jonas told John to set on a rock and keep watch while the rest of the family did the chores of the camp.

"Keep a good watch son, yell if you see any one approaching," Jonas commanded.

"We don't want any surprises," Jonas said.

"Remember what I told you about the gap area," he added.

"I think it's a good idea that we keep someone on watch round the clock, until we are well over on the other side of the gap," said Jonas.

The fire was built, and Rachel and Rhoda had a meal ready in short order.

The family gathered round and Jonas prayed a prayer of thanksgiving, and also a petition for safety. After the prayer every one was more at ease.

That night even Rachel and Rhoda took their turn on watch. They were both crack shots with the old Brown Betsy, as were most frontier girls.

There was a chill in the air next morning, and very foggy. The higher elevation was showing a different climate, than they were used to. A fire was blazing shortly after first light.

Rachel said, "look at the fog rising up in the mountain"

"Must be ground hogs making coffee," Jonas said.

Several chuckles rose from the children. Even Susannah laughed.

"We will be getting close to the gap today, I want every one to pay attention to whats going on around you today," Jonas said.

"I don't expect any trouble, but we will be ready if it comes," Jonas cautioned.

Emma and Elizabeth two of the younger girls were alarmed.

"Paw what kind of trouble might be a coming?" Emma asked.

"Now don't worry sweetie, your Paw will protect you," Jonas said.

"Now don't concern your selfs, but if any of you see any thing strange, let me know," added Jonas.

The Whitt's continued the steady climb onward and upward toward Rocky gap. The early fall sun produced a close humid condition. Even little Crockett sweated little drops of shiny moisture.

Every one seemed to be paying attention; they noticed the birds and animals on their daily adventures. High above were five or six lazy buzzards circling, and a deer was in the trail ahead. It stopped long enough to get a good look at the line of humans and farm animals ambling up the grade.

No shot was fired at the nice young buck, because there was no need of meat today. It seemed like a normal day on the trail except for the tiring climb.

They were about two hours from reaching the gap, when they came up on another nice mountain spring.

"I know it is still early, but I think we will camp here tonight," Jonas said.

"I want all of you to keep down the noise, and no fire tonight," Jonas instructed.

"We will be fresh tomorrow when we hit the gap," Jonas said.

"James I want you to go on first watch while we unload and hobble the horses," Jonas said.

Everyone gathered around the spring and got a good drink, and went about the chores of ending a day of travel.

All except Jonas.

"I think I am going on ahead for a mile or two for a look see," Jonas said.

"I will be back in about two hours," he said.

As Jonas stalked up the trail with the attention of a brave, he had seen no sign of bandits, or any trouble. He did see a large black bear tearing into a rotten log. He was thinking, awful big critter to be eating bugs, better bugs than me.

"Thank you Lord," Jonas whispered.

Jonas came up on the Whitt camp with caution.

James Griffith was paying attention.

"Here comes Paw," John announced.

"See any thing Jonas?" asked Susannah.

"Nothing but a bear, he is about a mile from here," Jonas said.

"He was not interested in me, he was having supper, eating bugs from a rotten log," Jonas added.

"I think we can have a small fire, and warm up supper," Jonas added.

It was a nice quite relaxing evening on the mountain.

Little Crockett was standing, holding on to first one then another.

"He will be walking soon," Jonas commented.

"He will be into every thing then," said Rhoda.

"I think you are right," replied Susannah.

"Well let's get ready for bed, every one get a good nights sleep," said Jonas.

"I will feel much better once we are on the other side of the gap," Jonas added.

"Every one remember your prayers, and good night," Susannah said.

Rachel had the last watch and as the early morning light crept through the camp she rekindled the fire, put some lard in a big skillet and set it in the coals to heat up. She also got the coffee cooking.

"Paw get up its morning, did you sleep well?" asked Rachel.

"Morning baby, yes I sleep fair, I was laying on a root or something," Jonas said.

All the sleepy eyes begin to open and greet the new day.

After a breakfast of dried beef moistened in water and lard, gravy and stick bread, every one was getting ready to shoot the gap and head for the Clinch Valley. Every one was business like and quiet, because they all knew that danger may be ahead.

After all the packing of the horses, and camp broke they were ready to move.

Jonas gathered the family around him and had a prayer for traveling mercies, and thanksgiving.

"Alright I want all of you to move along today, and get on the other side of the mountain," instructed Jonas.

"Hopefully in about four or five hours we will be through the danger, and we can calm down and enjoy the rest of our journey," he added.

They all took their traveling positions, James Griffith took the lead with his Brown Betsy ready for action. Next followed Jonas leading the way for the ones on horse back. The twins Rachel and Rhoda led pack horses and kept the live stock moving. Ol Jack the faithful dog was also a great help. Susannah and little Crockett rode along next. The other children helped move the animals also.

At the rear of the little caravan followed John Bunyon with his watchful eye and his old Brown Betsy ready for action.

After about an hour and a half traveling up the mountain, James Griffith turned and whispered, "I can see Rocky Gap."

"Good," said Jonas, "stay ready."

After another twenty minuites or so James Griffith lead them into the gap. All eyes were looking for any sign of danger. It looked like trouble may not come!

Old Jack barked, then "Paw, Paw," was the alarm from the rear.

John Bunyon passed the word forward, "two men riding hard toward us."

Immediately Jonas and James Griffith run to the back.

"Keep an eye up the trail," he told Susannah and the twins.

Jonas handed his Musket to Rhoda and put his hand on his Cap and ball pistol.

The riders began to slow down to a fast walk.

The riders were rough looking beardy men wearing dirty buck skins. Both of them held a musket across their saddles. They were soon about twenty yards from the Whitt's.

First words came from the riders, "Howdy folks, good day to you."

"Hold it right there," came a commanding voice from Jonas, "we don't want any trouble."

All the muskets and a drawn pistol was pointing at the two riders.

"Wait a minute mister., we don't mean any harm," said the front man.

Jonas replied with a quick answer, "why were you coming up on us so fast?"

"What is your business?" Jonas asked.

The riders were at a stand still, faceing muskets and a repeating pistol.

"We are just pilgrims traveling west, one said.

"How about lowering those guns, mister?" the other one asked.

"Not so fast, not until you explain your rush up on our rear," Jonas answered.

"Oh! We were just giving our mounts some exercise," replied one of the riders.

About that time Susannah shouted, "rider from the north."

Jonas said to James Griffith, "Get up front with Rhoda and be ready for anything.

John Bunyon and Jonas held the two riders in the rear at bay. The rider from the front came at a slower pace than the two from the rear did. He came with in twenty-five yards and stopped.

"Whoa there folks, don't be pointing them guns at me," he said.

"I mean no harm," he added.

James and Rhoda held the muskets at ready, pointing them at the stranger.

"What's your business?" asked young James.

"I'm just a traveler, going home to North Carolina to see my sick Maw," he replied.

The rider from the north looked about like the ones at the rear. He was wearing dirty buck skins, had a bushy red beard, and also had a musket across his saddle.

"James Griffith, march him on down here with these other fellows," Jonas shouted.

"Mister you heard Paw, now move slowly toward the rear," James said in his roughest voice.

"Don't try any thing, or I will cut you in two with this ol musket," James added.

The front rider traveled slowly toward the rear looking everything over as he traveled.

As he reached the rear, Jonas spoke sternly, "alright mister, hold it right there.

"If you think we won't blow you to hell, think again," Jonas said in his strongest voice.

"Mister you are all wrong about us we don't even know this fellow from the north," said one of the riders from the south.

"Sorry to disagree with you," Jonas said.

"I saw how you looked at each other," he added.

"Now I am going to make it simple for you," Jonas said.

"I want you three rascals to head back down the trail just as fast as you came here." Jonas commanded.

"I ought to blow you into to Kingdom Come right now, but the Lord wouldn't approve of that," said Jonas.

"If I see you following us I promise we will shoot you on sight." Jonas said.

"Now get going," Jonas shouted!

The three riders wheeled their mounts around and headed down the mountain at a full gallop. They didn't even look back.

They watched the three riders go out of sight.

Jonas turned to the family and said, "you done real good."

"Those jaspers were up to no good, and with the Lord's help we turned back trouble," Jonas said with a pleased look!

"Paw do you think they will try it again?" asked Rachel.

"No honey, I think we put the fear of God in them," replied Jonas.

"They knew we were not bluffing," Jonas added.

"We will rush down the mountain towards our new home, but stay ready if those devils try to come up on us again," warned Jonas.

"Get back into your positions, stay alert, and keep putting distance between us and them," said Jonas.

"I want for you to hurry down the mountain, but be careful," Jonas instructed.

"Thank you Lord for delivering us," said Susannah out loud.

The Whitt's traveled briskly down East Mountain toward East River! Soon they will resume a south western direction toward the head waters of the Clinch River and their new home in Baptist Valley.

CHAPTER 3

HOW FAR TO JEFFERSONVILLE

The Whitt party decended from Rocky Gap in record time, putting distance between them and the mountain outlaws! Now they can breathe a little easier.

"We still need to stay alert; those rascals could come back for revenge," Jonas said.

"We gave them a black eye, by being ready for them," added Jonas.

"Why do people become robbers?" asked Elizabeth.

"Don't know cept the devil gets into them," said Susannah.

"They don't want to work like honest folks, and they think it fun to take from other people," Susannah said.

"Once they start they get worse after each encounter," she added.

"Well don't you worry, I think that is behind us, just be aware of what's going on around you," Susannah continued.

"Enjoy God's creation as we travel through this beautiful land," inserted Jonas.

Jonas explained that they were in this valley now and will not have to cross another high mountain the rest of the way. There will be some big hills but no big mountains.

Another night on the trail and the Whitts move on in a south western direction toward Jeffersonville. They pass a little town or a farm ever now and then.

Rachel noticed the grass in this area was different.

"The grass is kinda blue looking," she said.

"Blue grass, that's what it is," Jonas said.

"We have a little in Montgomery County" Jonas said.

"I hear Kentucky has lots of it." Jonas added.

"That sure is a blue field," Rachel said.

"That would be a good name for this place, if we got to name it,"

Rachel added.

"It may already be called that," replied Jonas.

"We in Tazewell County yet Paw?" asked little Elizabeth.

"I think we might just be," answered Jonas.

"We should be with Grand Paw Hezekiah in a few days," Jonas added.

"We should be seeing the Clinch River any day now," said Jonas.

"Is it a big river like the New River Paw?" Rachel asked.

Jonas explained to the family that the Clinch is small at the head waters, one fork of the Clinch is sometimes called Little River. It is not much more than a creek this far north, but it runs for many miles plumb down into Tennessee.

"I reckon it gets pretty big by the time it winds that far south," added Jonas.

Another day passed, and the travelers are bone tired, yet excitement grows with each step toward Jeffersonville. As late afternoon comes they see the mighty Clinch.

"Don't look too mighty to me Paw," said James Griffith.

"I know, I told you it wouldn't be very big," Jonas reminded them.

"But all things start out small," said Jonas.

"Let's set up camp here in this flat area, under the trees," Jonas suggested.

"We can get our water right out of the Clinch," Jonas said.

"If we get an early start, and have good luck we might just see Grand Paw tomorrow," Jonas continued.

"Does he live right on the Clinch Paw?" asked James.

"No but close, he lives closer to a creek called Indian," Jonas said.

"Do you think there will be Indians there Paw?" asked Elizabeth.

"No I doubt that, most of the Indians have traveled west across the big Mississippi," explained Jonas.

"But you will see Grand Maw Rachel, do you remember she's part Indian?" Jonas asked.

"Some folks refer to her as Indian Maiden," Jonas Added..

"She wouldn't be wearing feathers and such," said Susannah.

"She will be just like any other Grand Maw,"she added.

"Reckon they will be wanting to see us Maw?" asked Elizabeth.

"They surely will," answered Susannah.

The Whitt's set up camp in a level area beside the Clinch River. Everyone went about the chores of camp and cooking. There was plenty of grass and good clear water for the animals. This was indeed a good land.

It was still in the early evening and the cool water was inviting.

Susannah said, "I'm going to get a bath and get some of this travel dirt off me."

"You girls get a change of clothes and follow me up the river, I seen a good little hole we can bath in," instructed Susannah.

"Here Jonas you take Crockett and let him play in the water, he will enjoy getting clean and cooled off," said Susannah.

So Susannah and the girls went in a line up the river to their heavenly pool.

Jonas and the boys decided to do the same thing right here at the camp. Jonas took little Crockett, and the boys followed. They dropped their clothes and went right in the cool refreshing waters of the Clinch.

Crockett was the biggest duck in the puddle, he had such a good time thrashing and splashing around.

Just as Jonas and the boys finished and were getting on some clothes, a scream broke the silence from up river. Jonas handed Crockett to John grabbed the first musket he saw and went in a run up the river. As he rounded the curve and ran down the little bluff, he saw all the girls splashing in the water.

"What's wrong?" he hollered.

"We are alright now," replied Susannah.

"Rachel stepped on a big slick lizard creature," Susannah said.

"I have never seen any thing like it," she exclaimed.

"Where is it?" Jonas asked.

"It swam off," explained Rachel.

"How big was it?" asked Jonas.

She held up her hands spread to about 14 inches.

"Bout this big," she said.

"What color was it?" Jonas asked.

"Brown, about the color of the bottom of the river," Rachel said.

"You scared us half to death," Jonas replied.

"It was just a was a Water Dog, they are real big salamanders," said Jonas.

"They wouldn't hurt you unless you catch them, then they will try to bite," Jonas explained.

"I'm going back to camp so you all can get out of the water," Jonas announced.

"See you back at camp, in a minute," replied Susannah.

As late evening shadows stretched long, the sky grew dark with storm clowds gathered. They could see the flashes of lightning back in the west. Also the faint rumble of thunder could be heard.

"We better secure the camp, looks like we are going to get a bad storm," said Jonas.

"Get that canvas tied real good, cover the fire wood, stretch a rope over there and tie the animals," instructed Jonas.

"They all may decide to leave if the storm scares them very bad," Jonas added.

Just at the finishing touches of securing camp, the wind came as an unwelcome guest. The trees waved and loose leaves filled the air. The Whitt's all gathered under the large lean-to, and pulled down the extra canvas securing it with rope to rocks and bushes.

The lantern was lit and its little flame waved back and forth giving off an eerie illumination under the canvas.

Soon the lightning flashed brightly and the thunder boomed like a hundred cannons going off. The wind blew violently; shaking the canvas. The horses and cattle made desperate sounds outside. Then here come the rain, like pouring water out of a bucket.

"Don't be afraid it will soon pass," Jonas said trying to calm them.

"God's just showing some of His awesome power," said Jonas.

"He knows we are here and will protect us," added Susannah.

Finally the storm passed and everyone slipped off to slumber land. Some dreamed of their new home and seeing Grand Paw Hezekiah Whitt again. Some just rested in the security of the canvas and of course, God's pertection. Things will be different in the morning.

"Things sure are wet this morning," John said.

John noticed all five of the sheep are missing.

"Well only thing we can do is take ol Jack and round them up," said John.

"Old Jack has been such a help in moving the animals along the trail," said John.

"I hate to say it but he is getting old he will be nine next March," John added.

John and James Griffith set out to find the lost sheep.

John said, "This reminds me of the Bible story, Jesus left the ninety and nine sheep to go and search for the one lost sheep."

"Yes but we don't have a hundred sheep, and all five of ours is lost," replied James.

"Don't worry we will find the dumb things," said John.

"Dumb things, what do you mean?" asked James.

"Well they ain't smart are they?" asked John.

"Reckon not they are lost," said James.

"They are so dependent on us to take care of them," said John.

Jack picked up the trail and the boys ran after him. They followed an old game trail up out of the little valley, toward a ridge. About one quarter mile from camp they seen the sheep, one is hung up in a briar thicket, and the other four are just standing there.

They look like they are trying to figure out how to get it out.

"Here Jack, don't scare them," called James Griffith.

John ran ahead and looked over the situation.

"Guess I got to go in there and get her," said John.

"Guess so, but watch out for snakes, and oh yeah, also the briars," warned James.

John waded into the brier patch gently and speaking softly to the little ewe.

"I will get you out you little dummy," John said softly.

There he said, "I got a hold of her."

"You called her little dummy," said James.

By the time he got out, his hands were bleeding with all the scratches.

"Glad we just got five of these little dummies," James said.

They, with the help of Jack had them back to camp in short time.

Jonas and the rest of the family just about had camp broke, when the boys arrived.

"Here boys have some tea, and hard-tack we will eat better at dinner," Jonas said.

"With good luck we might be able to eat supper with Grand Paw Hezekiah," Jonas added.

The little caravan once again was on the move following the Clinch. There seemed to be new energy in each step. The distance is now short; a great reunion with the Whitt's of Tazewell County is coming soon. Jonas and his clan are just outside of the little town of Jeffersonville.

When they get their final directions to the Hezekiah farm, they will feel much better. They only hope it's not too far from Jeffersonville.

Even the animals seemed to pick up on the excitement. The Whitt's were making excellent time. Now Jonas moved to the front as they traveled, not because he expected trouble, but because he wanted to see the town. Another hour passed, yet no town, it was pushing 1:00 PM as they reached the top of a little rise.

Jonas turned to the family and smiled.

"There it is," he said.

"Another half hour and we will be in town," Jonas said.

"We will find something to eat and I will get directions to Paw's farm," he added.

"Reckon Grand Paw will be looking for us today? asked Elizabeth.

"Don't know, bout that, he knows we are coming, he just don't know when for sure," Jonas answered.

"Paw, will he have everything ready for us?" James Griffith asked.

"I suspect he is ready for us," Jonas said.

"The last letter we got back in June, he said he would make provisions for us," Jonas said.

"Don't worry, I'm sure we will fare just fine," Susannah inserted.

"I sure like this beautiful land," said Susannah.

"A good ground to grow crops and young-uns," she exclaimed.

The Whitts march into Jeffersonville, they admire the handsome little town. Most of the buildings are quite modern, a church, a court house, a mercantile, livery stable, and several good looking houses. And also a tavern, which had rooms above.

"Looks like a real nice town to be this far west," said John.

"Yes it does," said Susannah as she held up little Crockett.

"Look baby, this is your new town," Susannah said.

Little Crockett smiled real big and jabbered something, that only he understood.

The people were moving about their business and many tipped their hats or said howdy as they passed.

The streets were still a little muddy from the storm last night, but the town had board walks in front of most of the buildings.

"Well let's get something to eat, and find out where the Hezekiah farm is," said Jonas.

"I am going to see if we can put all the animals in the corral," Jonas said.

"Just leave them packed, we wouldn't tary long in town ,we will eat and head for the farm just as soon as possible," Jonas instructed.

Jonas helped Susannah down from her mount.

He held Crockett and asked, "Well little man, how do you like it?"

The twins, old Jack, John, and James Griffith headed the animal to the corral.

Even little David Crockett Whitt was excited, as they headed toward the tavern and eatery.

"You know," said Jonas, "I should be hungry, but I don't feel too hungry."

"You will be once you see food," Susannah said.

"Now let's get in and eat, and find the directions to Hezekiah's farm," said Susannah.

"I can't wait to see Grand Paw," said Elizabeth.

"Well it's not going to be too long now," replied Susannah.

As they all headed inside Jonas saw a very large table over by the window.

"That table over there will do," said Jonas.

A man approached and said, "hello folks, welcome, how can I help you today?"

Jonas spoke up saying, "We hope to get a meal, four more are coming, they are taking care of the stock."

"Glad to see you folks, my name is James Vandyke, I own this place, and will take care of your hunger and thirst," he said.

"Glad to meet you Mr. Vandyke, I am Jonas Whitt and this is my family," he said.

"Mr. Whitt please call me Jim, and I bet I know some of your kin, "Jim said.

"I have a good friend by that name, Hezekiah Whitt and he is a prominent gentleman around Jeffersonville," added Jim.

"Well Jim, call me Jonas, and Hezekiah is my father," replied Jonas.

"We have traveled from the far side of Montgomery County, to settle here close to Hezekiah, added Jonas.

"He will be glad to see your family Jonas, he told me the other day he expected you all any day," Jim said.

"As a matter of fact I think Hezekiah will be in town today, he always has business at the court house," Jim said.

"Great, I hope he gets here soon, he can show us the way to Baptist Valley," said Susannah.

Now the twins and the boys show up from the corral, they come on over to the big table where the family is seated.

"This is Mister Vandyke children, and Jim, this is the rest of my clan, Rachel, Rhoda, James Griffith, and John Bunyon," Jonas said.

They seemed to speak in unison, "Hello Mister Vandyke."

"Welcome to the Vandyke Inn," replied Jim.

"Thank you sir," they said once again in unison.

"They sure are polite Jonas," replied Jim.

"Give Susannah the credit for that, she believes in being proper," replied Jonas.

"Nothing wrong with that," answered James!

Jim explained that the special today is beef stew, corn bread, and apple pie for desert. Got coffee, and some lemonade to drink!

"That will be fine, we will all have the stew," Jonas answered.

"I'll get right on it," Jim said.

"I'm going to send a boy over to the court house, and have them inform Hezekiah that you are here, when he comes in," Jim added.

James summoned a small black boy from in front of the inn! James whispered something to him, and the boy ran toward the court house.

"Thanks so much Jim for your hospitality," Susannah spoke up.

"Not a problem, we are always glad to get another good family in Tazewell County," replied Jim.

"Now just relax and enjoy your dinner," Jim said with a big smile.

"I think this will be a good day for all the Whitt's," Jonas said.

Jim left the table and began taking care of the dinner for the Whitt family. They were enjoying the welcome and hospitality.

Jonas had noticed the boy head out toward the court house.

"I hope Grand Paw is already over there," he said.

"Me too," Rhoda spoke up.

"Me too," said about three more voices!

"Well just relax and enjoy your dinner, Lord willing we will see him today, exclaimed Susannah.

In a short time a young lady with beautiful red hair, came carrying large flat bowls filled with steaming beef stew.

The stew was real meaty; you could see large cuts of beef, and big chunks of potatoes, carrots, and onion. On the side was a big piece of yellow corn bread.

"Welcome folks, hope you are hungry, my name is Mary Jane Vandyke," she said.

"Paw said you all are the Whitts from Montgomary county," said Mary Jane.

John Bunyon had a special twinkle appear in his eye as he gazed up on the beautiful young lady.

In a cracking voice John Bunyon blurted out, "Thank you Ma-am."

The twins chuckled under their breath.

"Sure looks good Mary Jane," Susannah spoke up.

"Hope you folks enjoy," replied Mary Jane.

"Do you think you will want some apple pie?" Mary Jane said.

"It is the best in the county, some folks say," Mary Jane added.

"My Maw does the baking and most of the cooking, which seems to be her gift," Mary Jane continued.

"Well Mary Jane, let's see if we are going to have room for pie after we take care of the beef stew," said Susannah.

Mary Jane went around the table filling glasses with cool clear water.

"Need any thing just let me know," she said.

"Thanks dear," said Susannah.

John Bunyon couldn't seem to take his eyes off the handsome young filly, as she swayed her way back to the kitchen.

As the bowls became empty, Mrs. Vandyke came to the table with Jim.

"I wanted to meet you folks, I'm Mrs. Vandyke, call me Susie," she said.

"My real name is Susannah but folks know me by Susie, she added.

Susannah Whitt spoke first, "so nice to meet you and James, and your nice daughter Mary Jane," she said.

"Glad you folks are settling here, it's always good to get another good family in our county," said Susie.

"Thanks so much for your hospitality, this seems to be a great land, filled with good people, said Susannah.

"Yes for the most part," said Susie.

"Now can I get you some of my famous apple pie," asked Susie?

"Anybody up for pie," Jonas asked?

Hands went up all around the table.

"Well I think so, bring it on," Jonas answered with a smile.

In a few minutes Mary Jane and her mother were serving up apple pie.

Just as the Whitts polished off the last of the tasty apple pie, a tall straight handsome man with silver hair appeared in the door of the tavern.

Rachel was the first to see him.

"GRAND PAW!" she exclaimed.

All eyes turned toward the door!

A big grin was on the face of Hezekiah Whitt as he looked up on his son and family. Rhoda was the first to reach him. She was welcomed with a great big bear hug. The family formed a line from their table all the way to the door where Grand Paw Hezekiah stood. He worked his way toward the table, giving each of his grandchildren a big hug.

He finally made it to Jonas.

"Welcome son, you sure are a site for sore eyes," said Hezekiah.

"Susannah you are pretty as always; who is this fine little fellow you are holding," asked Hezekiah.

"Grand Paw Hezekiah, meet your new grandson, this is David Crockett Whitt," stated Susannah.

A big smile appeared on both faces, Little Crockett and the patriarch Hezekiah.

"Here Susannah, let me hold that young man," Hezekiah said as he took the baby.

Hezekiah held him up and exclaimed to the whole room, "this is my grandson, David Crockett Whitt.

"Well he has a good name, David Crockett died a hero's death for the liberty of Texas," he added.

"This is a fine looking family you have Jonas," Hezekiah said.

"I got you a house ready not far from my place," he added.

Hezekiah looked around and said, "Are you about ready to see Baptst Valley?"

"Thought you would never ask Paw," said Jonas.

"Let me settle up with the Vandyke's, and we can be on our way," added Jonas.

"I got it, James put the dinner on my bill, please," Hezekiah said.

"No need for that Paw, we can pay, " Jonas said.

"I know but you will need your money for other things," Hezekiah said.

"You gotta get set up before winter comes, you know after September it's not that long till winter," added Hezekiah.

"Thanks so much Paw, but did you get your business taken care of?" asked Jonas.

"Partly," replied Hezekiah.

"Nothing that can't wait a few days," he added.

Jonas and Susannah went over and shook hands with James and Susie Vandyke.

John Bunyon awkwardly made his way over, and took the hand of Mary Jane Vandyke.

"Nice meeting you miss," he said weakly!

"Same here, you can call me Mary Jane," she replied.

"Same here," said John Bunyon, "just call me John."

"Alright John, time to get the stock and head down the road," Jonas broke in.

As the twins, James Gritthth, and John, move to get the stock Jonas turns to Hezekiah, and says, "You look real good Paw."

"Well I don't do too badly; for seventy six years old," he answered.

"Are you that old, you sure don't look it," said Jonas.

"Well son the twenty eighth of March according to my ciphering, I was seventy six," he replied.

"Paw how is Maw and the rest of the family?" asked Jonas.

"Your Maw has her good days, and some bad, I guess you could say she is tolerable," replied Hezekiah.

"James and Nancy are doing fine, still no young-uns, "Hezekiah said.

"Griffy is way out in Missouri, Richard is out in Carter County, Kentucky, John Bunyon is in Kentucky, I think Floyd County," Hezekiah stated.

"Let me see now, Susannah married Joe Webb, they have three young-uns, the baby is about five now," added Hezekiah.

"Well son lets get going, we can talk on the way, and we have some time since you are moving here," said Hezekiah.

"Alright Paw, about how long will it take us to get to your house?" Jonas asked.

"Not far if you are on a nice walking horse, I make it in about thirty minuites when I'm in a hurry, said Hezekiah.

"I would guess, driving sheep, cows, and pigs, about two hours," added Hezekiah.

"We will come to your new house before we get to my house," Hezekiah said.

"Well It's not new, but it will be new to you," he added.

"It's roomy and built well, got a barn, and a spilt rail fence around about an acre of ground," Hezekiah said.

"Over one hundred and sixty acres all together," he said.

"I put out a little garden for you, not much, tators, late corn, and some squash," said Hezekiah.

"There's a good spring about thirty paces from the house, and the house sits on a little knoll about a hundred paces from the Clinch," added Hezekiah.

"By the way there's a honey hole not far from the house, I catch fish every time I go there," said Hezekiah.

"Well I guess I better shut up and let you say something," Hezekiah said.

"Paw it just sounds so good to hear you talk, it was real good luck that you were in town today," said Jonas.

"Glad I was son, It is always easier to show some one the way, than to tell them," answered Hezekiah.

The little caravan moved southwest from Jeffersonville for about seven miles then cut back toward the Clinch.

"We are just about to your new home place," said Hezekiah.

"My house is across a big hill from your place, some folks call it Green Mountain," added Hezekiah.

"It's not really a mountain, guess it's about a mile and a half from your house," added Hezekiah.

"Hezekiah lifted his hand and pointed, "There it is over there on that rise above the river," he said.

"It is beautiful," Susannah spoke up, "a wonderful view," she added.

"The meadow fenced in with split rails, the barn, and a good roomy house, it's like a picture," she continued.

"Will it be hard crossing the river Grand Paw?" Rachel asked.

"No, not most of the time, there is a ford just below the house," answered Hezekiah.

"Now in spring when the river swells up, there ain't no getting across," added Hezekiah.

CHAPTER 4

A New Beginning

This is just a wonderful moment, finally being back with you Paw, and seeing our new home, it makes the whole trip from Mongomery worth while," Jonas said.

"Well son, I am glad you brought your family here to be with us," answered Hezekiah.

"You know I ain't getting any younger, already exceeded my time here on earth according to the Bible, "added Hezekiah.

"Yes Paw but seventy years is for most folks, a long life is promised for those who honor their father and mother," Jonas said.

"I think you lived a good life, being fair to all you come in contact with, and you did honor your father and mother," exclaimed Jonas.

"Well I tried, I loved my parents, and they loved their children, just like you do yours, Jonas," Hezekiah said.

"Lets get this Whitt clan across the Clinch, you got a lot of settling to get done," said Hezekiah.

"Yes we do," answered Jonas.

"John, James, will you and the twins water all the animals before we take them up, and turn-em loose in the pasture?" asked Jonas.

"I am going to get Susannah, and the little ones up to the house, so they can start getting ready for tonight," added Jonas.

Little David Crockett was wanting down off that horse, he was tired of being wallowed for the past weeks. He seemed to know he was home, and was ready to settle down, just like everyone else.

Hezekiah went up to the house with Jonas and Susannah.

"Reckon it will need some cleaning , there is some furniture, and beds," said Hezekiah.

"You will be wanting to make some more furniture when you get a chance," he said.

"Well any way, you can live here as long as you want, and make any improvements you like," Hezekiah said.

"It ain't costing me nothing but a little tax each year, so you don't have to worry about any rent for now," added Hezekiah.

"Son you may want to buy it some time down the road," Hezekiah said, "but for now just move in and enjoy it."

"It's gotta be better than sleeping on the trail," added Hezekiah.

"Thanks Paw, it's like a mansion to us, and we are entirely thankful for you and your hospitality," exclaimed Jonas.

"Just glad you finally got here," Hezekiah said.

"Got any questions before I cross over the hill?" Hezekiah asked.

"Well when will you be back?" asked Jonas.

"I will bring your Maw over in the morning and let you visit some," Hezekiah said.

"Any thing you want me to bring when we come?" Hezekiah asked.

"Don't know of anything right off, Paw," Jonas said.

"I'm sure Rachel will want to bring something for your house warming, see you all in the morning," Hezekiah said.

"Thanks Paw, see you then," answered Jonas.

Jonas opened the door to their new home, It wasn't in too bad a shape!

There was one little problem, a family of Wasps, will have to be evicted. Jonas put his buck skin jacket on, picked up a broom from the corner and proceeded to clear the house of the waspers.

"Well come in and see your house Susannah," Jonas exclaimed.

"Sure it's safe now," said Susannah.

"Don't want waspers on the baby," she said.

Susannah came through the door cautiously.

"This will be a great home!" she exclaimed.

The house was made of hewed out logs with locking at each corner. To the right was a kitchen, and dining room together, with a large fire place. The fire place was built with a oven of stone on one side. There was a large table, and eight chairs, also in one side of the kitchen was a cabinet running about eight feet with a smooth board top for mixing and cutting of food. Also a nice window was over the counter top.

Straight ahead they could see a stairway up to the second froor. To the left was a sitting room and also a bed room, with a high back bed, a washstand with a bowl and pitcher sitting on it. The sitting room had a davenport, a smoking stand, and two straight chairs.

Susannah was beside her self.

"Jonas I am so happy with this big house," she said.

"Paw has really helped us with this place," said Jonas.

"Thank God he is so wonderful," Susannah said.

"Let's look up stairs and see whats up there," Susannah said.

Susannah pushed forward like she was afraid Jonas would pass her. The steps were a might steep, but no complaints were heard.

At the top they turned down a hall way that ran straight toward the front of the house. On the right side was two doors and on the left was one door. At both ends of the hall was a window for illumination. Susannah moved to the first door and looked inside.

"This is a bed room," she said.

Jonas looked at her with a puzzled look.

"What's wrong?" she said.

"Nothing, but it does have a bed and a fire place," Jonas answered.

"Alright, I am thinking out loud," she exclaimed.

Jonas laughed as they moved toward the single door on the left.

They saw a big bed room, two sets of bunk beds, and a fire place. A big wardrobe on one side, and a wash stand to the right. This room had two windows. There was also candle stands on both walls and one on the mantle.

"Can you believe this fine old house?" Susannah asked.

"You are right this is a fine new place to start over again," answered Jonas.

Once again they moved down the hall to the last door on the right.

The door was closed, so they opened it slowly, and a hairy little racoon run up the wall to an opened window, and out he went.

To the right was another bunk bed, with a messed up cover on it. They could see a mess of hair in one area.

"Looks like we just evicted the prior resident," Jonas said.

"Look around, there may be more of the little bandits," Susannah said.

Jonas walked over and closed the window. As he turned he noticed that this room also has a small fire place.

Susannah went to the window and looked out over the little farm.

"I see the garden over there, corn looks to be getting ready for harvest," she said.

"Hezekiah has been getting ready for us for some time," Susannah said, "Bless his heart, he is a fine man."

"Yes he is," said Jonas.

"He appears to be in real good shape for seventy six," he added.

"Yes he is, and a good Baptist to boot," replied Susannah.

"Well lets get down stairs and start getting things moved in and in order," Jonas suggested.

"Yes we better," answered Susannah.

Jonas headed out side to coordinate the unpacking and where to put this and where to put that.

He told James Griffith to take the two mules that carried the tools and farming implements to the barn and start lifting the burden from them.

"Just unload them for now, we will put every thing in its place when we find out where that is," Jonas said.

"I know what you mean Paw," James Griffith said.

"Want me to turn-em out in the pasture when I get em freed up?" he asked.

"Yes son, I see you already got the pigs, sheep, and cows over there," answered Jonas.

"The animals seemed so relieved to be home," said James Griffith.

Jonas laughed and turned to the twins and said, "Girls, as I unload the rest of this stuff, you all start packing it in the house."

"Your Maw will tell you what to do with it," he added.

John Bunyon went to help James Griffith. The small children stayed and helped Rachel and Rhoda.

They had spread a quilt under the Oak next to the house, there sat David Crockett acting like he was in charge of the whole operation.

"Look at that young-un, he thinks he's the boss," said Rhoda.

"He's not far from it," Jonas said with a wide smile on his face.

Every one stayed busy bringing things into the house and putting things where Susannah instructed. Rachel and Rhoda started a fire and started fixing supper. They pealed potatoes, cut up an onion, opened two glass jars of brown beans, that had been cooked, and sealed with wax, and brought from Montgomery County.

Next they mixed up some corn bread to a thin consistency so they could fry corn cakes. The smell filled the house and stirred the appetites of every one of them. James even brought in some green onions from the garden.

They had a full day, besides being weary from the journey they had just completed, the unpacking! After supper, every body pitched in again, to prepare the beds and get ready for bed.

"I don't care if this is the last time we move," Susannah said to Jonas.

"Know what you mean Darling, I ain't in no hurry to be moving either," replied Jonas.

Finally things were ready for the Whitt's to go to bed, and it was about to get dark out side. Jonas came back from the barn , he had been checking out the animals and the corral.

"That's a real nice barn," he said as he came in the house.

"Come on Jonas, I think we are all just about ready to go to bed in our new home," replied Susannah.

As all the children crawled into bed, they called out, "Good night Paw, good night Maw," and each child went through each and every name.

"Takes about an hour for all the good nights to get said," Jonas whispered.

"Well that's all right, they love each other, even though some times they don't show it," Susannah said.

"Good night Jonas," Susannah said to Jonas.

"Good night honey," replied Jonas!

The last of the good nights were said, and it was so peaceful. They could hear a bull frog down by thr river, a whip-per-will sound came from the ridge, and a distant Owl sounded a low hoot, hoot. And if you listened real good you could hear the eddie in the river just below the house.

Susannah whispered to Jonas, "This place is almost heaven."

"Yes Tazewell County is almost heaven, I see why Paw talked so highly of it," answered Jonas.

Sleep came to the Whitt house.

The rain danced on the roof as the morning light first shown through the windows of the new home of Jonas Whitt family.

Little Crockett roused up and gave a little, " whine."

Susannah looked at little Crockett laying on the blanket she had spread for him to sleep on.

"Guess he's wet and hungry, Jonas, " Susannah said.

"He slept all night, how did you sleep," asked Susannah?

"I slept fine," said Jonas, "I think the whole family slept like logs."

"This trip and all the excitement has taken something out of all of us, "Susannah said.

"I still haven't gotten over the ordeal at Rocky Gap," added Susannah.

"Well that was dangerous, we were ready and the Lord was watching over us," said Jonas.

"Yes it pays to put your trust in the Lord," confessed Susannah.

"Amen to that," replied Jonas.

"I hope this is just a summer shower, don't want your Maw and Paw to get wet," said Susannah.

"You know they will come rain or shine," Jonas said.

Susannah picked up Crockett, changed his diaper, and laid back in bed, with little Crockett at her breast.

"I might as well lay in bed until our little feller gets a full belly," exclaimed Susannah.

"Go ahead I am going out and try out the little building out back, you know the one with the crescent moon on the door," said Jonas.

"Better hurry, there will probably be a line forming," replied Susannah.

"I will try and win that race, " answered Jonas.

"Got to get ready for the days work, we have a lot to do you know," said Jonas.

"Just ease into it, we don't have to get everything done in one day, and we will have company," said Susannah.

"Alright, darling, I will see you a little later," replied Jonas.

As Jonas went through the door, she could hear him whistling.

He's happy thought Susannah. I hope he can find some work soon, he does better when he's working at a mill or building a house.

Breakfast was over and everyone got busy with more moving in, chores. The boys had let the five chickens out in the barn last night. They were a little worn by the trip.

They had been cooped up in a little crate, and rode on top of the packed mules, all the way from Montgomery County. Each night they had been set down on the ground, watered, and fed cracked corn.

"Looks like they made it alright," said Jonas.

"Lets leave them in the barn another day or two before we let them out," Jonas added.

"Take special care of that old rooster, he's the only one we got," added Jonas.

"Alright Paw," said John Bunyon.

"Do you want us to get water out of the spring or the river to fill the watering box for the stock?" asked John.

"Get it out of the spring, then we will know how good our spring is," Jonas answered.

"Just as soon as I can get to it I'm going to build a big spring house over it," said Jonas.

"We need it to keep our milk, butter and other things cool," Jonas said.

"It will keep the water cleaner too," Jonas added.

"That will be a real good idea, Paw," said John.

About that time loud voices came from towards the house, Jonas and the boys turned their attention toward the house.

A buggy pulled by a springy chestnut mare pulled up to the back of the house. Everyone was running to meet it, It was Hezekiah and Rachel Whitt.

"Look it's Grand Maw, and Grand Paw," John Bunyon exclaimed as he took off in a run toward the buggy.

James Griffith and Jonas came in a fast walk.

About that time another buggy came round the house. Jonas looked intently to see who it was.

"Well my goodness, that is my big brother James and his wife Nancy," he said.

"We are having a family reunion, huh Paw," said James Griffith.

"Looks like it," Jonas said.

"You were named for your uncle James, partly any way," Jonas added.

"I know Paw, I remember," answered James.

The whole Jonas Whitt clan gathered around the two buggies and started hugging and tears of joy filled their eyes.

"What a wonderful day," said Grand Maw Rachel!

"Where is little David Crockett Whitt?" was the next thing out of Rachel's mouth?

"He's napping, just fed him and laid him down," Susannah said.

"I will get him, he can sleep later," she added.

By now everyone was in the house, Susannah come carrying a sleepy little boy to meet his Grand Maw Rachel and of course uncle James and aunt Nancy.

"Oh what a fine little fellow this is," Rachel said.

"He is long and lanky, bet he will be a tall man," replied Hezekiah.

Rachel held him up to get a good look at her grand son.

"Are you David Crockett?" she asked.

Little Crockett spread his mouth with a big grin.

"I think he likes his Grand Maw," said Susannah.

Next she passed the baby to the open arms of Nancy, James's wife.

"He is a beautiful baby," said aunt Nancy.

"Handsome," uncle James interrupted!

"Well I guess you are right," Nancy said.

"Boys are handsome, not beautiful, "James said.

My turn, may I have him for a minute?" James asked.

Crockett was passed to his uncle James, once again the big smile came on his face.

This brought a smile to all that seen him.

"How old is he now, can he walk any." asked Nancy.

"He's bout nine months old, and he is pulling himself up, but not took that first step yet," Susannah said.

"It will be soon I think," Nancy said, "He is a strong little man."

After Rachel hugged all the children, she turned to John Bunyon.

"I need a strong man to go and get the crates from the buggy," she said.

"I'm strong Grand Maw," James Griffith said.

"Yes you are, you go with John and help bring in the crates," replied Rachel.

The boys headed outside at once.

Susannah spoke up, "You should not have brought anything."

"Only right, we got plenty, you will need it this winter to feed this family." replied Rachel.

The boys came dragging in the first crate, and set it on the floor beside the counter.

Look at all this canned food, green beans, pickled beans, pickled corn, canned tomatoes, cans of jams and jelly and a can of honey," said Susannah.

"Makes my mouth water," said Jonas, as he looked over the food.

Here the boys are again, another crate, this one had more of the same, and about five cans of chow chow. Some canned apples, about everything you could think of.

Rachel said to the boys again, " There is some little sacks out there also, go and fetch them."

They were gone and back in short order, this time they carried cloth bags, one of coffee, tea, flour, mill, and salt.

"Boys did you see one more big sack in the very back?" asked Rachel.

"Yes Grand Maw," said John.

"Well run and fetch it, that's the last of them," she said.

The boys come carrying a large sack.

"Put it up on the table boys," instructed Grand Maw.

Rachel went over and opened the sack and pulled out a nice sugar cured Virginia Ham.

"Maw you and Paw are just too good!" Jonas said.

"We really appreciate all of this food, I sure hope you don't run your self short," replied Susannah.

"Not a problem, we have plenty, your Maw puts up a mess of stuff every year, God has really been good to us" said Hezekiah.

"Well it wouldn't go to waste," said Jonas.

Next James went out to his buggy and come back carrying a box.

"Well brother, Nancy and I wanted to bring you a house warming present too," said James.

First Nancy pulled out a bolt of calico material, and held it up for Susannah to see.

"You can make a dress or two, and some shirts," Nancy said.

Then she pulled out a bolt of musslin material, "you can use this for what ever you need it for," said Nancy.

Then she pulled out a big platter, "you can use this for your turkey or ham on Thanksgiving day," added Nancy.

"Thank you so much Nancy and James," Susannah said.

"Feels like Christmas, I feel so bad we don't have any gifts for you," added Susannah.

"You and the family moving here is a gift in itself," said James.

"We have not got to see you much for a long time," Nancy added.

"I know what you mean, I think we are going to love Tazewell county," exclaimed Susannah.

"Yes it is a good place to live, winter is a little rough sometimes, that's about the only drawback," said James.

"Can't be as bad as the winters way up north," said Jonas.

"Well you are right about that," James said, "but the elevation does have a bearing on it."

"We have a lot of catching up to do," said Hezekiah.

"Since this is Saturday, we can spend the whole day visiting and resting," said Susannah.

"Long as we get home by dark, Church Day tomorrow, you know," Hezekiah said.

"Didn't know Paw, all my days run together since we have been on the trail," replied Jonas.

"How far is it to the church?" asked Jonas.

"Bout six miles from here I reckon, you can be there in less than an hour," said Hezekiah.

"Well that is if you ride, don't forget you don't have a wagon yet," he added.

"Well Paw we sold ours because we couldn't take it on some of the trails you know; I am going to make us one before long, or buy one," Jonas said.

"Yes you need one, that's for sure," Hezekiah answered.

"Me and Susannah will come to church and see where you live," replied Jonas.

"Yes you come to our house and you can travel with us to the church," said Hezekiah.

"That's settled, lets all sit down and and get to visiting," said Grand Maw.

"Let me and the twins get some dinner on, we will be hungry after a spell," Susannah said.

"Rhoda you and Rachel come and help, I'll see you don't miss any thing," Susannah added.

The three headed for the kitchen.

"Well lets get some potatoes peeled, and I will russle up something to go with them," said Susannah.

"How about some of that Virginia Ham?" asked Rhoda?

"Well I don't know why we can't enjoy some of your Grand Maws special ham she brought us," she answered.

Nancy and Grand Maw Rachel took turns holding little Crockett and playing with the other children.

Hezekiah, James, and Jonas headed out to look over the barn and farm.

Jonas said, thinking out loud, "This farm has great potential."

"Yes it does, I think you have more level ground than I do, and I reap a good harvest of corn, tobbaco, and cane every year," replied James.

"You can plow all that upper area under, before cold weather, you got room for tobbaco up by the woods, corn over to the right," pointed out Hezekiah.

"You still have room for cane or wheat," added James.

"Over here by the barn, you can have a big garden," added Hezekiah.

"I tell you Jonas, this ground is so good, you can grow most anything," Hezekiah said.

"Yes Paw I believe we have good opportunity here," Jonas said.

"Thanks so much for all your help," Jonas added.

"I wanted to ask you and James about contacts regarding house work and mill building," said Jonas.

"Do you know anybody that is looking for a millright or house builder?" Jonas asked.

"Not now, but you can bet someone will need someone like you," said Hezekiah.

"I will start asking around," said James.

They walked around the barn and also looked at the corral.

Jonas said, "The barn is in good shape, not much needing fixing."

"Yes you are right, some of your rail fence could use some fixing," Hezekiah said.

"Yes Paw, all in all, everything is in pretty good shape," Jonas exclaimed.

James spoke up, as he looked over Jonas' stock, "You got a real good start on your herd, looks like good beef cattle, and a good looking milk cow."

"Is she still fresh?" asked James.

"She has been giving real good milk, but I think the trip has just about dried her up," replied Jonas.

"If you run short, let us know, I got a good milker, you do too, don't you Paw?" asked James.

"Well that's good to know, don't know when Susannah's going to ween little Crockett, but we will need milk for him, and of course the rest of the young-uns," said Jonas.

A voice was heard coming from the house.

"Paw you all come on, dinner is ready," Rhoda announced.

"Alright honey," Hezekiah answered.

"We are on our way," shouted Jonas afraid she didn't hear Hezekiah.

Rhoda waved and went into the house.

The doors and all the windows were all open for cool air flow through the house and also to help cool the heated kitchen.

In a short time the men came single file into the kitchen. The big table was set, and the smaller children were sitting along the wall on quilts with filled plates. None were eating yet, they were waiting on something!

Susannah turned to Jonas, "Well Jonas you are the head of this house, how about asking blessing?"

"All right, lets join hands, all but you young-uns, no need you getting up with your plates," said Jonas.

The bigger children and all the adults circled the table and took hands. All heads bowed.

Jonas spoke up addressing God almighty. "Holy God, we come to you today with Thanksgiving, we ask that you be a part of this house and bless this whole family. We thank you Lord for your watch care. We thank you for your loving kindness. Lord we thank you for the bounty you have provided for us. Now Lord bless all the food and all the hands who prepared it, Be with us, and lead us away from temptation. Forgive us for our short comings. I ask all of this in the Name of Jesus Christ. Amen!"

Each and every voice sounded, "Amen."

Jonas sat at the head of the table, with Hezekiah on his right and Susannah on his left.

"Pass the ham please," came a plea from James Griffith.

Hezekiah chuckled, "boys hungry!" he said.

All the little ones around the wall were pretty quiet, the good food went well. The whole family got quiet after they got the plate passing done. Every now and then you could hear a, "sure is good!"

"After the dishes are done you children can go a swimming if John Bunyon will watch you," announced Susannah.

"I will do it Maw," spoke up John, "If I don't have to do the dishes."

"We don't bargain in this house," Susannah said, "You know you hardly ever have to do dishes."

"Sorry Maw, it just jumped out," replied John Bunyon.

As supper finished up, Jonas said, "Everybody grab a chair, we will go out under the big oak."

"Nice breeze out there, and we can talk," added Jonas.

"Little Crockett can sit on a quilt and entertain us," said Susannah.

"I plumb forgot," said Grand Maw as she pulled out some stick candy.

"Good thing I forgot I guess, or they may not have eaten their dinner," she said.

All the children gathered round Grand Maw Rachel as she handed each of the children a piece. Even the big ones got in on this treat. She started with the smallest and worked up. John Bunyon was the last one in line.

All of them said, "Thanks Grand Maw."

She had one piece for little Crockett. She picked him up and held him on her lap. She stuck the stick of candy to his lips. He got a taste, and grabed her hand to pull the candy closer.

"Wait honey, you can't have it all at once," she said.

Every one had a laugh, as they watched little Crockett go after the sweet candy.

The men all took a chew of tobacco, and leaned back in their chairs. The women gathered on one end so they could talk.

Soon the dishes were done and the children headed down to the river, all wearing country swim wear. (old worn clothes)

Rachel and Rhoda came to sit with the grown ups, after all they were practically grown.

"You children be careful," shouted Susannah.

"If you get drowned, I will beat you to death," she added.

Every one laughed at that.

John turned and hollered back, "They will be fine Maw, I will keep a good watch over them."

"All right," she hollered back.

"Have a good time," she added.

As the men talked the subject of the trip from Montgomery county came up.

Hezekiah wanted a day to day accounting of their journey.

"We had to be patient traveling with children, and driving stock," Jonas said.

"It was not too hard I guess," he added.

"The only real danger was running into outlaws on Rocky Gap," Jonas said.

"Tell us what happened," replied Hezekiah.

Jonas went ahead and told the whole story of his brave children, how they were ready when trouble came.

The mountain outlaws backed down and went down the mountain.

"I guess I would to, if I had three Brown Betsy's and a six shot cap and ball pointed at me," said Hezekiah.

"You were lucky," said James.

"Not luck, the Lord was with us, and we were ready," Jonas said.

"I have no doubt if we needed to fire, the children would let go on them devils," Jonas said.

"Well I'm sure you taught them about shooting and when to shoot if needed," replied Hezekiah.

Jonas nodded, and spit some tobacco juice over in some tall grass.

About that time all heads turned toward the river as a scream sounded from the frolicking children in the water.

Jonas jumped to his feet, and ran toward the river.

As all watched, it became clear what was happening.

John Bunyon had a stick in one hand and a rock in the other.

A nasty water snake decided the children were intruding on his space and was chasing the children. It was funny in a way, children screaming while they ran out of the river, the snake right after them, and John Bunyon right after the snake.

The snake turned toward John, he let go with a wild swing of his stick, he connected and the snake headed down stream in a crazy swim.

Jonas was laughing by the time he got to the river.

"Just a mean water snake, it's not poison," he exclaimed.

"But Paw that thing was chasing us," said Elizabeth.

"I know honey, they do that, don't worry," Jonas said.

"I think John put a hurting on him," Jonas added.

Jonas turned toward the house where everyone was standing.

Jonas waved his hand.

"It's alright, just a water snake," he said.

Up at the house Hezekiah sat back down, all the others followed his lead.

Hezekiah broke the silence.

"I had one of them get after me one time, they can get real mean," he said.

"They think they own the whole river, I reckon," he added.

"The main thing, the children are alright," said James.

Grand Maw Rachel spoke up.

"That mean ol snake disturbed the children's play, it may be some time before some of them will get back in the water," she added.

Grand Maw Rachel got out her little corn cob pipe, filled it with fine ground tobacco, walked to the fire place in the kitchen, and lit it with a twig of fire. She came out of the door with a puff of smoke coming from her mouth.

"A good smoke after a good meal is enjoyable," she said.

She went back over and sit in her chair.

"Grand Maw, how long you been smoking?" asked Rhoda.

"Shucks honey, don't rightly know; but a many a year," she said.

"I think I smoked when Grand Paw Hezekiah brought me to

Montgomery County back about 1780," she added.

By now all the children were coming up the hill, like a herd of turtles.

"No need to rush now I guess," said Rachel.

"Well we had our excitement for the day," said Susannah.

Little Crockett was standing and holding on to her dress.

"That young-un will be walking a fore you know it," said Hezekiah.

The Whitt family had a good time that day, and enjoyed the company of each other.

After a while Hezekiah spoke up.

"Rachel, don't you think we better get over Green Mountain?" he asked.

"Guess so, It has been so good to visit, I hate for it to end," she answered.

"Maw we will see you in the morning," Jonas said.

"Susannah, me, and some of the children will meet you to go to church," Jonas added.

"Paw how do we get to your place?" asked Jonas.

"Just follow the road cross the hill, down near the bottom you will see our house on the left," Hezekiah said.

"It's the only one there," he added.

About that time James and Nancy stood up and walked toward Susannah, to say good by. Susannah opened her arms and gave Nancy a hug and next James, before you know it everyone was hugging someone.

"Thanks again for all the gifts!" said Susannah.

"Now don't worry about what little we gave you, we are glad to help a little," Rachel said.

Nancy turned and said, "Enjoy your material."

"You know some of them young-uns will want a new dress or a new shirt for school," she said.

"School," said James Griffith.

"We got school in Tazewell county?" he asked.

"Sure," said Hezekiah as he helped Rachel up in the buggy.

"School is important now a days, got to be able to read, write, and cipher," explained Hezekiah.

"Education is something that will help you all the days of your life," Grand Maw added.

"We'll will see you all in the morning," said Hezekiah.

Hezekiah and Rachel waved as they pulled away.

Next James and Nancy waved.

All the hands of the Jonas Whitt family were in the air waving like the wind.

Soon both buggies were on the little road down by the river.

Then they could see them head up the hill of Green Mountain, and were out of sight.

CHAPTER 5

WE ARE HERE

Jonas turned to his family and exclaimed, "This has been a wonderful day."

"Time spent with loved ones, is as good as it gets," Jonas said.

"And it continues tomorrow with our trip to church," said Susannah.

Everyone was tired after such a busy day.

"Lets get our chores done, and get ready for tomorrow," Jonas suggested.

"Who all is going to church," asked James Griffith, knowing only two horses, and two mules were available to carry the them.

"Well we will have to decide," replied Jonas.

"Your Maw, little Crockett, and me," Jonas said.

"I guess you can draw straws to see who the other two will be," Jonas said sadly.

"Children, I will get us a wagon on the road real soon, then the whole family can go together," Jonas added.

Jonas went in the house and broke off broom straws, checked and made sure none were the same size. All the children gathered around.

As he held the straws out, they looked the same size as the varying lengths were concealed by his hand.

"Call it, short or long," Jonas said.

"Short!" shouted James Griffith.

"Short it will be, the two shortest straws will get the mules tomorrow, the long straws will stay home and take care of the younger children," said Jonas.

Each child took a straw.

When all the straws were taken Jonas said, "Let's see who got the short straws?"

The straws were compared.

James Griffith jumped with glee, he and Rhoda got the "get to go" straws. The other children had varies comments, shoot, shucks, and one darn.

Jonas gave a stern look at John Bunyon.

"Sorry Paw.," John said.

"Don't worry, you will rotate until I get the wagon," Jonas said.

"Me and your Maw want all of you to attend church as much as possible," Jonas added.

"John I want you to read the Bible to the children tomorrow while we are gone," Jonas instructed.

"All day Paw?" John Bunyon asked.

"No not all day, about an hour," Jonas said.

"You are a young man now, time to be a leader to the younger children," Jonas added.

"All right Paw, I can handle it, maybe I can go next week," he answered.

"Yes maybe," replied Jonas.

"James, you and Rhoda lay out your best Sunday clothes," said Jonas.

"James Griffith clean up your shoes," said Susannah.

"Shoes, I got to wear shoes?" he asked.

"Yes," said Susannah.

"You are going to church!" she said.

The other children took it pretty well, thought Jonas.

"I hate for things like this to happen," he said.

Susannah looked at him.

"I know what you are saying, it will be all right," she said.

He gave her a smile, and walked over and pulled her to him.

"Give me a big hug, I love you Susannah," Jonas said.

"I love you too," replied Susannah.

"Glad you got us here, in our new home," she added.

"We all pulled together to make it happen," Jonas replied.

"Got any more of that coffee, honey," asked Jonas?

"Yes Jonas, but you don't need coffee this late, you will not sleep tonight," Susannah said.

"Please get me a cup, I will sleep," Jonas said.

"I'm so tired a herd of buffalo couldn't keep me awake," he added.

"Alright, sit down in the sitting room, I will bring you a cup," she said.

Susannah poured out about a half a cup, then added water to finish filling the cup. I will not let him flop around all night she was thinking. Susannah brought the coffee to Jonas.

He took her hand!

"Here sit down beside me, lets enjoy a little time together," Jonas said.

She squeezed his hand and sit down close to her loving husband.

"Better enjoy this for now, It wouldn't last long," Susannah said.

"We got to get the young-uns all lined out for bed," she added.

Rhoda had little Crockett upstairs giving him a bath from the pitcher and bowl. He was getting a little fussy.

"I think every one will sleep tonight," Jonas said after hearing Crockett protesting from up stairs.

"Crockett usually loves his bath time, reckon you are right," replied Susannah.

Finally all chores were done and it was getting dark out side. The Whitt's settled down for a restful nights sleep. After all the good nights were expressed by each of the children, the house fell silent. Once again you could hear the river as it bubbled over the rocks.

Night creatures were out and on the prowl, something was disturbing the animals in the coral. The cows started bawling, and the horses were running back and forth.

Jonas spring to his feet and called out, "John get your clothes on an grab a musket."

Jonas was down stairs and lighting a lantern when John Bunyon got to him.

"What's going on Paw?" asked John.

"Something is bothering the stock, we better be quick," said Jonas as he headed for the door.

They ran toward the fenced in lot where the stock was. Jonas heard a thump as something jumped the fence. They ran toward the noise, and got a glimpse of a large animal heading toward the mountain.

"See that Paw?" asked John.

"Yes I did, don't know what it was, lets check the animals," Jonas said excitedly.

Jonas and John climbed the fence near where the noise came from. The animals were milling around with fear. The horses were still protesting as were the cows.

"Paw look over there, is that one of our?" said John.

"Yes," interrupted Jonas.

"That thing killed one of our sheep," Jonas said.

"Let's get her out of here so the stock can settle down," he said.

"We can take her to the barn and dress her out, may be we can salvage some of the meat," Jonas said.

"Alright Paw, do you think that thing will be back?" asked John.

"Not tonight, I think we scared it pretty good," Jonas replied.

"What do you think it was?" John asked.

"We will look first light, could be a bear, a panther, wolf, or even a wild dog," Jonas said.

"We will just have to wait and see," Jonas added.

"I'm going to skin out this mutton, you go to the house, get the twins up and build a fire up," Jonas instructed.

"We got to cook some of this meat, salt some down, and save it if we can," Jonas said.

John was off and got the twins up and went to the kitchen and started a fire.

Jonas came in the door carrying two hind quarters of the sheep.

"Maybe we can smoke some of this meat, boil some, and we can fry up some for breakfast," Jonas said.

Susannah was up and dressed by now, coming down to help.

"Something killed one of our sheep," Jonas replied as he seen Susannah.

"Better get James Griffith up also, he can help slice off strips for smoking," Jonas said.

"I'm going back to the barn and get what ever meat is usable," Jonas said.

By now everyone was busy trying to salvage the mutton. No one complained, they all knew the meat could not go to waste. Jonas was back with the last of the meat.

"John bring your musket and go to the barn with me," Jonas said.

"We got to bury the waste of the sheep and I want to look around a little bit to see if we can figure out what attacked our animals," added Jonas.

About thirty minutes passed, Jonas and John were back. The cooking and smoking was going good. Everyone looked so sleepy. By midnight work was done, meat was still smoking, but it would be all right to let it dry by itself.

"Thanks everyone, we saved most of the meat, now go back to bed and get some sleep," Jonas said smiling.

Everyone ambled off toward their beds. Finally all was quiet, and rest came to the tired family.

As day was breaking, Jonas and John were heading out with muskets.

"We should be back in time to leave for church," Jonas said.

"Go ahead and get breakfast, dress for church., we will be back as quick as we can," he added.

Now Jonas was a good tracker, his father Hezekiah had taught all the boys tracking and wood craft. He and John started out at the kill site.

Old jack showed up, all beat up.

"Where has that dog been, he should have been here last night," said John.

"Maybe he was," Jonas said.

"Lets see if he wants to help us track that devil," Jonas added.

"Here Jack, smell this scent, lets go hunting boy," commanded Jonas.

It didn't take Jack long to catch the scent, barked loudly , and headed under the fence.

"Come on John , Jacks got the trail," shouted Jonas.

Jonas and John jumped over the split rail fence and headed up the grade toward the mountain, the dew was heavy and their pants were already wet.

Jack kept his nose to the trail, and let out a confident yelp every little bit.

They had traveled about a mile where fields turned to woods. Jack kept right on the trail.

The quarry had done a double back twice but Jack caught on and was relentless in his pursuit.

Jonas and John had to do double time to keep up. They were doing some heavy breathing by now. Jack was slowing down some too. Jack came to an abrupt stop and pointed toward a thicket of mountain laurel. Jonas and John froze in their tracks.

"John that thing is in that thicket!" Jonas said.

"You stay here, I am going around to the upper side and try to flush it out, Jonas said."

"Remember how I taught you to shoot?" Jonas said.

"What Paw, aim little, hit little?" asked John.

"That's right son," Jonas said.

"You ready John?" he asked.

"Alright I'm going now, it should run down there where you can get a shot," added Jonas.

Jonas started his circle, Jack followed him up the grade to flank the thing, what ever it was.

Jonas moved slowly and precise.

John moved in about three paces and stood ready, musket raised in a relaxed position. He had his Brown Betsy chocked, and was ready as he could be. He had one eye on Jonas and one eye on the right side of the thicket.

Jonas gave John a little wave and headed into the thicket, Jack took the lead again and crept into the thicket in crouched position. What ever they had tracked was waiting in that thicket.

John whispered a little prayer, "Dear God, please protect Paw and Jack, and help me shoot straight, Amen."

In a moment the leaves shook and you could see something running toward the right side of the thicket, Jack was barking loudly now.

Out come a Black Bear, running on three legs. He paused and looked at John.

John unloaded and the bear crumpled to the ground. John started reloading in case he had to shoot again.

Now Jack ran out of the brush barking at the bear.

"Here Jack, hold it boy," Jonas hollered.

"Come Jack," Jonas commanded.

Jonas was just about to the fallen bruin.

"Good shot John, I couldn't have done any better," Jonas said.

"I don't know of anyone that could have made that shot any better than you did," Jonas added.

"Be careful Paw, he might still be alive," warned John.

Jonas walked up behind the bear, reached out his musket barrel and poked the bear.

"I think you got him good," Jonas said.

"Paw did you see him running?" asked John.

"No why?" replied Jonas.

"He was running on three legs," replied John.

"Well that would explain a lot," answered Jonas.

"What do you mean Paw? John asked.

"The bear was wounded, that's why he went after our stock," Jonas said.

"The sheep was easy prey for a wounded animal." he said.

Jonas stood there and looked at the bear, and patted John on the shoulder.

"Alright John, here's what I want you to do," Jonas said.

"Get back home, get the mules teamed up and bring that heavy rope," Jonas instructed.

"Get back as soon as you can," Jonas said.

"I'm going to gut this feller and we can drag him home," he said.

John and Jack were off like a flash.

Jonas went over and poked the bruin one more time.

No need to take a chance, he thought.

Jonas was thinking, that boy did make a good shot at a moving target.

John is a fine young man, even if he is mine, Jonas surmised.

Well I better get this critter gutted, he thought.

He rolled the bear over so he could get to his under side.

This bear is a young one just barely grown, but big, thought Jonas.

Jonas looked for the wounded foot. There it was his front right foot had a big splinter right in the center of it behind the front toe pad. It was festered up some but should not brother the meat.

Jonas got to the work at hand, he took his sharp skinning knife out and slit the hairy belly. In a short time he had the bear cleaned out.

John was back in no time, he was riding one mule and leading the other.

Jonas could see the mules had on their collars and were rigged to do some pulling.

"Did you tell any one at home about killing a bear?" asked Jonas.

"Yeah I did, I couldn't wait Paw, John said.

"They are all excited at home," John added.

"Me too," said Jonas.

"You got yourself a fine bear," Jonas told him.

"Lets get this thing back to the house John, some folks are going to church today," said Jonas.

"I forgot that," replied John.

Jonas and John had the bear rigged and headed home in no time, Jack was running back and forth with excitement.

As they come in sight of the house, everyone was out looking for them. In minutes they were at the barn with the carcass. Everyone gathered around to see the bear that turned John Bunyon into a man.

"Well John you killed it, you skin it," commanded Jonas.

John looked up quickly.

"I ain't never skinned a big ol bear!" he exclaimed.

"You have skinned rabbits, squirrels, ground hogs, skinning is skinning," Jonas said.

"Just do the same thing in a bigger way," Jonas explained.

"Rachel, since you aren't going to church will you help your brother?" asked Jonas?

James Griffith spoke up, "Paw let me help John, skinning a bear is man's work"

"You got the short straw James, are you sure you want to stay home and help John?" asked Jonas.

"Please Paw, Rachel can go to church in my place," James said.

"I want to hear all about this bear hunt, and how John shot it," James added.

"Alright James get some work clothes on, and Rachel put on your good dress.

"We got to get over Green Mountain and meet Maw and Paw," Jonas said.

"John, cut off a hind quarter while we get ready, I will take it to your Grand Paw," Jonas said.

"He will be proud of you, killing a bear," added Jonas.

"Alright Paw, I will get it ready," replied the proud John.

Finally Susannah, and baby Crockett were mounted up. The twins were on the mules, and Jonas was in the lead with a hind quarter of bear meat tied behind his saddle.

They looked back and seen John, James and a audience of younger children skinning Mister Bear. It was funny to watch.

They headed down by the Clinch and hit the road to cross Green Mountain.

Jonas turned around to Susannah and replied, "Feels like I already lived this day, and it's just getting started."

"I know what you mean, nobody got much sleep last night, with all the excitement," she replied.

"Hope your Paw has salt to put on the bear meat," she added.

"I'm sure he will have some on hand," replied Jonas.

"Well let's try and forget about all that went on, and try to concentrate on worship today," said Susannah.

"We have not heard any preaching for about two months, with the trip and all," she added.

"What did Hezekiah say the preachers name was, I'm not too alert this morning!" said Susannah.

"Elder David Young, is his name, Maw said he was a fine man, and tells it like it is," replied Jonas.

"I enjoy good preaching, but I wouldn't get mad if we get out early today," replied the worn Jonas.

Jonas turned around and looked at the girls.

"Awful quiet back there," he said.

"Aren't you all excited to go to Grand Paw Hezekiah's and to Church?" Jonas asked.

"We would be Paw, if we were not so tired," answered Rachel.

"I know girls, we promised them we would come today, and we keep our promises don't we?" asked Jonas.

"We will be fine," replied Rhoda.

"This is a nice view up here, look over there, we are coming into Baptist Valley," announced Jonas.

"How big is this valley?" Susannah asked.

"I think Paw said about a mile wide and nine miles long," Jonas replied.

"Of course the width varies, according to what part you are in," he added.

As they descended the hill, Susannah said, "I see it over there on the left, see it girls?"

"Grand Paw and Grand Maw have a beautiful house," said Rhoda.

"A real nice house to be this deep in Virginia," Jonas added.

"Somebody is sitting on the porch bet it's Grand Maw Rachel," said Rachel.

Susannah turned back to her and smiled.

"You know you were named for her don't you dear," asked Susannah?

"Yes Maw, I remember you all told me about that," she answered.

"Rachel is a fine name, I'm glad its my name," Rachel added.

Jonas turned around again.

"Sounds like you ladies are all awake again," he replied.

"Smells like little Crockett is awake," replied Rhoda.

"Well I can change him while Jonas tells the bear story," Susannah said.

"Not much time, we will have to head up the road, we don't want to be late for Church," Jonas said.

They rode up to the porch where Hezekiah was waiting.

Rachel had been waiting , but went in to get her shawl.

Hezekiah said with a loud voice, "How's the Whitt's this fine Sabbath morning?"

"Just fine Paw, how are you and Maw?" asked Jonas.

"Good I guess, got up a little stiff in the back, but that is normal for an old man," Hezekiah said.

"What's that you got tied on behind you Jonas?" Hezekiah asked.

"John Bunyon sent you some bear meat," Jonas replied proudly.

"Bear meat, where, how, where did he get bear meat?" Hezekiah asked.

"It's a long story, I will tell you all about it on the way to Church," answered Jonas.

"Got some salt to put on your bear meat?" asked Jonas.

"Yes, bring it around to the smoke house, we will salt it down and hit the road," replied Hezekiah.

Hezekiah spread out salt on the bench in the smoke house, put the big hind quarter in the center of it. Then he took salt and rubbed it all over the meat. Then he took some muslin material and wrapped it around it.

"There, that will do for now let me wash my hands and get my Bible, then we can be on our way," replied Hezekiah.

By now Susannah had little Crockett changed and he was wide awake.

He was jabbering, and looking around.

"Crockett feels good, he's the only one that got any sleep last night," Susannah said.

The buggy was hitched up in preparation, so Hezekiah helped Rachel up into the seat. He walked around and got up into his place. Took the reins and with a "Gitty Up", they were heading up the valley.

Jonas pulled his horse up beside the buggy so they could talk.

"Good road up through the valley Paw," Jonas said.

"Yes some is pretty good, some not so good," Hezekiah said.

"Now are you going to tell me before I bust a wondering about that bear?" Hezekiah asked.

Jonas told the whole story, and went in great detail as he told the part about John Bunyon dropping the bear with one shot.

Hezekiah smiled with great pleasure!

"That bear was really on the move, huh son?" asked Hezekiah.

"Sure was Paw," answered Jonas.

"John and the other children are skinning and cutting the meat right now," added Jonas.

"John told me he prayed for me and old Jack, and to help him shoot straight," Jonas said.

"You got your self a fine young man Jonas," exclaimed Hezekiah.

"Well the whole family is just fine," answered Jonas.

"Glad you all got that bruin, having a sore foot makes them dangerous," said Hezekiah.

"They will go after a child even, when they are hurt like that," he added.

"Yes I know, that is why I thought it important to get after him this morning at first light," replied Jonas.

"Wise decision," Hezekiah said.

Grand Maw Rachel finally got in a word.

"Was it a big bear son," she asked?

"Yes it was full grown, but a young one I think," Jonas said.

"Should be some good eating meat," Hezekiah said.

"Well you better get back there and ride with Susannah," Rachel said.

"Women don't want to be left out," she added.

"She's fine, she knows men have to brag on their boys, especially when one of them kill a bear," answered Jonas.

The road began to narrow now so Jonas dropped back to ride beside of Susannah.

"Well did they like your bear story?" Susannah asked.

"Sure did, Paw is so proud of John Bunyon," Jonas said.

"He's liable to bust his buttons right off his shirt," he said.

"That is good, I love to see men proud of their of their young-uns," she replied.

Jonas looked at her in amazement.

"How do you feed the baby on a jostling horse?" Jonas asked.

"Feeding a baby is a natural thing, no matter where you do it," she answered.

"He is in control, he don't turn loose too easy," she added.

"Maw," replied Rhoda, "You are embarrassing us."

"Silly girl, it is just a part of raising children," Susannah said.

"You should have seen me when you all were babies, I had one on each nipple."

"Maw, we don't want to hear about that, especially since Paw is listening." Rachel protested.

Rhoda changed the subject, "Bout how much further Paw?" she asked.

"Don't know, never been there before," answered Jonas.

"I would say we are better than half way there," he added.

Hezekiah kept a good pace with the buggy, but not too fast. He knew the ladies were riding behind them.

Jonas was thinking now, this is a good day that the Lord has made. He was with us last night, and this morning in a time of danger. Now they would be in the Lord's house soon. Good preaching and Christian fellowship is what they need.

"We are just about there," Hezekiah announced.

It was a fine strong church building. It had a steeple with a bell. They could hear the clang, clang of the bell as they neared the church.

"That is like music to my ears," said Susannah.

To the left of the church was a cleared field and about six or seven buggies were there. The horses were tied to a weight, so they could do a little nipping on the grass. Over to the right was a long pole horse hitch.

Hezekiah went to the left. Got out and dropped his weight, then tied his horse to it. He walked around, and helped Rachel down out of the buggy.

By now Jonas had dismounted, hitched his horse, and went to assist Susannah. She handed down David Crockett, and stepped down off her horse like a veteran rider.

The twins were down and heading toward Grand Paw Hezekiah.

"Come on girls, we can just about fill a pew today," said their Grand Paw.

Grand Maw Rachel was all smiles, she would have her sons Jonas and James in church today, plus all the ladies, Susannah, Nancy, Rachel and Rhoda.

Sure enough The Whitt's filled a pew. James and Nancy were already seated when they arrived. James and Nancy stood up and hugged all the Jonas Whitt family, and also hugged Hezekiah and Rachel.

"Coming to our house today?" whispered Rachel to James?

"Yes Maw," James answered.

"We will stop for a little while," he added.

Hezekiah turned to Rachel, "I count thirty five here today," he said.

"That is good," Rachel replied.

Elder David Young walked to the front and stood before the pulpit. All talking stopped, silence fell upon the congregation.

"Welcome to the house of the Lord, Ye children of God," said the preacher.

"Brother Hezekiah would you open our service with a prayer," asked the Elder?

Hezekiah nodded, and stood and prayed a prayer of Thanksgiving. It was a short Prayer but to the point. He sat back down.

John Hankins went to the front to lead in some hymns.

Rachel turned to Jonas.

"That is our neighbor, he only lives about two miles from us," she said.

John Hankins worded the first verse, then the whole congregation joined in together. Then a pause and John Hankins worded the next verse, then the whole congregation joined in again to sing together. Each hymn was sung and enjoyed in this manner. After about four or five hymns were sang, Elder David Young came forward again, carrying his Bible.

Brother Young flipped open his Bible and what ever passage appeared he would preach on it.

Elder Young acknowledged the visitors and bid them a welcome. He had Hezekiah introduce Jonas, Susannah, Rachel and Rhoda. Everyone nodded their heads as a welcome.

Now Elder Young became earnest in his message. He preached for about an hour on the subject of the Blessed Hope. "It is a funny thing that Bible always opens to that subject," Hezekiah whispered.

"Shhhh!" Rachel said.

Brother Young extended in invitation to the congregation to come up and accept the Lord Jesus into their life.

After another hymn, and a closing Prayer the service was ended. Everyone made it a point to shake the hands of the visitors.

By now young Crockett had about all the church he could handle. He was tired of being held, tired of Susannah whispering be quiet, and he was hungry and wet.

Everyone had a little bit of fellowship on the way to their buggy's and horses.

Susannah and Grand Maw Rachel headed to the buggy, where they could take care of little Crockett's needs.

Hezekiah took Jonas around to each man for a formal introduction.

Jonas met John Hankins the song leader, and also Hezekiah's closest neighbor, besides James.

Jonas also met Lawyer David McComas, John Wynn, William Williams, and Thomas Perry, and of course Elder David Young.

Brother Young wanted to know if all of the family was with him.

"No," replied Jonas, "Two daughters Emma, and Elizabeth, and two sons John and James were at home skinning a bear."

"A bear," replied brother Young.

"Yes," said Jonas.

"My son John Bunyon killed it this morning," Jonas said.

Jonas gave him a quick version of what had happened during the night and early this morning.

Brother Young said, "You must be proud of that John, making a shot like that!"

"Yes I am, of course I'm proud of all my young-uns," replied Jonas.

"I look forward to meeting the rest of your family," the Elder said.

"I guess you know I am the school master here locally," he added.

"No I hadn't learned of that," Jonas said.

"When does school start, and what ages do you take?" Jonas asked.

"Starts about the middle of October, that gives most folks time to get in their harvest," replied Elder Young.

"There is no age limit long as they can get to school, I don't mean babies of course," Elder Young added.

"Well brother Young, we will be talking before then," said Jonas.

By now Susannah had little Crockett soothed down, changed his diaper and was feeding him again.

As Hezekiah and Jonas walked toward the buggy, Grand Maw Rachel told them to take the horses, she would drive the buggy so Susannah could feed the baby.

"Maw that's alright, I can ride the horse," Susannah said.

"Nonsense honey, you sit right there and take care of that young-un," replied Rachel.

Hezekiah untied the horse, picked up the weight and put it in the floor of the buggy.

"Alright Rachel be careful," said Hezekiah.

Rachel backed the horse enough to make a turn back toward the road. Hezekiah, Jonas, and the twins mounted up, and fell in behind the buggy.

The Hankins buggy was in the lead as they headed back down the valley.

James and Nancy followed behind the riders.

Rhoda said to Rachel, "Looks like we got a caravan to Grand Paw's house."

"Did you notice Thomas Perry rode his carriage to church?" Hezekiah said.

"His nigger drives him and Mrs. Perry ever where they go."

"Yes I seen he had a servant, I noticed he was up close to the church listening to the service," answered Jonas.

"How many slaves does he have?" Jonas asked.

"I think He has about five or six," answered Hezekiah.

"He has house slaves, and field slaves," added Hezekiah.

"I'm not sure how I feel about that," said Hezekiah.

"Me neither," replied Jonas.

"I know the Bible don't really speak against having slaves," said Hezekiah.

"I always got by with out any," said Jonas.

"Me too," said Hezekiah.

"Of course I never run a plantation like Thomas," added Hezekiah.

"The people up north are starting to express their views of how us southern people ort to live," said Hezekiah.

"They would be better off, to mind their own business," Hezekiah exclaimed.

"Some of the people up north are hypocrite's, they have slaves and call them servants," added Hezekiah.

"That is right Paw," replied Jonas.

"I am starting to run down a bit Paw, it will be nice to get back to your place," said Jonas.

"I bet you are," Hezekiah said.

"It will not take us long," he said.

"Rachel is taking that buggy on down the Pike," Hezekiah added.

"Pike, Paw, is that what you call this road?" asked Jonas.

"Some call it Baptist Valley road, some call it Kentucky Turnpike," replied Hezekiah.

"You know this is the road to Kentucky, don't you son?" asked Hezekiah.

"I didn't know that Paw," exclaimed Jonas.

They followed for a while in silence, as they watched the buggy wheels throw up little clouds of dust.

"I see the house, we are just about home," Rachel announced.

CHAPTER 6

NOW WE LIVE IN TAZEWELL COUNTY

The Whitts converge on the Hezekiah home. Grand Maw Rachel had a lot of food cooked up.

"It will be ready in about two shakes," she said.

Nancy and the twins went in to help her.

Susannah got baby Crockett laid down on the bed and put pillows on both sides. She came in to help set the table and finish up the dinner.

"Crockett is sleeping hard, hope he don't wake up for a while, I don't know if the pillows will keep him on the bed," Susannah said.

"Let me know if any of you hear him," Susannah added.

Rachel replied, "Yes dear," as she mashed the big bowl of potatoes.

"Here Rhoda put some more butter in for me," Rachel said.

In the sitting room Jonas , James, and Hezekiah talked on different subjects, but conversation kept coming back to the bear.

"I hope John and the other children had good luck cutting up that bear," said Jonas.

"Don't fret Jonas, I am sure they did just fine," replied Hezekiah.

"I guess you are right Paw," Jonas answered.

"Jonas you are so lucky to have such wonderful children, I wish Nancy and I had some," James said.

"I think you are right James, I take them for granted some times," Jonas said.

"I was concerned this morning when we had that bear cornered," Jonas added. "We left him a way out, and had a plan for him to run out like he did," Jonas explained.

"You never know what will happen in situation like that," Jonas added.

"Sounds like you had a good plan," said Hezekiah.

Hezekiah Whitt House. Baptist Valley, Tazewell County, Virginia. Log underneath.

"You got to have a good plan for anything you do, if you want to succeed!" pronounced Hezekiah.

James nodded his head and said, "Paw is right about that."

"Jonas I was wondering, reckon you might let some of the children spend a little time with Nancy and me?" James asked.

Jonas looked up surprised.

"Well I think that would be alright, maybe one or two at a time, they could visit over night, right now I need them all to pitch in and help us get settled," Jonas replied.

"I understand," answered James.

"That is a splendid idea, the children could get to know Uncle James and Aunt Nancy," remarked Hezekiah.

"Not to mention Grand Paw and Grand Maw, you know we live close to each other," James added.

"Come and get it, dinner is ready!" announced Grand Maw Rachel.

"Wash your paws and we can eat," she added.

"Paws!" said Rhoda.

"Maw always says that, you would think we were pups or something," Hezekiah said.

Jonas chuckled, "Maw is something, that's for sure," he said.

They all gathered around the table, Hezekiah offered grace, and the family enjoyed the dinner.

Hezekiah told a little story about an old man that was hard of hearing.

"There was an old man eating with a visitor, when supper was over the old man ask if he would have more?" Hezekiah said.

"I have had sufficient," the visitor said.

"Huh you been fishing?" the old man said.

"I have had plenty," the visitor replied.

"Huh you caught twenty?" ask the old man.

"I have had enough," said the visitor.

"Huh they were tough?" ask the old man.

Every one laughed at the story. All had heard it many times except the twins Rachel and Rhoda. They thought it was the most wonderful story, because Grand Paw Hezekiah told it.

Jonas stood and said, "It has been a wonderful day, good company, good food, and a good church service."

"I hate to say it, but we better get over Green Mountain," he added.

"James come by, and I am sure John Bunyon will give you a hunk of bear meat," Jonas said.

"By the way we can spare some mutton also, I would have brought some Maw, but things happened too fast this morning to remember every thing," Jonas added.

"Don't fret son, you all better get home and get settled in," Grand Maw said.

"No more bear hunts fer a spell!" she added.

"I agree with that Maw," answered Jonas.

"Come on girls lets get going," said Jonas.

"Thanks again for everything," Susannah said as she waved toward the elder Whitt's.

"You know you are welcome," said Rachel.

"Good to see you and Nancy again ," Jonas said.

"We will let the young-uns visit you some a little later," he added.

By now Susannah was mounted, and Jonas was going to hand up baby Crockett.

"Let me hold him on the trip over the hill honey, you have held him all day," Jonas said.

"Well alright, just be careful," answered Susannah.

"I will, don't worry," replied Jonas.

He put Crockett on his saddle like he was a big boy. One leg on one side the other leg on the other side. Crockett set up and smiled from ear to ear.

"Look at my big boy, a regular horseman," Jonas said.

The ladies all smiled at the sight.

"Now Jonas you watch that boy, don't let him fall," Susannah said sternly.

"Now Susannah, you know I am careful," replied Jonas.

"I guess," she said, and dug in a spur.

"Come on Clementine, take me home," Susannah commanded.

"How did that horse get that name?" ask Rachel. (daughter)

"Don't know, when your paw brought her home, she looked like a Clementine," answered Susannah.

"What about Paw's horse, does he look like a Jake?" asked Rachel.

"Reckon so," replied Susannah.

"What time is it Paw?" asked Rachel.

Jonas looked up at the sun.

"I would think about 4:30!" he said as he felt for his watch.

He flipped open the cover on his watch and looked intently at it.

"Well not far off, it's about twenty till five," Jonas said.

"Girls he looked at your Grand Maws clock as we were leaving, that helps out a might with his guessing," said Susannah.

"Paw you are always tricking us," said Rhoda.

"What, you ask me what time didn't you?" asked Jonas.

"Yes sir, didn't know you were going to trick us again," Rhoda responded.

Jonas laughed!

"Gotta have fun, life is too short to be a serious all the time," Jonas said.

Rhoda said right out of the blue, "Paw I love you, and you too Maw."

"Well honey we love you too, and Rachel," Jonas said.

"All our babies, we love every one of them," added Susannah.

Crockett was jabbering again, like he knew every thing they said.

"Look down there, there is our Clinch, we have just about talked our self's home," said Susannah.

"Our Clinch?" asked Jonas.

"Of course our Clinch it's right in front of our home, that makes it ours," replied Susannah.

"Well I know of a certain water snake that thought it was his," exclaimed Jonas.

"That's not funny, bout scared the young-uns to death," answered Susannah.

"Alright honey, I agree it's our Clinch, at least this part," Jonas said.

James Griffith came running from the house, Old Jack right with him.

"Hello James, did you have a good time?" asked Rhoda.

"We sure did, got that old bear hide hung on the barn wall," exclaimed James.

"Where is every one else?" ask Susannah.

"Chores," he replied.

"I been cleaning up the dishes, John and the girls are out checking the stock and stuff, probably they are in the barn looking at the bear some more," James Griffith added.

"What did you all eat?" Susannah asked.

"We had beans, taters, bear meat, and mutton," answered James.

"That old bear sure was greasy, but pretty good," he added.

"Sounds like you all handled everything just fine," said Jonas.

By now they were dismounted. Susannah and the twins headed into the house, Jonas and James Griffith were leading the horses, and mules toward the barn.

John was walking toward them with Emma and Elizabeth at his heels.

"Paw, what did Grand Paw say about his bear meat?" asked John.

"He was really surprised, and very proud of you," replied Jonas.

"We skinned a bear Paw!" Emma announced.

"I know you did honey, was it fun?" asked Jonas.

"Yes, we hung his old hide on the wall," Emma exclaimed.

"He won't be a killing no more little sheep, Paw," Elizabeth said.

"That's for sure, John Bunyon took care of that!" Jonas answered.

"Sure did!" James Griffith resounded.

"Lets get Clementine and Jake taken care of, and the mules too," Jonas said.

"They have been working all day," Jonas continued.

"We can look at mister bear later," Jonas added.

"Maybe we can make a bear skin rug for the sitting room, that way every body that comes to visit can see John's trophy," Jonas surmised.

"Paw, that would be great," sounded John Bunyon.

John and James took care of the horses, and mules needs, while Jonas and the girls headed to the house.

"Paw did Grand Maw miss us today?" asked Elizabeth.

"Grand Paw and Grand Maw both missed you," answered Jonas.

"Me and your Maw missed you to," Jonas said.

"You will get to go next time, we all will be going as soon as I can get us a wagon on the road," Jonas exclaimed.

"When you gonna get us a wagon Paw?" asks Elizabeth.

"That is number one on my list," replied Jonas.

"I think I will go to Jeffersonville tomorrow, and see what I can round up," he added.

Susannah was in the sitting room as they entered the house.

"What are you going to round up Jonas?" she asked.

"A wagon, or at least some wheels," Jonas said.

"Wheels Paw, we can't ride wheels," Elizabeth said.

"Sure you can," said John.

"When we build a wagon on them," added John.

"We will just have to wait and see what I can round up," Jonas said.

Everyone was exhausted, So as soon as it was dusky dark, every one was in bed.

"Hope we don't get another bear tonight," James Griffith said quietly.

"Me to!" sounded everyone.

Then the good nights were heard as usual, each child had to say goodnight.

Jonas whispered to Susannah, "By the time we all say good night, it will be morning!"

"Yes," she chuckled.

"Hope the baby don't get us up tonight," she added.

The house fell silent, and a snore here and there could be heard. The Clinch was making her restful sounds, and night creatures were about. Sleep, restful sleep came to the Whitt house. Morning came quickly to the tired family. Today is Monday, what a week end the Whitts have had in their new home land. Today they will start living their new dream in Tazewell County. They all knew that many things needed to be accomplished, before cold weather.

Grand Paw had warned them that winters are longer and colder here, than in Montgomery county. He said it was the elevation.

The family had breakfast together, then Jonas started handing out assignment to the children. He announced, "I am going to Jeffersonville to check on a wagon, or at least find some wheels, to build a wagon around."

Everyone listened intently.

"John, I want you and James to set up a saw frame out by the barn, then take the mules to the woods and start dragging in dry wood to cut up for fire wood," Jonas said.

"I want all four of the girls to go and dig up the potatoes, that Grand Paw Hezekiah planted for us," Jonas instructed.

"You can put them in the empty stall," he added.

"Susannah you and Crockett can do your house work," Jonas suggested.

"Crockett will get a lot done, I'm sure!" Susannah replied.

"I guess he will keep me entertained while I put stuff away," she added.

"I need the wagon to help in our other projects, I need to build a hog pen, chicken coop, a wood shed close to the house, and also a spring house," Jonas said.

"We have to get enough wood cut to heat the house this winter, we have to get all the corn in, and the potatoes dug," Jonas continued.

"I would like to get the ground turned over before the snow comes," Jonas said.

"I'm sure we have other little things we will want to do," Susannah added.

"School starts about the middle of next month, Elder Young is the school master, he told me this yesterday," Jonas related.

"Paw can't we skip school this year since we got so much to do?" James Griffith asked?

"Don't think so, we can fit it in" Susannah spoke up sternly.

"You heard your Maw," replied Jonas.

"Any body got any questions before we get started?" Jonas asked.

Everybody got up and headed out, Rhoda turned and said, "Maw do you want me to help with the dishes before I go to the field?"

"No, honey, I will take care of the house, and start some dinner," Susannah replied.

"James Griffith I do need some wood brought in, and a fresh bucket of water," announced Susannah.

James grabbed the water bucket and headed for the spring.

Jonas kissed Susannah and headed out to saddle up Jake.

"I will be back as soon as I can, is there any thing you want from town?" asked Jonas.

"Not today dear, I will go in to town with you next time and get a few things," Susannah said.

"Love you!" she added.

"Love you too!" answered Jonas.

The girls headed to the barn to get hoes and a couple wood crates for the potatoes.

John got a shovel and an ax, then gathered four poles to build the saw stand.

Jonas saddled Jake and headed toward the ford in the Clinch.

He wheeled Jake around to face the children.

"You all be careful, see you after while," he said.

Every one turned and waved, and went back to their chores.

Jonas was excited about going to Jeffersonville.

He whispered a little prayer, "Lord if it be your will, help me get a wagon for the family."

Jonas rode Jake along at an easy but steady pace.

As he rode along he admired the great beauty of this new homeland. There was Clinch Mountain over looking the valley. It appeared bluish and smoky. Jonas marveled at the natural beauty of the Creator.

He also let his mind wander back to the farm, he could see John and Jim dragging logs to the newly built saw stand. He could see the girls all working to get the potatoes in. He could see Rachel and Rhoda digging with hoes, and Elizabeth and Emma picking them up and putting them in the barn. Jonas was proud of the children, they all had learned to be good workers.

Jonas noticed that the trees were already getting a brownish color. The Fall was almost on them. He was thinking, good thing we got here when we did, it has been a busy year. Getting ready to move, making the hard trip with family and live stock, now getting settled before winter.

God has been with us Jonas thought, he whispered another prayer, "Thank you Lord for your loving kindness."

Jonas was almost to Jeffersonville.

He patted Jake on his neck.

"You are a good boy," he said out loud.

Jakes ears twitched, as he received the complement.

Jonas could see smoke rising from the town in little gray streams as it drifted into the heavens. The town was coming into clear view now.

Back at the Whitt house, Susannah has been busy cleaning the kitchen and getting ready to start dinner. Crockett has finished up his nap and is now ready to play.

About that time she heard a horse trot up to the back door. She went and looked out, she saw that it was Hezekiah.

"Well hello Paw," she said.

"Hello there young lady," he replied.

"Young lady, you Whitt's sure no how to make a women feel young," she replied.

"You missed Jonas, been gone about an hour," Susannah added.

"Did he head for town?" he asked.

"Yes sir, he went to check on a wagon, got us all to working and took off," she said.

"That's a Whitt for you!" said Hezekiah laughing!

"Well honey, I will not disturb the work's in progress, I think I will go on to Jeffersonville," Hezekiah said.

"I have unfinished business, and I want to catch up with Jonas," he said.

"I might know where he can get a wagon," Hezekiah added.

"Alright Paw be careful and have a good day in town," replied Susannah.

Hezekiah tips his hat, wheels his mount and heads toward the Clinch.

Jonas heads for the livery stable, hoping to start his search there.

As he comes close a voice sounds out, "Hello Mister Whitt how you doing this fine morning?" a stranger asked.

"Fine sir, do I know you?" Jonas asked.

"Well I guess not, word travels fast in these parts," he said.

"I seen you folks Friday when you came through, now everybody knows you are Hezekiah's son," he added.

"Glad to get good folks here in Tazewell County, we all have a lot of respect for your Father," he added.

"Well since you know me, guess you should introduce your self," Jonas replied.

"Sorry for my manners Mister Whitt, I am John Laird," he said.

"Anything I can do for you?" John asked.

"Well to start with call me Jonas," he answered.

"Good," John answered.

"You just call me John," he added.

"Well John, I am in need of a wagon," Jonas answered.

"Wagon huh, I know where you might find one," John said.

"Bill Russell lives over by the Perry's in Indian, not too far from you and your Paw," John said.

"Heard he had a wagon for sale, don't know much about it, I saw it here in town, but I never paid it no mind," John said.

"He seems to be a fair fellow to deal with," John added.

"Well thanks John," said Jonas.

"I will check it out after I see Mister Vandyke at the tavern, he might know somebody looking to sell a wagon also," Jonas said.

"James knows a lot of folks," John answered.

"I reasoned that he would," Jonas said.

Jonas went in the tavern and had a seat at a small table. The young lady with red hair came up to greet him.

"Well hello Mister Whitt", how are you today?" she asked.

"Fine thanks, Mary Jane, right?" Jonas asked.

"You are right, where is your family today?" she asked.

"I left them on the farm, hated to but we have a lot to get done, and I'm looking for a wagon," Jonas said.

"By the way that boy of mine, you remember, John Bunyon, killed him a bear yesterday," Jonas announced.

"Yes I remember that handsome young man, why did he kill a bear?" she asked.

"Killing sheep!" Jonas replied.

"Is your Paw here today?" asked Jonas.

"Yes sir, want something from the kitchen?" she asked.

"A cup of coffee would go good," Jonas replied.

"I will find Paw for you, and fetch your coffee," Mary Jane said. Mary Jane is right back with the coffee.

"Hear you are, Paw said he would be right out," she said as she set down a hot cup of coffee.

"Maw has him in there stringing beans," Mary Jane said.

"By the way tell John congratulations for me," she said.

"I will Mary Jane," Jonas answered.

Shortly, James comes from the back.

"Thanks Jonas for getting me out from under them beans," Jim said laughing.

"Hello Jim, thought you might know where I can get me a wagon," Jonas said.

"Russell, a feller that lives over in Indian had one not long ago," Jim said.

"Well that's what John Laird told me, thought you might know somebody here in town that was looking to sell one," Jonas added.

James sit down and talked for a while about the Whitt's first week end in Tazewell county. Jonas told him all about the goings on and the bear.

James sit up straight.

"Bet you are proud of that young man, making a shot like that," Jim said.

"Yes we are, hope he don't get the big head." replied Jonas.

The coffee was finished and Jonas thanked James.

"I better get going, I got all my children working, and I need to be with them," Jonas said.

"Good luck Jonas with the wagon," Jim said.

"Thanks James, see you next time," Jonas said.

As Jonas walked out, Hezekiah rode up.

"Well hello Paw, how you doing today?" asked Jonas.

"Fine son, did you find a wagon yet?" asked Hezekiah.

"No but I got a lead on one," Jonas answered.

"I know where you might get one," Hezekiah announced.

"Where is that Paw?" Jonas asked.

"Bill Russell has one over in Indian, about four miles from my place," Hezekiah said.

Jonas laughed!

"What's funny son?" Hezekiah asked.

"That is the third time I have heard Bill Russell, guess I better go see Mister Russell," Jonas said.

Hezekiah agreed, the third time is charm.

"Are you going there from here?" Hezekiah asked.

"I might as well, got to get one," Jonas exclaimed.

"Well I got to finish my work at the court house, and that might take some time," Hezekiah said.

"I will stop by your place on the way home," he added.

"I can just follow the river to Indian can't I Paw?" Jonas asked.

"Yes that will take you there, it is a fair road," Hezekiah answered.

"You have to cross the river twice, so be careful," he added.

"Jonas you tell Bill Russell hello for me and that I sent you to him," Hezekiah said.

"Yes sir, I will Paw," Jonas answered.

Jonas headed Jake toward the Clinch, going to see Mister Russell.

Hezekiah goes toward the court house.

Jonas is very anxious to talk to Bill Russell, and anxious to get the family a wagon.

Jonas is thinking, I will get to travel a new road, and see new things today, and meet a new man. Jake seemed to be glad to be out and about again.

"We better get going boy, got about 15 miles ahead of us, then back home," Jonas told his faithful Jake.

Jake trotted a little sideways, as a reply.

In about two hours of steady riding Jonas could see the little village of Indian. As he came into the village he saw a lady out doing some garden work.

"Good day Ma'am, could you point me toward Mister Bill Russell's place?" Jonas asked.

"Yes sir, go on down just past the mouth of Indian creek, up on the hill to the right," she said.

"Look for a little cabin and a big barn," she added.

"Well thank you so kindly," replied Jonas.

Jonas did not want to get in to a long conversation today, he had too much to do. So he hurried Jake on down the road.

"Welcome mister," she said and got back to her work.

In a short time Jake had Jonas up the hill, and in front of the Russell cabin.

"Hello in the cabin," Jonas said with a slightly raised voice.

A lady opened the door.

"Can I help you?" she asked.

"Yes Ma'am I'm looking for Mister Russell," Jonas replied.

"He is in the barn, ride out there and holler for him," she instructed.

"Thanks," Jonas replied.

As Jake wheeled toward the barn, Jonas could see a wagon sitting in the barn yard.

"Hello Mister Russell, you in there?" Jonas hollered.

A short thin man slid between the barn doors.

"I'm Russell, can I help you Mister?" he said.

"Yes sir, maybe, I'm Jonas Whitt, and I heard you might be looking to sell your wagon," Jonas replied.

"Whitt, you any kin to Hezekiah?" he asked.

"Yes sir, he is my father," Jonas replied.

"Good man, that Hezekiah, well get down Jonas, call me Bill," he said.

"Thanks Bill, and you can call me Jonas," Jonas answered.

"I didn't know Hezekiah had a Jonas," Bill went on.

"I just moved here," replied Jonas.

"Well Jonas, I do want to sell the wagon," Bill said.

"That is it," Bill said as he pointed toward the wagon.

Jonas shook Bill's hand and walked toward the wagon.

"She needs some work, but is a solid wagon," Bill said.

Jonas walked around looking it over, looked real close at each wheel.

"Seems pretty sound, except for a few loose boards, what do you have to have for it," Jonas asked?

"Well since you are Hezekiah's son, and she needs some work, how does eleven dollars sound, reckon a new wagon like this would go for as high as forty dollars, I think I'm offering you a good deal," Bill said.

Jonas walked around the wagon one more time.

Jonas looked at Bill and said, "Think I will take you up on it Bill."

Jonas dug down for his purse, from deep in his pocket. He counted out eleven dollars to Bill.

"Thank you Jonas." said Bill.

"Thank you Bill, now I got to figure a way to get it home," Jonas said.

"Where do you live Jonas?" asked Bill.

"Across Green Mountain from Paw," replied Jonas.

"Well I have an idea, do you need rigging for your team?" asked Bill?

"I have a set for my mules, what you thinking?" Jonas asked.

"If you want the rigging you could borrow my team, and bring them back tomorrow," Bill said.

"That way you could use the wagon and plow at the same time," Bill continued.

"What are you asking for the rigging?" Jonas asked.

"Well let me see, two collars, four long reins, two singletrees, everything you need to pull the wagon, I will let you have them for, lets see three dollars," Bill said.

"Come in the barn and look at them," Bill added.

"Jonas I will do you one better, I was planning to come up that way," said Bill.

"Take the rigging too, and I will pick up my team tomorrow," added Bill.

They went in and looked the rigging over. Jonas noticed the rigging was in excellent condition.

"Well Bill, I wasn't looking for rigging, but it would be good to be able to work two teams at the same time," Jonas said.

"It's a deal," Jonas added.

Jonas dug into his pocket again, and counted out three more dollars.

"Well Jonas you made your self a good buy today, tell Hezekiah I helped you a might on the trade," replied Bill.

"I will and thanks, you are a prayer answered," Jonas answered.

Bill and Jonas rigged the team, and led them to the wagon. In a short time, they were hitched up, and ready to roll. The two men shook hands to seal the deal.

"Jonas I will be by your place some time tomorrow, nothing happens," Bill said.

"I will be a looking for you," replied Jonas.

"Bert is the leader, John just follows what Bert does," Bill instructed about the team.

Jonas went around and tied Jake to the back, and got up on the wagon.

"Bill which way is the best, up the river, or over the Kentucky Turnpike?" Jonas asked.

"Turnpike through the valley is a better road for a wagon," Bill replied.

"Thanks again Bill, see you tomorrow," Jonas said.

"Giddy-up Bert," Jonas sounded loudly.

The team came to life and headed down toward the Kentucky Turnpike.

Jonas felt a sense of relief, God has helped me today he thought. Three people pointed me to Bill Russell.

"Thank you Lord for your loving kindness," Jonas whispered to his God.

CHAPTER 7

WE GOT A WAGON

Jonas drove his new wagon up Indian creek on the Kentucky Turnpike. He passed a farm that had to be the Hankins place, traveled another mile or so and went by another place. This other place may be James and Nancy's farm. Before long he turned up Green Mountain Road. There was Paw's place on the right, Jonas was thinking. Before he knew it he turned in to see his Maw Rachel sitting on the porch.

Rachel stood up, and looked!

"Thought that looked like you", said Rachel.

"Hello Maw, got us a wagon, and was going home, I thought I would stop for a little spell," Jonas said.

"I need a drink of cool water, think you can accommodate me, Maw?" Jonas asked.

"Why sure son, just got some water out of our fine limestone spring" she answered.

Your Paw went to town, he said he hoped to see you," Rachel added.

Jonas drink a tall glass of cool clear water.

"Thanks for the drink, it sure is pleasing," Jonas exclaimed.

"I did see Paw, he told me about Bill Russell having a wagon for sale," Jonas added.

"Good, looks like it worked out," She answered.

"I think Gods hand was on me getting this wagon," Jonas said.

"I don't doubt it for a minute, God is so good" replied Rachel.

"He is so good," declared Rachel again.

"Yes He is Maw, I better get on home, I want to show the family our new wagon," Jonas said.

Jonas hugged his mother and got back up on the wagon.

"See you Sunday Maw, if not before," Jonas said.

"Giddy-up Bart," Jonas commanded.

Bart moved into his collar, John joined in, and the wagon headed up Green Mountain.

This has been a good day, the Lord knew we needed this wagon, and He helped me find it, Jonas thought. Three people, the first three I asked, all sent me to see Bill Russell, Jonas surmised.

The family will all be glad to see me roll in, riding our new wagon, he thought.

Before long the Clinch River was coming in sight to Jonas. There's our Clinch he thought.

Jonas drove down by the Clinch and up the hill to the Whitt House.

James Griffith looked down from the barn yard, and saw his Paw arriving.

"There's Paw and he got us a wagon," James Griffith said loudly.

Before Jonas knew it the whole family was around the wagon. Rachel came out of the house carrying Crockett. She had a big smile on her face as did all the children.

"Here let Crockett look it over," she said.

She handed Crockett up to Jonas on the wagon. Jonas just sat there on the wagon holding Crockett, telling of his whole day. He told the whole story of how God had helped them get their wagon.

Crockett slid slowly down into the wagon and walked around holding on to the seat.

"Well David Crockett Whitt, what do you think?" Jonas asked.

Little Crockett grinned from ear to ear.

"I think he approves of it, Paw," John said.

"Well people let me get down, got to take care of the team and Jake," Jonas said.

"Mister Russell will be coming by tomorrow to pick up his team, he was so nice to loan them to me, you boys park the wagon up there by the barn and put the animals in the corral," Jonas instructed.

"Give them a little oats and fill up the drinking trough," he added.

James Griffith jumped up in the wagon, and took the reigns.

"Let me drive it over there John," he asked?

"Go ahead little brother, but be careful," John Bunyon said.

"Everybody get ready for supper, it will soon be ready," Susannah announced.

Jonas followed her into the house carrying Crockett. They had no sooner got in the house, and Hezekiah rode up.

"Come on in Paw, you can eat with us," Jonas said.

A good meal and good conversation was enjoyed by all.

Jonas told his story of the day, followed by each of the children, telling their story.

"Sounds like every body had a good day and got a lot done," Hezekiah said.

"What about you Paw, how did your day go?" asked Jonas.

"It went fine, I was involved as a witness on some property exchanges," Hezekiah related.

"I also did a little visiting around Jeffersonville," he added.

Crockett was walking around holding to Susannah's dress, jabbering up a storm.

"Sounds like baby Crockett is telling his story," Grand Paw Hezekiah said.

Everybody laughed!

Everyone was tired, and they wanted to go to bed early again tonight.

Hezekiah didn't linger for long after supper. He wanted to get across the hill, before too late. Rachel would be looking for him.

The evening chores were done and everybody could relax. Jonas sat on the floor and played with the baby. Emma and Elizabeth joined in on the fun. John Bunyon was sitting on one of the kitchen chairs talking with the rest of the family.

"By the way John, a certain little red head, was asking about you," Jonas said.

John blushed a little.

"What did she say?" asked Rhoda, listening intently.

"She said congratulations," Jonas answered.

"What for?" Rachel asked.

"For killing a bear," replied Jonas.

"Paw, you mean you told Mary Jane about me killing a bear?" John asked.

"Yep, sure did," said Jonas.

John turned a little redder.

James Griffith became envious of his brother John Bunyon, but said nothing.

"Well it's almost dark, lets all get ready for bed," said Susannah.

Jonas quoted his little night saying.

"To bed, to bed, said sleepy head, oh no said slow, put on the pot said greedy gut, and we will eat before we go." Jonas said in a funny way.

Everyone chuckled, and headed off towards their beds.

The good nights, were all exchanged and quietness came to the Whitt House.

The days came and went, time moved swiftly. The boys had a mountain of fire wood cut. Jonas had built a wood shed close to the house, and the boys filled it to the brim.

The girls had harvested all the potatoes, some were stored in a catch in the ground. They dug a pit, lined it with leafs put in the potatoes, covered them with leafs, then covered it with soil. This would keep them for long periods of time.

Fall plowing was started, Jonas wanted all the fields turned to prepare for spring planting.

They had enjoyed the Lords Day each week, attending church, and keeping the day restful and respectful.

The new wagon had been very useful, Susannah got to go to town with Jonas a couple of time for supplies. This was a treat, getting out of the normal routine .She had bought sewing items needed to use with the new material they got as house warming gifts from James and Nancy.

By now the children had matching clothes, shirts for the boys, and matching dresses for the girls.

"Nobody can mistake our children with their new clothes," Jonas stated.

School time was here, the children were all excited. A change from farm work to reading, writing, and arithmetic, was a welcome change except for James Griffith. James enjoyed the farm and felt trapped by sitting in school.

Jonas let one of the older children take the others to school in the wagon. He did not insist that the twins or John go to school. They knew the three "R's" pretty well, and were almost grown. So they took turns driving the smaller children to school.

James protested some.

"I am plenty big enough to take the others to school," he explained.

"For now John, Rachel, or Rhoda will be in charge of the younger children, even you James Griffith," Jonas said.

"Alright Paw," he said reluctantly.

This way two of the older children could be great help on the Whitt farm.

Jonas and John Bunyon have started plowing now that school started. Also they built a chicken coop, and a new privy.

Each evening they would take the wagon and gather the corn, and take it to the barn. It had to be shucked later, and put in the crib. Everything was coming together, to meet their goal to be ready for winter.

Susannah announced, "All work and no play makes the Whitts very dull."

"What are you thinking about?" Jonas asked.

"We have had our nose to the grindstone all year," she said.

"Let's have a corn shucking, and barn dance," Susannah said.

"The election is coming up soon, you will want to talk to some of the men before then," she added.

"I could do with some visiting too," she declared.

"Well that sounds good to me," replied Jonas.

"The boys have not had time for a hunt either," Jonas said.

"We will need a turkey for Thanksgiving," Jonas added.

"I think we all need a break, Crockett will be a year old in about six weeks," Susannah said.

"We can have him a little party, just family," she added.

"Sounds like you been thinking all of this over dear," replied Jonas.

The Children all agreed with their Maw's thinking.

"All right, you set a date a date for our corn shucking and I will spread the word," Jonas said.

"Guess we better get the rest of it gathered though," chuckled Jonas.

"Paw who you going to vote for in the election?" asked James

Griffith.

"Don't think Jackson is running, and the Vice President, Van Buren is a Yankee from New York," Jonas said.

"I think he will side with the North on every issue," Jones continued.

"I heard that he would block Texas from joining the Union because it would be a slave state," Jonas said.

"I'm not for slaves myself, but it should be a free choice I think," he added.

"Jackson is gathering up all the Indians from North Carolina and Tennessee, and he is marching them with bayonets held to them all the way across the Mississippi river," Jonas said.

"That is a disgrace," Jonas added.

"Also Jackson makes everyone pay gold when they buy property," Jonas said.

"How come Paw? asked James Griffith.

"A lot of folks lost their land because of the banks failing," Jonas said.

"Maybe Jackson was right on that," Jonas sighed.

"Credit can be very dangerous," Jonas added.

"This country is in a mess because of some greedy politicians," Jonas said.

"Wow! Paw, I didn't know you knew so much stuff about voting," replied James.

"You have to inform yourself all that you can," replied Jonas.

"You want someone in office that thinks like you, if you can get them there," Jonas said.

"Enough politics for now, how about having our corn shucking the thirty first of October?" she asked.

"Halloween would be a good time," said Jonas.

"I will spread the word, and you children can tell everyone at school, added Jonas.

"Alright Paw!" Elizabeth exclaimed.

Before they knew it, the thirty first rolled around, several families said they would be there. Jonas and the children cleaned out the barn, put new straw down, set up a table for food and drinks, and made a dancing area out in front of the barn. Jonas borrowed extra lanterns from Hezekiah and James. He also got the corn out in a working area so everyone could take a turn at the shucking!

There was excitement in the air. The twins had not got to meet any young folks.

John Bunyon, and James Griffith also wanted to meet some young folks.

"I hope Mary Jane will come," said Rhoda.

"Me too," said John before he thought.

The twins both laughed.

John turned a little pink.

People were arriving by four O'clock. Jonas had arranged for some folks to bring their fiddles, and banjo's. Susannah and the twins had worked most of the day getting bake goods and punch ready. The best plates and cups including those borrowed were carried out to the table.

Hezekiah, Rachel, James and Nancy were there by now, and a host of others. Even Elder Young was there. The music was started and the corn shucking began.

Mary Jane Vandyke, and John Bunyon sat together shucking corn. The twins, Rachel and Rhoda joined them, as did a few more young folks.

Everyone took a turn at the corn pile, and before they knew it all the corn was shucked and thrown into the corn crib.

Dancing was going on out in front of the barn. Eating and drinking was enjoyed by all. Some of the men gathered around to talk man talk.

The ladies did the same, except they were talking woman talk.

A few of the young adults and children took a time on the dancing area.

Truly everyone had fun, and many people met for the first time.

Jonas brought out a jug for those who wanted a swig of corn squeezins. Go easy on it fellows, was the word. Jonas got it from an unknown source. Even brother Young took his turn for a swig.

A good time was had by all, and it began to get late. Each family came around and thanked the Whitts for the good evening.

Lanterns on the buggies and wagons were lit, and folks began to leave. Most of them went to the ford below the house and crossed the

Clinch. There would be a train of buggies and wagons headed toward Jeffersonville. The rest crossed Green Mountain toward Baptist valley. Every one was jolly.

David Crockett had a wonderful time, everyone wanted to hold him and play with him. He was ready for all of this attention.

"We all had a good time, but I'm glad it's over," related Susannah.

"Me too," said Jonas!

James Griffith spurted out, "I know something!"

John Bunyon gave him a look, and said, "You be quiet little brother!"

"What is it?" asked the twins in unison.

James Griffith couldn't hold it in any longer.

"John kissed Mary Jane!" James announced.

John took off after him, and the family all laughed.

"Well lets get our lanterns put out and get ready for bed," said Jonas.

"Paw and James took theirs with them," said Jonas.

"We don't have many to put out," he added.

The family all went in the house to get ready for a night's rest. Every one settled into a good sleep.

Susannah had pulled Jonas close to her, because the late October air had a chill about it.

Time was passing fast, It was almost Thanksgiving time. John, James and Jonas, were all looking forward to a hunt. They wanted a turkey, and a deer would be nice.

Jonas had been up on the ridge at least two times. He had scouted out the area, and put out some cracked corn. There was a good chance one of them would get a shot at a turkey, and maybe a deer.

The day before Thanksgiving, James, John and Jonas were in the woods before day light. Jonas put John where he could see anything coming, and James where he could see John, and Jonas. Jonas and John had it made up to let James Griffith have a shot if it came to him. James was a crack shot, even though he was young.

Jonas knew John Bunyon was a good shot also, after all he killed that bear in September with one shot.

Everything was set, the boys sat quietly while being alert to everything around them. The November's sun rays crept over the ridge and toward the hunters.

Gobble, gobble, gobble, a nice Tom turkey and three of his wives come toward James Griffith. He raised his musket ever so slow. He watched while the turkeys, meandered through the Virginia woods, closing the distance between them. Tom turkey was looking in all directions for trouble. He pecked at something on the ground, when he raised his head this time, James squeezed the trigger, and the turkey's head disappeared. The three Hens were gone in a flash.

Jonas had a big smile on his face.

"Paw I got him," he said as the smoke cleared.

"You sure did James, that was one great shot," Jonas said in praise.

John also came over to see the prize.

"Little brother you sure took care of Tom turkey, Maw will be proud of you too," John said.

"We are having turkey for Thanksgiving!" James announced.

Jonas put his hand on James's shoulder.

"I'm proud of you son, now you go ahead and take your turkey home and give him to your Maw," Jonas said.

"John and I will get back on our stand, we might get a shot at a buck," he added.

"After you help clean your bird, you can come back and hunt some more," Jonas said.

"We will be out the ridge a little further, so be careful if you come back," Jonas warned.

"Alright Paw, I will take care of this old Tom," replied James Griffith.

"You all be careful, and good luck," James Griffith said as he turned to leave.

James was out of there, carrying his trophy.

"John lets slip out the ridge and get back on stand, we still have a chance to get that buck," Jonas said quietly.

They had only been on their stand minutes, when along came a doe with her yearling twins following her. The hunters froze and watched them pass. A few more minutes passed, and they saw a nice big buck following on their trail.

That buck is in rut, Jonas thought.

He would sniff the air, sniff the ground, and trot out the trail a little further. Jonas waited, he wanted John to have the first shot. The buck was not as cautious as usual, being love sick.

John Bunyon had him in his sites, next time he raised his head, John turned loose on him. The big buck lunged forward, and ran about ten paces, and fell to the ground.

The two hunters slowly walked to the buck. Jonas kept his musket on the ready just in case. John touched The buck with the barrel of his Brown Betsy, the buck never moved.

"Another great shot son," Jonas exclaimed.

"The way he took off, I thought I missed him Paw," John exclaimed.

"Sometimes they do that, I guess they run on stored up energy," Jonas said.

"Look at that rack," said Jonas.

"It's a twelve pointer," John exclaimed.

John started dressing out the buck, Jonas cut a pole to carry the big deer on. Before 10:00 AM, they were back at the house. They had their turkey and a buck for Thanksgiving dinner.

Grand Paw Hezekiah and Grand Maw Rachel were planning to come, also James and Nancy would be there to share the feast.

"James and John had something extra to be thankful this year, they both made good shots, and both bagged their quarry," Jonas said proudly.

Grand Paw Hezekiah had plenty of praise for both the boys.

"Now we will have a plenty of good meat for this special dinner, and then some," he added.

Jonas had no extra hog, or beef to kill this winter. The stock he brought from Montgomery County were for breeding. The family would be fine, they had the mutton, bear, and now a big buck for food.

They may make an excuse to make another hunt, for fresh game. Maybe a hunt for rabbit, grouse, squirrel, or even quail could be enjoyed in the winter months to break the blahs of cabin fever.

The children have been making the long ride to school everyday, doing chores, doing home work, and not having much time to play. Little Crockett's birthday would come up soon. He would be a year old on the 13th of December.

Susannah decided to have a family party to celebrate. Everyone was looking forward to this day.

Hezekiah, Rachel, James and Nancy were planning to come and have a day of family fun. The day Susannah picked was the Saturday before Crockett's birthday. This would not interfere with school or work around the farm.

Susannah cooked up a big pot of venison stew and made a big sheet cake.

To make a sheet cake she had to make three small ones and put them together. She made a nice sweet icing, and lovingly spread it over the entire cake. She didn't have any little candles, so she put one of her finest home made candles right in the center of the cake. Rachel was not in school this Friday, so she helped her Maw with all the planning.

It was a cold December day.

"I hope the children don't get too cold," she said to Rachel.

"Me too, it is really cold out there," replied Rachel.

"School will probably be let out soon if the weather keeps getting colder," she added.

"We will have to teach them here at home when that happens," replied Susannah.

"It is important for all of you to get the best education possible," she added.

Saturday morning was here, and the family was ready to have a family day and celebrate little Crockett's day.

The fire in the kitchen was stocked and burning steady. Jonas also had a nice cheery fire burning in the sitting room. Little Crockett seemed to know something special was going on. By now he was an expert at crawling, and could walk if he would just turn loose. He was in the sitting room walking around holding to chairs or who ever extended a hand to him.

"Horses out side," said James Griffith.

Emma opened the door, "Grand Maw, Grand Paw," she said in a loud voice.

Then another buggy rolled up.

"There's Uncle James and Aunt Nancy," John said.

"John you and James hug everybody, and unhitch the horses, put them in the barn and give them some feed," Jonas said.

"Alright Paw," they said as they greeted their grandparents, and James and Nancy.

"Hello everybody," came from Hezekiah.

"Thanks for seeing to our horses, you boys are as handy as a pocket on a shirt," said Uncle James.

James Griffith spoke up as proper as he could, "It is no problem sir," he said.

"Sir, that makes me feel old," James exclaimed.

Every one had big smiles on their faces.

Jonas was at the door waving them in.

"Get in this house before you catch your death, it is cold as whiz out there," he said.

Grand Maw stepped down from the buggy holding on to Hezekiah's hand.

"It's not too awful bad," she exclaimed.

Everyone came in to the house, and hugged each awaiting child.

Grand maw picked up Crockett.

"Here is my birthday boy," she said.

Little Crockett was all smiles.

After some good family visiting Susannah asked, "Anybody hungry?"

"I am, I am, I am," came from all directions.

"Well come and get it," was her next words.

"I just got out a big pone of cornbread, and the stew is hot and ready," Susannah announced.

The family all enjoyed the meal, with many good compliments on the stew.

Hezekiah stated, "I can't tell this stew from good beef stew, Susannah knows her venison cooking."

"Thanks so much Paw," she said.

"Now Jonas hold Crockett here by the table, I want to see what he does when I set up his cake," Susannah said.

Everyone gathered around the little boy. Susannah lit the big single candle, and carried the cake to the table. Ooohs and Aaahs were heard around the circle of family.

David Crockett Whitt straightened his back, and let out some talk that only he understood. He was smiling, and his eyes sparkled like the stars of heaven. He knew beyond a shadow of doubt, all of this was for him.

"Wish we had one of them picture taking boxes we learned about at school," James Griffith said.

"What's he talking about," Jonas asked?

"They call them cameras, right now only rich people in big cities have them," Rhoda answered.

"Well I be!" Hezekiah exclaimed.

"What are they going to come up with next?" he asked.

"Hard to say, next thing they will want to fly," said Grand Maw Rachel.

Every one chuckled at this outlandish prediction.

Jonas helped Crockett blow out his candle, and the cake was served.

"It taste like heaven," said Elizabeth.

"Not quite that good honey," Susannah exclaimed.

The day passed fast, and it was another good family day.

Hezekiah, Rachel, James, and Nancy were headed across Green Mountain in a jolly mood. Jonas was still out on the porch waving. He shivered and rubbed his hands.

"Smells like snow in the air," Jonas exclaimed.

"Could be, we haven't had a snow yet!" said Susannah.

"I hope Maw stays covered up good on the trip home," said Jonas.

"It's cold for sure!" replied Susannah.

CHAPTER 8

DAVID CROCKETT WHITT
IS ONE YEAR OLD!

Jonas was right about smelling snow, It started about first light the next morning. It snowed almost non stop all day long. They had celebrated little Crockett's birthday, but today is December 13, 1837 his true birthday. It looks like they will get a big snow for David Crockett's gift.

Jonas and the boys went out and put all the animals in the barn, except the hogs. They were in their hog house and new straw was added for bedding.

The snow was over a foot deep, and still falling. The boys kept shoveling a path to the outdoor privy, and to the wood shed. Extra fire wood and water was carried in. A path was shoveled to the spring and barn. It seemed futile to clear out paths, with the heavy snow on the ground and still falling. At least they could find the trails tomorrow morning.

They had awaken to a beautiful winter wonderland.

Jonas held little Crockett up to the bedroom window.

His eyes opened wide to take in the sight. Crockett had never seen a big snow, he was so amazed!

Jonas said to Susannah who was making the bed, "Look at this baby!"

He was mesmerized by the great whiteness, and beauty the Creator had laid out before them.

"This is part of our worship today," Susannah said.

"You do know that it's the Lords day, don't you Jonas?" she asked.

"Yes dear, we will not be heading across Green Mountain today,"

Jonas said.

"You mean White Mountain, don't you Jonas?" Susannah asked?

"Guess I do, it is definitely white today, not green," Jonas answered.

"It's chilly up here, lets get downstairs, I can start breakfast," said Susannah!

"Sounds good to me, I hope somebody has fixed up the fire down in the kitchen," Jonas said.

When Jonas got to the kitchen, John was still adding kindling to the fire.

"Morning Paw, it will be warm in here in a little while," John announced.

"Morning John, thanks for building up the fire," replied Jonas.

"Have you looked out yet?" asked Jonas.

"Yes Paw, I went to visit the little house, I waded snow in the path over a foot deep!" John replied.

"Bet we got two feet," Jonas exclaimed.

"Close to it," agreed John.

"After breakfast me and James will get to shoveling again," John said.

"Thanks," Jonas said.

"Let's have a little home church after breakfast; then we can work on that," Jonas added.

"Sure Paw that would be good," John answered.

After breakfast Jonas read from the Bible, led in a couple of hymns, and closed in prayer.

Everyone said, "Amen!"

It was a big wet snow, the temperature rose during the day.

Jonas took his measuring rule out and stuck it in the snow.

"How deep is it," asked James?

"Wow, it is a full twenty five inches," exclaimed Jonas.

The boys and Jonas had little roads to all of the important places in no time!

"Thank the Lord for this thaw or we would be shoveling all day," exclaimed James Griffith.

"Yes James, the ground has still got some warmth to it," agreed Jonas.

The Whitts enjoyed some family closeness for a few days while the snow hung on. Christmas was almost here, time to think about baking and cooking.

Jonas and Susannah had some little items to put in the children's stockings. Jonas also brought a few thing from town after the snow was gone. Susannah had purchased some items when Jonas took her with him on one of the trips.

It will be a good Christmas at Whitt House. Christmas came with a clear but frozen ground. At least travel would not be impeded. Once again everyone congregated at the Whitt House as it was now becoming to be known.

James Griffith brought in a turkey for dinner again. James and Nancy had provided some nice yams, and turnips. Grand Maw Rachel had baked pumpkin and apple pies. Hickory nuts, chestnuts, and black walnuts gathered in the fall would be great snacks in this festive season.

The children got to their presents early on Christmas morning, they had a great time looking in their stockings. Boys got items such as jack knives, gloves, and big red apples acquired in town. The girls got things like a pendant to wear on Sunday, clothing items, and fruit. Everyone got stick candy.

Jonas had found time and privacy to build sleds for the younger children. Saint Nick, of course brought it all, and filled the stockings the children had hung the night before.

James and Nancy brought items as did Hezekiah and Rachel, to give to the children. John Bunyon, Rachel, and Rhoda the oldest children got a Bible each from Grand Paw and Grand Maw. Blankets, and homemade quilts were given to Jonas and Susannah!

Susannah had made fancy sweets, and some baked items of the day to give as gifts to visitors.

Every one had a great time that day. They gathered around a pretty Cedar Tree, that the boys had set up for the family Christmas Tree. The twins popped corn and threaded it into chains to wrap the tree. Elizabeth and Emma made paper people and animals, and hung them to the boughs.

Carols were sung, and when everyone got quiet, Hezekiah opened his Bible to Luke and read the Christmas story. The children sat intently, their eyes sparkling brightly as they listened to every word. John, Rachel, and Rhoda followed every word in their new Bibles.

James and Nancy came to Jonas and Susannah, and asked a special request.

"Brother, we would love to take Emma, Elizabeth, and James Griffith for a visit in our home," James said.

"They will not have school until sometime next month weather permitting," he added.

"If they want to go you can have them for a week or so," said Jonas.

"That is a good idea, they will get to know their Aunt and Uncle, and you all will find out about young-uns," said Susannah.

It was agreed the children would go for a visit, this was exciting for everyone.

Little Crockett was starting to wind down, he had been going strong all day with all the Christmas spirit in the household.

"I think that's our sign to go home, it's getting late, and the baby needs to lay down for a nap," Hezekiah said.

"Probably Hezekiah needs a nap," Grand Maw Rachel said.

Hezekiah smiled!

The three children got some clothes and their Christmas presents gathered to take to Uncle James' house.

"I wondered why you rode the wagon, instead of the buggy, now you have room for the children and all of their stuff," Jonas committed.

"Well Jonas, we were hoping," said Nancy.

"Just make them behave," replied Susannah.

"They are good children, there wouldn't be problem I'm sure," said uncle James.

The house seemed extra quiet after everyone left. Crockett took a little nap, and woke up for another round of Christmas. The family sat around the table to leftovers.

"I think its even better the second time around," said John Bunyon.

"I have to agree, it sure is tasty," said Jonas.

"We have so much to be thankful for, I wonder what 1838 has in store for us," Jonas said.

"Good things I hope," said Susannah.

"We will have the Lord watching over us, and family sticking together," Susannah added.

"With that, we can face most anything," replied Jonas.

"I hope that Van Buren will make a good President, and this great state Virginia, will be blessed," Jonas added.

Jonas and the boys used the winter months to make some needed furniture, Susannah and the girls did sewing and made some clothes. Every day some time was allotted to teach the children the three R's, and even some history. A hunting trip or two was enjoyed by the boys.

That old bearskin was tanned out, and made into a rug. They put it in the sitting room. Little Crockett loved it, he would sit on it, and pull the bears ears. He patted it, rolled on it and simply enjoy the black hairy thing.

"Good thing it don't come to life and eat us all up!" exclaimed James Griffith.

Everyone laughed!

Early Spring 1838 came to Tazewell county, and it was welcome! Winters seem long when you spend much time in the house. The mountain of firewood was now a little hill. Thoughts of planting, and preparation for summer was on everybody's mind. It was hard to believe they had lived there for six months already.

Soon the busy season would be up on them again. The children had gone back to school in February, weather permitting.

James Griffith had gone enough to get tired of it, and longed for April to get here. He knew he would be needed soon to help put out crops, and help on the farm. James was a smart boy, but a typical boy. Fishing, hunting, and skinny dipping appealed to him much more than the three "R's".

Hezekiah had talked to Jonas just lately about the farm.

"How do you and Susannah like the farm you live on, Son?" Hezekiah asked.

His reply, "We love it Paw!"

"Well son would you like to own it?" Hezekiah asked.

"Yes Paw, but I'm not sure we can get it, so many banks have failed," Jonas said.

"You know land has to be bought with gold or silver," added Jonas.

"Yes I know, do you have a Dollar in silver or gold?" Hezekiah asked.

"Yes sir, I do have that," Jonas answered.

"Well pay me a dollar and we will go to Jeffersonville," Hezekiah said.

"We will transfer the deed to you, and it will truly be the Whitt House, Whitt farm too I guess," said Hezekiah.

"Are you sure Paw, we don't want to take anything away from you and Maw," Jonas said.

"Your Maw is for this as much as me," he answered.

"Don't worry, you are not taking anything away from us, you have to pay the tax on it from now on, not me," said Hezekiah laughing.

Jonas laughed too.

Jonas and Susannah would start out the planting season 1838, as proud owners of the Whitt House!

Crockett was walking all over the place and getting into any thing that amused him.

"It seemed like he had five or six hands," Susannah said.

He had learned to talk a little bit too.

The whole family enjoyed watching him and playing with him.

The bear rug was his favorite place to sit and play. When he got tired, he would just pass out for a nap.

It was warm to him and no splinters, Jonas told them.

"I think sometimes he thinks its alive," said Jonas.

"He loves to pull its ears," added Susannah.

Everything went good this spring, the fields were planted and were getting off to a good start. They even had out a large cash crop of tobacco. A big garden with a great variety of vegetables were also planted. By now the weather was warm and nice.

Hezekiah told Jonas that he would be down on Tuesday to take the boys to his favorite fishing hole. Jonas had replied that would be fine because they needed a break from the farm.

"If you don't mind I want to go also?" Jonas asked.

"Sure you can go, we will see who is the fisherman of the family," replied Hezekiah.

"Sounds like a contest is brewing," replied Jonas.

"Could be, if you fellers are lucky we can have a fish fry," said Hezekiah.

Hezekiah showed up early on Tuesday morning, he was set for a day of fishing!

Jonas and the boys were ready!

Out comes Rachel and Rhoda.

"Paw can we come to?" they asked.

"Well girls I can't think of any reason why you shouldn't," replied Jonas.

James Griffith spoke up, "tell them they can't scare the fish Paw."

"We don't scare fish, if any thing we will catch more than you James Griffith," Rachel said sternly.

Grand Paw Hezekiah said, "That settles it, the twins are going too!"

"Boys did you get the worms dug?" Grand Paw asked.

"Yes Grand Paw, and we caught some crawdads too," James Griffith answered.

"We all have fishing poles except the girls," Jonas said.

"That is not a problem, we have line, hooks, and lead, we will cut them a pole on the way," said Grand Paw Hezekiah!

"Grand Paw how far is the fishing hole from here?" asked John.

"About a half mile down the river, but we can start right below the house and fish our way down to my honey hole, we might catch several on the way down the Clinch," Hezekiah explained.

"I usually catch some Red Eyes and sometimes a Small Mouth or two on the way down the river, crawdads work wonders on the Small Mouth Bass," added Hezekiah.

James Griffith was excited and raring to go. He was baited up before they reached the water.

Jonas cut two nice long poles and rigged them with hook, line, and sinker for the girls.

Grand Paw quoted a tongue twister that the poles made him think of.

He said, " A long, slick, slim, slender, sycamore, sapling."

Rhoda tried to say it fast and twisted it up.

Everyone laughed!

The fishing started with James Griffith throwing in first. A little Red Eye hit the worm he presented. He yanked it way up on the bank.

Everyone laughed!

Soon everyone was fishing their way down the Clinch.

Grand Paw Hezekiah pulled out a scrappy Small Mouth!

"Here's one for the table," he said in a jubilant voice!

Then Rachel hooked a real nice Small Mouth.

"Paw, Paw," she yelled, "I got a big-un"!

"Well pull him in!" James Griffith said in disgust!

Jonas ran over and helped her land the nice bronze back.

"Thanks Paw," she said.

"Here's another one for the table," she added.

Grand Paw grinned!

By and by each of them caught a fish as they worked their way down the river.

James Griffith even caught a nice one.

John Bunyon fished behind all the rest. He waded down the river, fishing around each protruding rock. He was catching twice as many Red Eyes than any one else.

Hezekiah said to Jonas, "John is fishing like an old hand!"

"He is a real fisherman. I expected him to do well," replied Jonas.

When they got to the Honey Hole that Grand Paw had told them about, they already had a big string of fish. The Honey Hole was a deep hole of water about one hundred yards long.

"Now we can sat down and do some lazy fishing," said Hezekiah.

"Watch your poles close, there's some big cat's in here, and maybe a big old Bass or two," Hezekiah instructed.

Every one set there poles, spaced about ten feet apart, and sat down.

Rhoda screamed out, "I got a big one Grand Paw!"

Her pole was bent double.

Hezekiah went over to assist her.

"Take your time honey," he exclaimed.

"Got to wear him down a bit before we can get him out," he added.

She fought the fish for a time. Seemed like for ever, but was only a couple of minutes. She drug the fish up close to the bank, Hezekiah grabbed the line and flung the two foot Channel Cat out on the bank.

"Whooe, Weee," exclaimed Rhoda, "That's at least two for the table!"

"I think you are right," said Grand Paw.

That was the biggest of the day! They all had good luck, and had two stringers full before three o' clock.

"Looks like we have a good mess of fish, are you all ready to head for home?" Hezekiah asked.

"Wrap them up young uns!" Jonas said.

"Lets head for Whitt House, we have a mess of fish to clean," he added.

Everyone was pleased with the days catch of fish. They had Catfish, Small Mouth Bass, a couple of Large Mouth Bass, some Sunfish, and a host of Red Eyes.

When they got back home, Susannah walked out with little Crockett to see the catch.

Her eyes grew large as she looked them over.

"Wow, you all really did good!" she exclaimed.

"Pish, Pish," Crockett hollered.

He wanted to play with them. Every one laughed at little Crockett.

"Better get to cleaning them," said Susannah.

"We can have some for supper, and Paw can take a mess home with him," she added.

They had a tasty supper of fresh fish, which was enjoyed by all. Hezekiah eat with them, and shortly after started for home. He took several fried fish for Grand Maw Rachel, and several uncooked fish that had been rolled in salt to have later.

It was a great day on the wonderful Clinch! A day to break up the routine of a busy farm.

Jonas always said you have to have a play day ever now and then.

This spring brought some new arrivals to the farm, Clementine had a handsome foal. There was two calves, and a litter of eight pigs born on the farm. The two hens were sitting also. Should be a bunch of little biddies any time.

Jonas had done some work for the neighbors, building a barn for one family and added a room on a house for another. He had helped set up a mill wheel for a McGuire man, on his new grist mill.

The crops were out, and also a big vegetable garden was growing close to the house. Summer of 1838 was just about gone. Soon would come the harvest season and time to get ready for winter once more.

Texas was trying to be annexed to the United States, but President

Martin Van Buren was against it. He said it may cause a war with Mexico.

The southern states all said it was because Texas would be another slave state.

The North didn't want any more southern states added, this would give more power to the South. There had become a tug of war between the North and South. Both sides trying to gain strength by adding new states for their side. It would be some time yet before Texas would join the union.

Hezekiah always said, there will be a war in this country one of these days.

"Jonas said in agreement, the North will not leave us alone."

"After you all fix all the problems in the country, how about inventing something to take the place of this scrub board!" Susannah said in an almost hateful tone.

"It takes all day to do the washing, and another day to do the ironing," she said strongly.

"Honey if I could I sure would," Jonas answered.

"I'm sure some day they will have many inventions to do away with some of our hard work," he added.

"Well it ain't helping today!" she said.

Jonas went on explaining, back in 1807 a feller by the name of Fulton put a steam engine on a boat. Now I hear tell they travel up and down the Mississippi River. Just four years ago in 1834 Hiram Moore made a Combine Harvester to gather wheat. The same year a Cyrus McCormick made a mechanical reaper. And you have heard of Eli Whitney's Cotton Gin. The cotton gin picks the seeds out of cotton. It is a real slow job to do that by hand. After the gin come on the scene, they started growing cotton all over the south.

"So you see, there will be a mechanical washer some day," Jonas said.

"In the old days they rubbed them on a rock I heard," added Jonas.

"Well don't expect me to do no rock rubbing!" Susannah said strongly.

"I'm sorry honey, do you feel alright today?" Jonas asked timidly.

"I'm just a little tattered Jonas," Susannah answered.

"Well Susannah go sit down for a break, I will go brew you a cup of tea," Jonas said.

"You have been working too hard here lately," Jonas added.

"I guess that a little break wouldn't hurt nothing, I will take you up on it," she said.

Hezekiah ask Jonas, "Is Susannah doing alright?"

Jonas replied, "She has been acting a little different. I wonder if she could be, naw she couldn't be!"

"Couldn't be what son, in a family way, now I have said it," Hezekiah answered.

"She shouldn't be, Crockett is not weaned yet", Jonas explained.

"Well Jonas that is just an old wife's tell, women get pregnant every day while they are still nursing," Hezekiah said.

"You better get in there and fix that tea for her," Hezekiah added.

"I wonder if she knows if she is or isn't," Jonas asked?

"Well Son when the time is right you will just have to ask her, I don't know I am just your Paw," said Hezekiah.

Jonas went in and threw in a little kindling to put some heat to the tea pot. Then he went in to the sitting room to check on Susannah.

"You alright honey?" he asked.

"I guess so, this feels good to put my feet up for a little while," she answered.

"Well sit right there, I'm fixing you a nice cup of tea," Jonas said lovingly.

"Thanks so much Jonas, you are such a dear," said Susannah.

Jonas went back into the kitchen.

Hezekiah stuck in his head through the door way. "I'm going to get back over the hill son," he said.

He gave Jonas a puzzled look and said, "Do you know anything yet?"

"No Paw, I will let you know; do you want a cup of tea with Susannah and me?" he asked.

"No Son you need to be alone with her," replied Hezekiah.

"I will see you in a day or two, son," Hezekiah said as he headed for his horse.

"See you Paw," said Jonas.

Jonas went on and brewed two cups of tea, and carried them into the sitting room.

"Susannah, I thought I would have a spot of tea with you," Jonas announced.

"Good," she said, "you work way too hard!"

They sat quietly for a minute enjoying their tea, then Susannah looked up at Jonas and said, "Yes!"

"Yes," Jonas said, "Yes what?"

"You know what you sly dog," Susannah said with a smile.

"You know I am expecting a new little Whitt," she added.

Jonas let his mouth drop open as if it was a great surprise.

"You mean you really are going to have us another beautiful baby?" asked Jonas.

"It looks like it to me," replied Susannah.

"When do you think it will be a coming," ask Jonas?

"I think in early May, or late April," Susannah replied.

"Well glory be, that is wonderful news honey, a new little one for 1838," Jonas said.

"Jonas lets keep it under our hat, for a while," said Susannah.

"Alright, but I must confess, Paw already is suspicious, he ask me if you were going to have another little Whitt," Jonas said.

"Why did he ask that?" said Susannah.

"Paw is a wise old man, he can read people like a book," replied Jonas.

"I will have to swear him to secrecy," said Jonas.

"That is another thing about Paw, he is good at that." Jonas said.

"What do you mean," she asked?

"He can keep his mouth shut, something he learned back in the Militia," Jonas said.

Things went on pretty normal, it was a busy time with the harvest, and extra work that comes with the fall. This year they had the added work of hanging the tobacco in the barn loft. Also they had a much bigger corn crop to get in. Wood to saw and chop for winter heat, would always be a chore.

Susannah had ask Jonas if they could have another corn shucking , like they had last year?

"I reckon we can, it was fun and our corn all got shucked," replied Jonas.

Susannah smiled with her sweetest smile and said, "Yes and it gives our children a chance to meet other young people."

"We will have a bigger and better gathering this year," said Susannah.

"What do you mean honey?" asked Jonas.

"Well I mean we will invite more folks, and have a bigger group for one thing," she said.

"I think we should have every one bring a covered dish, and come earlier for another thing," she continued.

"We can get extra chairs set up and surround the dancing area in the level we used last year," she added.

"That would be good," Jonas said.

"We can have everybody bring their own chairs," said Susannah.

"Well we better get to inviting folks, what day do you want to have it?" asked Jonas.

Lets see now, looking at the big calendar on the wall.

"Looks like the last Saturday of September would be good," she surmised.

"That will give us two weeks to get everything ready," answered Jonas.

"We can go in to Jeffersonville, and start the news, and also tell everyone at church," Jonas said.

"Elder Young will tell the Methodist Pastor over at Pisgah, and his flock can come too," Jonas added.

Once Grand Paw Hezekiah knows about it he will tell everyone around the Court House.

"Sounds like we already got a good start on our plans," said Susannah.

"Yes it does," replied Jonas.

"We will tell the children at supper, they will be so excited," said Susannah.

Plans were made and everyone was invited. Those invited were asked to bring chairs, lanterns, and a covered dish of pot luck! Be there by 4:00 PM to have plenty of time to visit and meet folks was agreed on.

Jonas and his family had worked on getting every thing ready. Saw dust and straw had been spread wherever there was a chance of mud.

The corn was all gathered in and put in a pile to be shucked.

It was already after noon, folks would be arriving soon.

The first to arrive was Hezekiah, and Rachel, followed by James and Nancy. They came a little early, in case they were needed to help with last minute preparations.

By a quarter till four, it looked like a caravan on the road from Jeffersonville. Also buggy traffic was thick coming across Green Mountain.

James Griffith was out front meeting the folks, and directing them to the field to the right of the house for parking. Jonas had made some makeshift tables to serve as a place to put the food. Two large Crocks were filled with lemon aid, and home made punch. Two little brown jugs were also provided for the gentleman to enjoy some spirits after supper. Jonas even had several twists of tobacco put out for those that enjoyed a good chew.

The late September weather was beautiful. It had the makings of a great community affair!

The Whitt children were anxious to meet some folks, preferable the opposite sex of their same age group.

A great crowd arrived at the Whitt farm, all were in a festive mood!

Jonas said to Susannah, "I was worried about having enough food, but after looking on the tables, I am worried about getting it all eaten."

"I agree," exclaimed Susannah laughing.

Jonas had the visitors bring their chairs and place them in a large circle around the dancing area. The boys had set poles in the ground around behind the seating area to hang lanterns.

This was to be the social event of the year. Many folks knew that Hezekiah would be there, which prompted their decision to come. Hezekiah was a well known, and respected gentleman in Tazewell County.

It never hurts to know people of purpose and prestige!

Jonas and Susannah stood by to greet each family as they approached the area. Many people had not met the Whitts and were looking forward to this get together.

One family was Alexander and Sarah Beavers, which had children about the age of the Whitt's children. John Bunyon and the twins were next in line to greet the guests. Rachel would meet Adam Beavers for the first time. John Bunyon would meet Catherine Beavers also. These meetings would lead to significant meaning in time to come.

Another couple with courting age children was James and Rebecca Lowe. Their son John Bunyon Lowe would put a twinkle in the eye of Rhoda Whitt. This would develop in to a lasting relationship also.

Jonas stood in the center of the great crowd and ask for them all to stand for the blessing of the food.

Jonas turns to Elder Young.

"Brother Young would you mind to bless the food?" Jonas asked.

After the blessing a line was formed by families to fill their plates of the great abundance of food.

After eating the dishes were raked into a barrel, and placed into a great tub of soapy water. The scraps in the barrel would give the hogs a banquet tomorrow.

Soon the music of the fiddles, banjos, and even a jug blower was heard. The young people all headed to the barn to make quick work of the shucking. They all laughed and flirted as they took care of shucking the ears. Adam Beavers made sure he sat beside the lovely Rachel Whitt. John Bunyon Whitt sat beside the attractive Catherine Beavers, even though Mary Jane Vandyke was making herself visible to him. Also John Bunyon Lowe followed Rhoda the other twin, to a convenient place to set by the heaping pile of maze.

A young man by the name of William Tanner saw his chance to sat close to the red headed Mary Jane Vandyke, and took it. The young people were having a good time and the corn shucking went great also. Outside the barn the music was lively, and the grown ups were all dancing and visiting each other.

In record time the ears were relieved of the shucks and the young people made their way to the dance area.

The dance area was full of old and young alike. There was much joy in this harvest moon festival! The sun was setting and the big orange moon was rising over the Clinch Mountain.

Word went around to light the lanterns. What a sight, the great circle of lanterns shining brightly made!

Jonas turned to Hezekiah and said, "This reminds me of the Bible story Gideon and his three hundred warriors," he said.

"Remember they had circled the enemy and lit their lamps, it had to be a site like ours," Jonas surmised.

Hezekiah responded, "I hope they don't break their pitchers and blow their bugles."

Jonas laughed!

The evening passed so fast. Even the little one's enjoyed the affair. The Toddlers had been placed on quilts where they could be watched by their Maws. Little David Crockett Whitt was right in the thick of things. They all played together so well.

The older and younger folks begin to tire. Folks begin to gather their broods and head for their wagons and buggies. Each family came by to thank Jonas and Susannah for inviting them. Some made sure to shake hands with the prestigious Hezekiah Whitt, before taking their leave.

Some hugs and a few stolen kisses took place in the shadows! Little by little the circle of lanterns were transferred to buggies, and become little moving lights headed down to ford the Clinch.

"What a wonderful evening this has been," said Susannah!

"Everything went really well, the weather was perfect, and we had a big showing of folks from all over the county," she said.

Jonas shook his head in agreement.

"Yes and we had good food, and made new friend," Jonas said.

"This is truly a good place to live," said Susannah in a quiet voice.

"Jonas I am just about tuckered, I am taking Crockett in and get him ready for bed," announced Susannah.

Jonas nodded his head in agreement.

"I will round up everybody; and get done what ever we have to, and leave the rest for tomorrow," he said.

Soon the barn yard was dark and silent. The pale light of candles shown from the windows of Whitt House. After the good night's were exchanged the house became quiet. Now the thoughts of the evening danced in their heads. Rachel thought of the handsome Adam Beavers. Rhoda thought of the handsome John Bunyon Lowe. John Bunyon Whitt was thinking of the wonderful Catherine Beavers.

Everyone drifted off to sleep with good thoughts running their minds.

CHAPTER 9

A NEW BABY IS COMING

Next morning seemed to come quickly. The weather was taking a change. It was almost October 1838.

"Get up every body, get ready for church, It's the Lords day;" said Jonas in a loud voice so every ear could hear.

Susannah was sick at her stomach when she got out of bed. Jonas went to her side.

"Wait a minute, hopefully it will pass in a little while," she said.

Susannah was starting out differently with this baby. She had never had trouble bringing any of the other children into the world. She had never been in her mid forties before either. The morning sickness passed in a little while, but Susannah felt weak, and her ankles were swollen.

"Do you feel like going to church today?" Jonas asked.

"Yes just give me a little time to get to feeling better," said Susannah.

"You over done it yesterday with the corn shucking party," Jonas replied.

"I may have, but wasn't it a great gathering?" she asked.

Jonas went down stairs and got the cooking fire going and the coffee on.

The twins came to the kitchen.

"Is Maw alright?" Rhoda asked.

"Yes, she just needs some time to get herself together this morning," Jonas answered.

"How about you girls fixing a pot of oats for a quick breakfast, then you can go get ready for church," Jonas said.

"That will be fine Paw," answered Rachel.

Elizabeth brought Crockett down when she came down stairs. He was still sleepy, but had a big smile for Jonas and the twins.

"Good morning little Crockett," said Jonas.

"Are you hungry?" Jonas asked.

Crockett reached for his Paw.

Jonas took him and gave him a hug.

"Just as soon as John gets back from milking, you can have some of it, and some oats too," Jonas said.

Crockett offered up a big grin with hearing that.

Susannah came down dressed for church, every one hurried up and got ready for the trip up the valley to church. Everyone went to church that day, the morning went slow for some reason.

After church the Whitts didn't stop and spend time at Grand Paw Hezekiah's as usual. Jonas thought it might be better to get Susannah home and let her rest up.

In late afternoon two guests arrived at Whitt House. Two new friends of Rachel and John Bunyon drove up in the Beavers family buggy.

Adam and Catherine Beavers came for an unexpected visit.

Adam came to the door and knocked.

Jonas went to the door and opened it.

Adam spoke right up, "Sir do you mind if I and my sister Catherine visit with John and Rachel?" he asked.

"I reckon it will be alright." Jonas said.

"Thank you Mister Whitt, we will not stay too long," Adam replied.

"Come on in Mister and Miss Beavers," Jonas said.

"You may take a seat in the sitting room, I will locate Rachel and John Bunyon for you," Jonas added.

"Thank you sir," was the reply from Adam.

John, Rachel, and Rhoda came in to meet the waiting guests.

"What a lovely surprise," said Rachel.

"I will put on some tea," said Rhoda, and left the room.

John took the hand of Catherine and gave it a little squeeze. She responded with a wide smile. Adam did the same with Rachel. They all took a seat, and had some small talk. Rhoda returned in a short time with four cups and saucers, and a tea pot steaming with hot tea. Also on the tray was a sugar bowl, and a cream pitcher. She sat the tray on the little table in the center of the room. Next she poured out a cup of tea into each of the cups.

"Sugar or cream?" she asked as she served each one.

Some of the smaller children came in to take a look at the guests having tea in the sitting room.

Elizabeth brought in little Crockett and sat him down on his favorite spot. He rolled around on the bear skin rug, and gently pulled the ears and said, "bar, bar!"

Everyone laughed!

Then Adam said to John, "I heard about you killing that bear John, it's a nice trophy."

John Bunyon was all smiles.

"Thanks Adam, It was a lucky shot I guess," John said.

Catherine then spoke up saying, "That's not what I heard, I heard it was a very good shot from a very skilled hunter."

John's face took on a pink color as he blushed.

Next thing they knew, Crockett was walking around to each of them and showing off!

Catherine picked him up.

"You have an adorable little brother," she said.

"Think he is a little pain sometimes," John said laughing.

The little visit didn't last too long, Adam and Catherine did not want to wear out their welcome, John and Rachel walked them to their buggy. John helped Catherine up while squeezing her little soft hand. Rachel walked to the other side with Adam, he also squeezed her hand while helping her up into the buggy.

Rachel spoke up saying, "You all will have to visit our church next Sunday, and maybe come for another visit."

"That is a fine idea, don't you think so Catherine?" John asked.

"Yes that is a fine idea, we will try to see you next Sunday," replied Catherine.

Time seemed to go extra fast through the fall and winter.

John seen Catherine often. Rachel, and Rhoda saw their new beaus as often as possible.

Susannah continued to have some problems with her pregnancy, but she didn't complain ! Susannah did tell Jonas, this has to be our last baby. She told Jonas that she was just too old to go through this again.

"I agree with you, I am surprised that we are having this one," he said.

"Why?" she asked.

"I have not gone through the change yet," she added.

"Well I guess it is the Lord's will that we have this new little one," Susannah exclaimed in a low voice.

"Yes dear, It must be that God wants another little Whitt to walk up on the earth," said Jonas.

Susannah gave him that special smile.

"You know we had a real good time making our babies," she exclaimed.

Jonas blushed!

"Yes we did," answered Jonas.

"That is a wonderful gift that God gives his married children," added Jonas.

"It is a special way of expressing love, and produces love in a new little child," added Susannah.

"Glad we didn't get a baby every time," Susannah said smiling.

"Me too," said a smiling Jonas.

Winter wasn't too bad this time. It seemed long, but short at the same time.

Early spring was here already, time to think about spring planting and preparation for all that comes with it.

Susannah was quite large as the time was growing closer. She was suffering with swelling and retaining fluids. She did not sleep well, and did not get the rest she needed. By now the baby was moving about vigorously in the womb.

"I never remember any of our babies being so active," Susannah said.

"This one seems to want out in a bad way," she exclaimed.

"You are probably just paying more attention to this one," said Jonas.

"Maybe, one thing for sure it wouldn't be too much longer," answered the weary Susannah.

Jonas tried to make it easy on Susannah! The whole family has stepped in and helped! The Twins were a blessing taking care of little Crockett.

Jonas had also been busy with the seed beds, and the other work of early spring.

John Bunyon and James Griffith had been turning the soil, and delivering new arrivals to the cows, sheep, hogs, and one new little mule.

The grass had taken on a bright green in this new spring season in Tazewell county.

Susannah spent a lot of time in the bed as per orders from Jonas and the midwife that Jonas had located.

The midwife was a military type older lady by the name of Chief Carter. Everyone was afraid to ask how she got the name of Chief. She was a good old lady, but didn't go along with foolish talk. She had helped to deliver a great number of babies in her life time.

She has visited Susannah several times and made preparations for the upcoming event! Chief had talked with Jonas, and laid down strict laws about Susannah getting proper rest and good food.

"Keep her off lard and other fattening things," she said.

"Let her drink all she wants," she added.

Also Chief gave him some special herbal medicine she had mixed up just for Susannah. It was made to help her rest and also stop her from retaining fluids. She was to take it three times a day, morning, noon, and at bed time. Since she started taking it she had been resting better and her ankles looked more like her ankles. Susannah had protested at first, but now drinks the bitter stuff willingly.

Chief Carter had told Jonas to come and get her if any thing out of the ordinary took place.

"Your wife is too old to be having babies," she scolded!

Jonas had replied saying, "We didn't plan on another baby, we will just have to deal with it, It must be God's will!"

"Phoeey," Chief answered!

"We will deal with it, and Lord willing mother and baby will survive," Chief added.

"I have to be honest with you Mister Whitt, they sure could be some difficulties," Chief said.

"If all goes well, and we hope for that, you don't get her this way again, hear now!" Chief said.Jonas looked at her a bit surprised. Seeing the seriousness in Chief's eyes Jonas was humbled.

"I will not get her this way again," Jonas said.

Jonas is not just concerned anymore, he is starting to have a cloud of worry hang over his head. What if something happened to his beloved Susannah? Got to get that out of my head, he thought.

Trust in God, that will be the thing to do! Jonas went back to his work to try and not think of negative things. Nothing helped, no matter how hard Jonas worked he could not quit thinking of the grave danger his bride and baby were in. It was like God was telling him to prepare for tragedy. Jonas could not accept the idea of giving up Susannah or the baby.

I have been a good Christian man to the best of my ability he thought. Surely God would not require the life of his sweet Susannah.

Jonas went about his business on the farm, praying time to time. Lord please don't make me give up Susannah! Jonas could not turn this over to God, like he always did his other troubles and trials. He was selfish about this, because of his deep love for Susannah. This is just a test he thought, God will not really take my wife! That was his mind set for the whole month of March 1839.

He stayed busy and thought of everything he could to drive out the premonition of Susannah passing away. Surely God would change His mind. God would not take the good Christian woman that has served Him all these years.

Jonas came up with many good arguments why God should not take Susannah! Finally Jonas took the attitude of trust God, and wait and see.

The family could see a difference in Jonah the past month. He was not the cheerful happy father figure he once was, even though he tried his best to put up a front.

One day when Jonas was in the barn by himself he was praying to God to spare Susannah! A thought jumped into his head, God is God, He gave up His only son Jesus Christ. Why then would it be wrong to take a good Christian woman home to be with Him?

Also Jonas sensed a need to be prepared. About that time a calf run to his mother and started nursing! Jonas felt the urging to get bottles and nipples!

I will go to town and do this, maybe Susannah will not have enough milk for the new baby he thought.

The very next day Jonas got up early and rode Jake to Jeffersonville. He talked to God, and to Jake all the way there.

He bought several bottles and nipples, and a store bought outfit for the baby. He also bought a little heart shaped locket for Susannah.

Jonas decided that he would write a letter to Archibald, Susannah's Paw in Montgomery County. Jonas felt prompted to let her folks know that the baby would be coming. It might be that they could come for a visit. It has been over two years since she has seen them.

Who knows Archibald may want to move here close to his brother Hezekiah and his daughter Susannah. Jonas will write the letter today, he would try not to alarm them but still relay a sense of need for them to come.

Today is April 1, 1839, and James Griffith is getting April Fool on every one. It is good to have some laughter in Whitt House.

Susannah had a pretty good day. She is still staying in bed a lot.

She has not publicized it to the family, but she knows things are not completely right. She has been spotting for two weeks, and she feels drained of energy.

Little David Crockett has spent a lot of time with his Maw. He seems to know that his Maw is sick and needs him there. Crockett has not been the rambunctious two year old that he was a month ago. He has brought a smile to Susannah everyday for the past few weeks. Susannah calls him her little angel.

Grand Maw Rachel has come over and spent time with Susannah lately. She brings some of Susannah's favorite dishes when she comes. Rachel will be 78 her next birthday. She is not a spring chicken, but spry for her age. She has not said anything to Jonas, but knows everything is not right with Susannah.

James and Nancy have also paid a visit or two. They always bring something for the baby. They also bring a cake or some sweets for the rest of the children.

Jonas told his Paw that he wrote a letter to Archibald about a week ago.

"I hope they can come for a visit, I would love to see my little brother," Hezekiah said.

"I am sure Susannah would love to see her folks also," Hezekiah added.

In the early morning hours of April fifteenth 1839 Monday, Susannah awoke with a pain that she recognized instantly as a labor pain.

"Jonas get up honey, it's time to get ready, the baby is coming," she announced.

Jonas jumped to his feet!

"Are you alright Susannah, it is three fifteen in the morning," he said.

"No honey, I'm not alright, I am having a baby," she answered.

"I know that you are having a baby, I mean are you alright other than that?" Jonas asked.

"Jonas you are half a sleep, go and wake the twins, and get John Bunyon on the road to get Chief," Susannah instructed.

"Then you go down and fix up the fire in the kitchen," she added.

"Alright Susannah, you stay right there and I will take care of everything," Jonas said as he left the room in his long handles.

"Jonas, Jonas put your paints on," Susannah yelled!

A shy embarrassed Jonas come back into the room, and jumped into his bibbed over alls.

"Now Jonas we have time, just go about your business in an orderly manner, but hurry a little," Susannah said.

Jonas went to the boys room first and awaken John Bunyon!

"What is it Paw, something the matter?" John Bunyon asked.

"Get up John, we need for you to go and get Chief Carter, your Maw has decided to have the baby," Jonas said.

"Alright Paw I will be there in record time," John announced.

"Now John go in an orderly manner, don't want any accidents," said Jonas.

James Griffith roused up.

"What's going on Paw," he asked sleepily?

"Go back to sleep James, John is going to fetch Chief for your Maw," Jonas answered.

"Can I help some way Paw?" James asked.

"Not now son, you sleep for now," Jonas said.

Jonas headed for the twins room.

"Girls, Girls, better get up, your Maw needs you," Jonas announced.

The twins both spoke up, "Be right there Paw," they said.

Then Jonas went bask to check on Susannah.

"You alright honey?" Jonas asked.

"Yes Jonas, you got things happening?" she asked.

"Yes the girls will be with you soon, and John is already out the door," Jonas said.

"Now I'm going down and get the fire fixed up and get some water on to boil," he added.

"Thank you dear, I will be fine here for a while, you go ahead and take care of the fire and get the water on," she said.

John Bunyon had the horses rigged to the wagon in record time and was headed down to the Clinch.

The horses protested a little for the early wake up, but plunged right through the ford in the river.

Thank God for the light of the full moon John thought.

John had about a thirty minute trip to Chiefs house. When he arrived she was sitting by the door with her day clothes on drinking a cup of coffee.

"How on earth did you know I was coming," he asked in amazement.

"Well the moon changed for one thing, and I had a premonition I guess," Chief answered.

"I woke up about thirty minutes ago and something told me to get up and get ready," she added.

"Wow," John said.

"Well are you ready Mrs. Carter?" John asked.

"Let me grab my coat and I will be with you John," Chief answered.

As John helped her up on the wagon she said, "Call me Chief young feller!"

"Yes Ma-am, I mean Chief," John Bunyon said.

"Giddy up was the command," and the team pulled into their harness's and the wagon was on the way to Whitt House.

By now Rachel and Rhoda were with their Maw, trying to keep her comfortable. Her pains had intensified and were coming about seven minutes apart.

Jonas had a fire going and a big pot of water heating up. Then He went up to the barn and got a jug of his best corn whiskey, and a stick to whittle on.

The stick was for Susannah to bite on if her pain required it. He whittled off the rough outer bark and exposed the clean smooth wood for her to bite on. Of course the whiskey was for her pain and his nerves.

He would take a little for medicinal purposes. He brought the stick and corn whiskey and set them on the wash stand in their room.

"How you doing dear," Jonas said.

"Would you like little snort to dull your pain?" Jonas said.

"No not yet," Susannah said.

"Where is Chief?" she asked in a little abrupt manner.

"She will be here soon, as a matter of fact I hear horses coming up the hill right now," Jonas answered.

"That has to be John bringing Chief," Jonas added.

"That's record time," Jonas said as he looked at the clock.

"I don't see how he could get there and back this quick, unless Chief was up and ready," Jonas said.

"How could she be?" said an exasperated Susannah.

"Don't know honey, but she is out there and a coming to your aid right now," Jonas answered.

"I am going down and get out of your way," Jonas added.

"Pray for me Jonas," answered Susannah!

"Have no fear about that, I will be talking to God about you," Jonas said.

"Just don't you worry Susannah," Jonas added.

Chief was up stairs in short order, and started handing out instructions to the twins, and trying to settle Susannah down.

Little Crockett was aroused and getting up to see what was going on. Rhoda picked him up and his blanket. She carried him to the bed where Emma and Elizabeth were sleeping.

"Here honey you go to bed with your big sisters," said Rhoda.

Emma looked up and took Crockett into her bed.

"What's going on Rhoda, is the baby coming?" asked Elizabeth.

"Yes it is, we need for you to take care of Crockett," Rhoda answered.

"Come on Crockett, let's snuggle up and take a nap," said Emma in a quiet sweet voice.

By now John Bunyon had the team unhitched and loose in the field by the barn.

Jonas asked him, "How did you get to Chief's house and back in a little over an hour?"

"Paw, I know it sounds crazy, but she was sitting there waiting for me," John answered.

"Well I will not question that, some women know these things, and she is one of them," Jonas replied.

Jonas told John Bunyon, we might as well sit in the sitting room for now. It will be daylight in about an hour, and then we can get busy doing something!

"I hate this waiting and feeling so helpless," said Jonas.

"Me too," replied John.

"Lets go and keep up the fire and brew some coffee," Jonas said.

John replied by shaking his head.

Jonas didn't hear an answer but let it go. John was walking right with his Paw as they headed into the kitchen. They heard Susannah scream out!

"Poor thing," Jonas said.

"I hate for her to suffer like this, I hope it will be over soon," he added.

"Me too," said John, "I know it is the sin factor that Adam and Eve caused, when God drove them out of the garden," John said.

"He told them they would suffer," John said.

"God even mentioned women having pain when they would have their babies," John added.

"Yes, John you know your Bible, but it still is so hard to hear your Maw suffering," Jonas answered.

"I know Paw," said John.

They still hadn't got any news from upstairs by 9:00 AM. About 9:30 a blessed sound of a new born was penetrating the floors and doors all the way to the sitting room.

Jonas jumped to his feet, "Glory Be," he said.

"I hear my new baby crying," declared Jonas.

John and all the other children jumped up also.

"Sure sounds good, don't it children," Jonas asked?

"You all have a new brother or sister," Jonas added.

About twenty minutes passed and still no word from Chief or the twins, Jonas began to get a look of concern on his face.

We should be hearing something from them by now," Jonas said out loud!

Chief came to the head of the stairs and called down, "Mister Whitt bring your Bible and come up please."

"Bible, Paw you better get up there," John said.

By now all the children were worried.

Jonas had his Bible and met Chief at the door.

She said something to him but no one could hear. Then she opened the door and led Jonas in.

Jonas was stunned at what he seen! The twins were tattered and horrified.

Chief took the baby and handed her to Rhoda.

"Here girls take baby Hannah down and fix her some milk in a bottle because she's hungry," Chief said.

Jonas looked at his sweet wife laying in a heaped up bed.

She tried a smile and said weakly, "Sorry honey."

"Don't worry sweetheart, you will be alright," Jonas answered.

Jonas looked at the bed, it was scarlet in the lower half.

"Dear God," he said in a low voice.

Susannah was visible weakening as he stood there.

Chief turned and said to Jonas, "Open your Bible to Ezekiel 16:6 and start reading."

"That is the verse that stops bleeding," she said.

Jonas with his hands shaking, turned through the books of the Bible. He found Ezekiel 16:6 and began to read. With a shaky voice the words were heard!

"And when I passed by thee, and saw thee polluted in thine own Blood, I said unto thee, when thou wast in thy Blood, Live; yea, I said unto thee when thou wast in thy Blood, Live."

Jonas knelt down by the bed and took her hand and squeezed it softly.

Susannah gave a little squeeze back.

"Honey what on earth do you have to be sorry about," Jonas asked?

"Jonas, I am in trouble, I am afraid you will have to raise the children by yourself," Susannah said.

"Now, Now, Susannah, don't speak of things like that, you will be alright in a few days," Jonas answered.

Chief took another clean rag and exchanged it with a red one. She pushed it slightly up inside of Susannah hoping to stop the hemorrhaging.

"Mister Whitt pray for your wife, I will read the scripture again," Chief said.

Susannah was a pale gray with shallow breathing.

As Chief read the word to stop the bleeding and Jonas prayed aloud, Susannah drifted off into a coma!

Little Hannah screamed in protest of her new world.

Susannah heard the little darling, and opened her eyes to a small crack.

Jonas hollered down stairs, "Bring that baby back up hear right now."

"Susannah come back here, don't you leave me," Jonas pleaded.

Every time the baby cried, Susannah tried to rally and come back.

She faded again into a coma. This time they could not get her to acknowledge that she heard them!

"Rachel, honey take Hannah back down stairs and take care of her, we will take care of your Maw," Jonas said.

Chief looked at Jonas and Jonas looked back.

"Pray again, maybe the Lord will revive her," said Chief.

Jonas prayed like he had never prayed before, for God to save his Susannah!

Finally Chief said, "Maybe if we let her rest for awhile she will come back, I have seen it happen!"

Jonas nodded and said, "I will sit here with her and pray silently, you go down and check on the baby and the other children, please."

Chief Carter got up and went down the stairs.

"Girls do you have any tea in the house?" she asked.

"Yes Ma-am we do," said Rachel.

I will fix some, I could use a cup myself," Rachel added.

When the tea was ready Rachel brought a cup to Chief.

"Thanks dear," Chief said pleasantly.

Rachel looked at Chief, "How is Maw doing Ma-am," she asked?

"It doesn't look good for your Maw honey, we have done everything I know to do," Chief said.

"It is in Gods sweet hands, and she is resting, trying to come back," said Chief.

"All we can do is pray, it may be that God will bring her back," added Chief.

Everyone sat quietly praying.

James Griffith broke the silence and said, "I'm going to saddle up Jake and go tell Grand Paw, Grand Maw, James and Nancy," he announced.

"They need to know about Maw so they can pray for her," he said in such a sad voice!

"Good idea," replied Rachel.

Even little Crockett sensed something was wrong!

"I want my Ma, want Ma," he kept saying.

Rachel and Rhoda fought back tears!

"Honey Maw is resting right now, she needs to sleep," they explained.

Jonas sat holding Susannah's hand praying and talking to her.

Chief Carter went back up to see if she could think of any thing else to help in this sad occurrence. Susannah lay quietly with a smile on her face! She seemed to be in a sweet dream!

Jonas held her hand and talked to her in a soft soothing voice! Susannah gave no sign of hearing him. She just kept smiling, and taking slow breaths of air!

Jonas said to Chief, "Please sit with my wife while I go down and meet my new daughter."

"Of course Mister Whitt, her name is Henrietta, Hannah for short, Susannah named her that," Chief answered.

"A good name," answered Jonas as he was leaving the room.

Jonas looked back and said, "that is Susannah's Maw's name."

It was past noon already! James was back from his sad journey. He put Jake back in the field and ran to the house.

He seen Jonas holding the new little sister, "How's Maw doing," he asked?

Jonas looked at him with sad eyes and answered, "Not good son!"

"Did you find the folks, are they coming, son?" Jonas asked.

"Yes they will be here real soon," answered James Griffith.

"Maybe Grand Maw Rachel will know what to do," he added.

"Maybe," Jonas said, "We all need to keep praying for your Maw."

In a short time two buggies pulled up to the back door. Rachel came into the house like a young person.

"Where is she Jonas?" Rachel asked.

"Up in our room, Chief Carter is with her," Jonas answered.

"Chief is the best midwife around these parts," replied Rachel as she headed up the stairs.

Hezekiah, James, and Nancy headed over to see little Hannah.

Little two year old Crockett wasn't sure he liked his new sister. He went over and crowded in between Grand Paw and the cradle where little Hannah lay.

"Green eyes," said Nancy!

Nancy picked up little Crockett and held him so he could look down to see baby Hannah.

He looked down and said, "Baby."

"Yes," said Nancy, "That is your baby sister Hannah."

"Han nah," he repeated.

"That's right, baby Hannah," Nancy answered.

Jonas was back up the stairs after his mother in short order.

"Maw she has been like this for about four hours now," Jonas said.

"She seems to be having a wonderful dream," Jonas surmised.

Hour after hour passed and there was no visible change in Susannah's condition. Prayers went up from every one of the Whitts. Hezekiah prayed a long loving prayer out loud.

The entire family gathered around Susannah about 6:00 PM. They read scriptures, prayed, and sang hymns.

Susannah never opened her eyes. She seemed to be at peace as she continued to exhibit that sweet smile.

"She sees something beautiful!" Jonas said.

Chief felt of Susannah's hands and arms.

"She is cold as ice, get me another thick quilt," she commanded.

Rhoda ran to the trunk in the corner and got out a thick quilt.

Grand Maw Rachel lovingly spread it over Susannah, all but her face.

Jonas told John to build up a fire in the fire place. The fire had burned down, because everyone had been warm during the day.

John had a roaring fire in a short time. The room had become extra warm.

Jonas felt under the covers and touched Susannah's hands and arms. The expression on his face told the story. Susannah was not one bit warmer.

About that time Susannah mumbled something about beautiful!

Her eyes twitched a little, and she said real plain, "Sweet Jesus!"

Her breathing stopped!

Chief felt of her neck to see if she had a pulse.

Chief turned to the family and said, "She is gone to be with the Lord."

Then she walked over to the clock and stopped it at 6:47 PM.

Jonas cried out loud, "Why Lord did you take my Susannah," and fell on his knees beside the bed.

He hugged and kissed Susannah, and had great lamentations!

Hezekiah gathered everyone together in one big hugging group.

All were crying and holding on to each other. Rhoda was holding Hannah, and Nancy was holding Crockett.

Jonas got up abruptly and announced "I have work to do."

He walked down stairs and out the door to the barn.

Hezekiah and John Bunyon followed him. When they went into the barn, Jonas was sorting through his lumber pile and looking for certain boards.

Jonas turned to Hezekiah and said, "I got to build my Susannah a nice coffin Paw."

"Will you help me?" Jonas asked.

Jonas could not see very well through the tears that flowed from his eyes!

"I will help you and John will help too," Hezekiah said."

John spoke in a soft voice and said, "Yes I want to help Paw."

Back at the house the women, Chief, Rachel, Rhoda and Grand Maw Rachel lovingly cleaned the body of Susannah for her burial.

Nancy kept the smaller children down stairs and lovingly attended to their needs.

James Griffith got up and went to be with his Paw, Grand Paw and brother John in the barn.

CHAPTER 10

MY GOD WHAT WILL I DO?

The word spread through Tazewell county like wild fire. Jonas and Susannah were a well known couple even though they had not lived here long. The funeral was set for the eighteenth of April. That was a Wednesday. It would be at the Grave site in Baptist Valley.

Elder David Young would have the service. There would be a wake at Whitt House the evening of the seventeenth, Tuesday. Jonas laid down strict rules about this.

"We do not want people sitting around here all night, I want people out of here by 10:00 PM.," Jonas demanded.

Also a funeral procession was scheduled to leave from the home of Jonas and Susannah at 10:00 AM.

Hezekiah had a nice wagon that would be used to carry Susannah to the grave site. The funeral would be preached at the new Whitt cemetery, which was located on the hill straight across from Hezekiah's house.

Hezekiah set this plot aside for family to be buried in.

Hezekiah had some friends dig the grave, after so many volunteered!

Jonas had built a nice coffin out of Walnut Wood that he had been saving for something special. Susannah is the most special thing in my life he thought. Hezekiah had helped get it started, John and James did all the sanding, and applied Bee's Wax to the finish. It was a magnificent piece of finish carpentry. Jonas wanted the very best for his Susannah. The inside was lined with cotton, and covered neatly with blue muslin. Six strong wooden handles were added to the sides.

The women had prepared Susannah's body with loving care. Her hair was fixed the way she always wore it. She had her nicest dress on! They also added a little rouge to give her face a more natural look.

Jonas took the little locket that he brought from town only a few days ago, and put it on his beloved Susannah.

The men carried the new coffin up stairs, and with the help from the women laid Susannah into it. They closed the lid temporarily and carried Susannah down to the sitting room, being careful to keep it level. They set it on two small tables that had been set up for this. Candles were lit round about and the lid was opened for the family to visit Susannah in the final hours before burial.

It was such a sad and solemn time at the Whitt House. Many of the closer neighbors had brought in food for the family. The Jonas Whitt family was walking around in shock.

Rhoda had taken on the responsibility of taking care of baby Hannah, and Sarah was helping with little Crockett who kept crying for his Maw!

By 5:00 PM. many people had come to offer their condolence and respect for the family. A group from the church came and sang some hymns, and every one just mingled. Each family went around and tried to lift up the Whitts with words of encouragement. Jonas stood all evening by the coffin, holding the hand of his beloved Susannah.

Next morning many people had formed a line with their buggies and wagons in front of the Whitt House.

At 10:00 AM. Jonas had the pallbearers carry Susannah out and put her coffin in Hezekiah's new wagon. The wagon had a fresh coat of white paint and the wheels were bright red.

John and James had the family wagon next in line behind the one carrying Susannah. Jonas broke down and cried like a baby when he got up into the wagon with the coffin. He intended to ride beside the coffin all the way to the cemetery.

Hezekiah and Rachel would drive the wagon which carried Susannah. John would drive the family wagon with James as co-driver. The rest of the family sat about the wagon. Little Crockett and even little Hannah was in the wagon.

Crockett was beginning to understand that his Maw was in the fancy box on Grand Paw Hezekiah's wagon.

He kept whimpering and saying, "my Maw is gone, my Maw is gone."

The sad procession got started across Green Mountain. Hezekiah led the way carrying Susannah to her final resting place.

Jonas looked back at all the friends who were following.

"Paw look back at all the buggies and wagons, there must be sixty or seventy of them," Jonas said.

"Yes Jonas, she was well liked!" Hezekiah answered.

Jonas sat quietly and held tight to the newly built coffin to keep it from sliding around. He wanted to be as close as possible to his beloved Susannah. Time was passing fast and Jonas knew he would have to part from her soon.

When Hezekiah's wagon got to the cemetery, he drove right up the hill and stopped right beside the newly dug grave. Each wagon or buggy drove up close to the one in front of them. The driver of each wagon got out and tied his horse to the wagon in front of his wagon.

There was a nice level ground directly behind the grave. This is where every one gathered for the service. The pallbearers gently carried Susannah over and sat her on three timbers over top the open grave. Some benches had been placed for the family to sat on and all the friends were standing behind them.

Elder David Young stood and offered up a prayer. Next the singers from the Baptist church sang three of Susannah's favorite hymns. The service continued with time given for whoever wanted to speak of the life of Susannah. Three of her friends had a short story of their friend Susannah Whitt.

Then Grand Maw Rachel stood and gave a description of the lovely woman, and mother.

Jonas wept out loud.

Many of the family burst out in grief.

Elder Young stood and began to preach the funeral as the family became quiet. It was an inspiring message of how Susannah was now with her Lord Jesus Christ. She has no pain, nor tears. She is waiting happily for each of you in Heaven. She would not want any of you to cry and be sad! She is in a better place! Yet the family cried out from time to time.

The coffin was lowered into the earth slowly by ropes. When the ropes were pulled out Elder Young prayed. He stood again and said some words about dust to dust.

Jonas stood and got a hand full of dirt and dropped it down on

Susannah's coffin.

"I will see you over there some day honey," Jonas said.

"I love you and always will," he added.

He was followed by each family member who did like wise. Even little Crockett was allowed to throw a little dirt on his Maws coffin. He seemed so mature for a two year old.

"By Maw, by Maw," he said as Rachel carried him back to the wagon.

Every last person there did like wise. Each hand full of dirt fell on the coffin until it was almost hidden from view. As the folks went by and shook hands with the family they left for home buggy by buggy. Finally only the family was left with Elder Young and two neighbors who were going to take care of the grave.

Jonas and the children went to Grand Paw Hezekiah's house after the funeral. Grand Maw Rachel and Aunt Nancy had prepared a good meal. James and Hezekiah were trying their best to get Jonas to think of something other than the passing of Susannah.

"It is good that we can be with you in your time of sorrow, God and family is all we can hold on to in times like this," Hezekiah stated.

Jonas spoke softly saying, "Thanks Paw, you are right, but it is not easy."

About 3:00 PM Jonas and his family loaded up the wagon and headed across Green Mountain toward home. It was a sad trip home, but little Crockett tried to do some funny things to break the spell. He did get a few smiles.

Baby Hannah cried a few times.

"She is getting hungry again, I will feed her as soon as we get back home," Rhoda said.

Jonas was quiet all the way home. He dreaded to go into the house where there is no Susannah to greet him.

When the Whitts arrived at home Jonas took little Hannah from Rhoda.

"Let me hold her while you fix her bottle," Jonas said.

That brought a smile to Rhoda's face.

"Sure Pa, you carry her in and I will fix the bottle," Rhoda said.

John Bunyon said to James Griffith, "How about helping brother take care of the team."

"Sure will big brother," James answered.

They parked the wagon by the barn and unhitched the team. When they got inside the barn a new little calf was there. Betsy the cow had delivered her baby while they were away.

"Wow!, look John," James said in excitement.

"That sure is a purty baby cow," he added.

"Baby Bull," John corrected him, "It's a boy!"

"Paw will be glad to hear about this," said James.

"Yes he will, and little Hannah will have more milk," John said.

"Betsy will be fresh now, since she had this little fellow," John added.

"Let's hurry and tell everyone," James said.

James Griffith ran ahead of John Bunyon to the house. He ran in to where Jonas was sitting and holding baby Hannah.

"Paw guess what, Betsy found a calf, it's a little bull," he announced.

"Really she's got a baby boy?" Jonas asked.

"Yes Paw, he is purty too," James said.

"Well let's go and see this purty boy," replied Jonas.

"Come on everyone let's take the babies to see Betsy's calf," Jonas said.

All the children followed their Paw to the barn. Jonas carried baby Hannah, and led little Crockett. This was the diversion the family needed. They would have plenty of time to mourn and heal after the tragic death of Susannah.

James kept saying, "Look at his purty white face!"

"Yes it is," said Rachel.

"Look how little he is," said Elizabeth.

"Can I pet him?" asked Emma.

"Me too Paw?" said Elizabeth.

"Maybe we shouldn't brother him just yet," Jonas said.

"Let him get acquainted with his Maw and this new world he has come into," Jonas added.

Rhoda held Crockett up so he could get a good look at the new little bull.

Crockett said, "Purty Boy!"

He was repeating what Jonas called him earlier.

"Yes Crockett he is a Purty Boy, let's call him that," said Jonas.

Crockett said once again while pointing his little finger at the calf, "Purty Boy!"

"That does it, Betsy's baby will be named Purty Boy," exclaimed Jonas!

"Now lets get back to the house so Betsy can take care of Purty Boy," Jonas added.

They all meandered back to the house, talking about the new little calf as they went.

Jonas was in a state of shock, he was having trouble adapting to his new situation. He did not like being in the house. Jonas would stay out of doors from early morning until dark. Last night he was sure Susannah came and sat on the edge of the bed, and smiled at him. Was he going crazy, or was he just going through a period of grief? He would just go through the motions for a time and hope for the best. Jonas did not want to add to the problems of the family. It is such an adjustment to lose a wife and mother in an active family.

About a week after the funeral, Archibald and Hannah showed up. They were coming to see Susannah and the family. Archibald and Hannah broke down and cried when they found out their daughter was dead.

"Jonas, why didn't you write to us earlier?" Archibald asked.

"Why did she have to die, why did we not come to see her before now?" Archibald asked.

They were adding guilt to the grief!

Jonas sat them down and told them the whole story of Susannah's passing. He told them about her smile and saying Sweet Jesus, as her last words. Jonas was surprised that he could talk about it, trying to console her parents.

Archibald and Hannah stayed the night and went to visit with Hezekiah the next day. Jonas was glad, so that he could lose himself in the outdoor work.

Rhoda was doing a wonderful job with baby Hannah, Rachel was taking care of little Crockett. Everyone seemed to be doing fine, except Jonas. He was just going through the motions of living.

Baby Hannah seemed to be such a blessing in this time of distress!

Archibald and Hannah were back at the Jonas Whitt farm in a couple of days. They were like different people this time. They had time to adapt and come to reality that their daughter was gone! Hezekiah had talked with them, and soothed their souls.

Now they were having a good visit with their grand children, especially with Hannah and Little Crockett. The place seemed to be much more light hearted!

Jonas sat and talked for hours about coming to Tazewell county, and how Susannah loved it. She even claimed the Clinch River as ours.

"I can understand, this is a grand country, the mountains, and hills, and the winding waters of the Clinch," exclaimed Archibald.

Hannah was surprised and honored that Susannah had named the baby after her.

"You know baby Hannah even looks like me," Grand Maw Hannah said.

This brought a smile to Archibald.

All and all the visit was a good one.

"I am glad you came, it has helped us get over the shock of loosing my beloved Susannah," Jonas said.

The children were glad also. They had not seen their Grand Parents on their Maw's side for over two years.

One topic of talk came up about Crockett's favorite place. The bear skin rug. Of course every detail was told about the bear hunt, and how John Bunyon brought down the bruin with one shot.

Little Crockett still loved to play on the rug and pull on the bears ears.

"He's going to pull them ears off one of these days," exclaimed James Griffith.

The whole family laughed at that, and at the idea they pictured in their minds of Crockett holding detached bear ears.

Archibald stayed for about three weeks all together; about half of that time they spent with Hezekiah and Rachel. They even spent one night with James and Nancy.

Archibald gave Jonas Fifty Dollars to help the family. He told Jonas that Hannah and he had talked it over and wanted to do it. Archibald had sold some land back in Montgomery county and could help them now with the money. They had intended to give the money to Susannah, now they felt led to give it to Jonas for the family.

Jonas tried to reject such a gift, but Archibald insisted.

"That is a large amount of money," Jonas kept saying.

"Don't worry about it Jonas, just put it to good use for the family," Archibald said.

Next morning bright and early, Archibald and Hannah hugged all the children and headed back toward Montgomery county.

Jonas told them to be extra careful at Rocky Gap, that is where bad men sometimes way-lay pilgrims.

Archibald, tapped the handle of his revolver, and said, "We will let this fellow do the talking if trouble comes."

"Just be extra careful Sir, and write us a letter when you get back home," Jonas said.

Archibald turned his mount and headed toward Jeffersonville, Hannah right behind him. They turned and waved as they got to the Clinch. The whole family was out in the yard waving back.

The summer came and the crops were doing really good because of all the time Jonas spent with outdoor work. He still dreaded going in the house, because Susannah was not there to greet him.

Rachel, Rhoda, and John Bunyon were still doing a little courting.

Little Crockett was not only walking, he was running. He followed Jonas every where he went.

"Baby Hannah is growing like a little pig," James Griffith said.

"That is because she gets all the good creamy cow milk she wants," he added.

Jonas heard of a farm over on Indian Creek for sale. It was close to Hezekiah's and James's farms. One day he rode over on Jake to look it over.

He liked it real well. That evening at supper time he talked to the children about buying it and moving. He was surprised, the children, every last one was for it.

"Well I will go and see Mister Vandyke and see if I can strike up a deal," Jonas said.

"This farm will go back to Paw, when and if we get the new place," Jonas added.

Jonas was at his nerves end and had to get away from the house that Susannah called Whitt House. Too many memories were made at this house.

Jonas would talk this over with Hezekiah. The wise old patriarch would have words of wisdom for his son Jonas.

Jonas made an appointment with the Vandyke's to come and walk over the farm and talk about a price if he was interested. It was about the middle of August, Jonas left early in the morning and stopped at Hezekiah's home for a visit and talk.

Jonas told Hezekiah and Rachel about his problem with the place he lived at. It is almost torture to go into the house, let alone the bed room.

"Paw," he said, "The Vandyke's next to you all are selling their farm."

"I would like you to go and look at it with me," Jonas continued.

"If I could buy it, I would give you your old farm back," Jonas explained.

"I just have to get away from that house," Jonas said.

"The children, every one of them are for it," Jonas added.

"Yes son we will help in any way we can," exclaimed Hezekiah.

"I know that farm, it is a real good piece of ground, and the house and buildings are fine, there is a good well, dug close to the house," Hezekiah stated.

"You would be next door neighbors to James and Nancy, and real close to Me and your Maw," Hezekiah continued.

"When are you going to look at it?" Hezekiah asked.

"I am suppose to meet James and Susannah Vandyke at about 1:00 PM.," Jonas answered.

"Well we can eat dinner and leave here about twenty minutes till one," Hezekiah suggested.

"It is just around the bend on Indian Creek," Hezekiah said.

"No body has lived there since the Vandyke's moved to town," Rachel inserted.

"Any idea what they are asking for it Jonas?" Hezekiah asked.

"I heard something like Four Hundred Seventy Five Dollars," Jonas answered.

"How much land is there?" asked Hezekiah.

"One hundred eighty six acres I was told," Jonas answered.

"I went and looked it over a little while back by myself, but I didn't know the boundaries," Jonas continued.

"It is being taken over by weeds and brush, but that is no problem with a little work," Jonas added.

"You already know where it is then?" Hezekiah asked.

"Yes Sir," answered Jonas.

"Well son here is what I will do, you put your old farm back in my name, and I will give you Four Hundred Dollars," Hezekiah explained.

"Then we will bargain with the Vandyke's a might," added Hezekiah.

Jonas felt a mighty load lift from his shoulders! He even had a big smile come on his face.

They sat down to a tasty, but simple dinner Rachel had rustled up for them.

After they polished off a piece of apple cobbler and drink a cup of tea it was time to go see the farm.

"Now Jonas don't act so anxious, don't let James see your weakness in needing a new place," Hezekiah instructed.

"He and Susannah are good people, but business is business," Hezekiah explained.

"Do you understand what I am telling you son?" Hezekiah asked.

"Yes Paw, I do understand bargaining," Jonas answered.

"We will try to get it at the lowest fair price we can," Jonas exclaimed.

"Good son," Hezekiah answered.

"Look I see the Vandyke's sitting on the porch waiting for you," Hezekiah said.

James and Susannah Vandyke took Jonas and Hezekiah all around the property. They went through the barn and out buildings and even checked the fence. After the tour around the boundaries they got a drink of good cold water from the well.

James turned to Jonas and asked, "How do you like it Jonas?"

"Buildings seem fine; pretty good tract of land," Jonas said.

"Is it true that you have one hundred eighty six acres on this piece of ground?" Jonas asked.

"Yes it was figured out to have that amount," said James.

"The deed will say more or less as usual," James added.

Hezekiah looked at Jonas, Jonas turned to James and ask, "What will it take to buy this farm, James?

James looked at Susannah, and back to Jonas.

"Well Jonas we are asking Four Hundred Seventy Five Dollars," James said.

"Well James I was thinking more like Four Hundred Twenty Five," replied Jonas.

James looked at Susannah again, and Jonas looked at Hezekiah again.

"Jonas we will come down to Four Fifty, if you want it for that," James said.

Jonas looked around the fields and buildings in one sweeping glance.

"Well alright I will give you Four Hundred Fifty Dollars for your property," Jonas announced.

"When can we finalize the deal?" Jonas asked.

"Just as soon as we can get it done at Jeffersonville," James answered.

"I need for William Smith or Bird Lockhart to review everything, you see we got about four plots here and have to make sure all are included in the one hundred eighty-six acres when we get it on paper," James explained.

"Hezekiah you can review everything before we finalize," James said.

"Be glad to, just let me know when you fellers want to meet and sign the deal," Hezekiah said.

"Well since that's agreed on, would it be alright to start moving some things over from the old place?" Jonas asked.

"Yes that will be fine after we shake on it," James said.

Jonas smiled and stuck out his hand first to James, then to Susannah, and then to his Paw Hezekiah. Every one shook hands with all that were present.

"Our word will be our bond until we sign and transfer property for gold," James said.

Jonas said, "Yes," and everyone left with a good feeling.

Jonas went with Hezekiah to his home for another little visit before going across Green Mountain.

Jonas thanked Hezekiah, and Rachel profusely.

"You don't know how much better you made me feel," Jonas explained.

"I will get the crops harvested and everything moved as soon as possible," Jonas continued.

"I need to get away from where my Susannah passed away," Jonas said.

"I am glad to help, I think I understand Son," answered Hezekiah.

"You and I need to get to the courthouse before you and James meet to settle up," Hezekiah said.

"You put your farm in my name and I will get you four hundred in gold," Hezekiah added.

"Then I will try to sell your old place and get my money back," Hezekiah explained.

"You can take any and all of the furniture with you to your new place," Hezekiah added.

"Paw you are such a good father to me," answered Jonas.

"Thanks so much, and you too Maw," Jonas said.

Hezekiah nodded a sign of welcome and hugged his son.

"You are our son, and we love you," answered Rachel.

"We can go any day this week so you can get your property on the market," Jonas said.

"Who knows, you might sell it quickly," Jonas added.

Jonas is in a hurry to get back across Green Mountain.

Jonas hurries Jake along, so he can tell the children about the new place.

This will be the place Hannah and Crockett will grow up on, Jonas was thinking.

Jonas was in the best frame of mind since Susannah passed. Jonas was actually happy! He and the children will have a little celebration when he gets home.

A time is set to finalize the transfer of the Vandyke property to Jonas Whitt.

Monday the Second of September 1839, Jonas met with James and Susannah Vandyke at the court house in Jeffersonville, Virginia. Hezekiah also came to look over all the papers at the request of Jonas.

Everything looked in order.

Two Justices of the peace had signed as witness to the papers. Both of these men were close friends of Hezekiah Whitt and were completely trustworthy. Their names were William Smith and Bird Lockhart.

Jonas counted out $450.00 in Gold to James and Susannah! They put the Gold in a purse, each took a pen and signed the document. This gave Jonas Whitt the ownership of the farm on Indian Creek, a branch of the Clinch River in Tazewell County.

The Farm was not far from the little town of Indian. (Now Cedar Bluff)

Now Jonas was next farm neighbors to James and Nancy Whitt, and real close to his father and mother Hezekiah and Rachel Whitt.

He was also in walking distance of Whitt Cemetery.

Jonas felt like he could get a new lease on life with this new farm. He and his family could make new memories and not be reminded daily of that sad day in April, when Susannah went to Heaven!

Little Hannah was a robust baby girl now almost six months old.

David Crockett was now quite the little man. He would be three years old in December.

Everything was starting to look up for the Jonas Whitt Family.

CHAPTER 11

LIVING ON INDIAN CREEK

The settlement of Indian (now Cedar Bluff) on the Clinch River at The mouth of Indian creek got it's name because of a past Shawnee Indian hunting village located there. The creek also got it's name for the same reason. The Clinch valley was a coveted hunting ground of the Shawnee and Cherokee Indians. This was prime hunting grounds and often caused disputes among the Indian factions.

Even in this time of 1839 the mountains teemed with game. Buffalo was gone and Elk was sparse, but deer, turkey, small game abounded. And as you know from past chapters, bears roamed the woodland of Tazewell County.

The Kentucky Turnpike out of Baptist Valley followed the banks of Indian creek to the Clinch River. There it went down the river to present Raven, Virginia) Then the Kentucky Turnpike rose up to travel a ridge (now Road Ridge) westerly toward Kentucky.

The new Whitt farm was up on a hill overlooking the Kentucky Turnpike. The Turnpike was a dirt road with some stone added to keep wagons from sinking. During wet weather deep ruts and pot holes were prevalent.

Jonas and his family were apt to see folks traveling much more here than at the old place.

Jonas and the family had a lot of work to do before cold weather. They had most everything moved to the new farm by the middle of September 1839. Crops still had to be gathered at the old place, and brought across Green Mountain to the new Indian Creek farm. Also much work was needed at the new place.

The new house was not quiet as large as the old, but Jonas did not need a bed room of his own. Jonas would bunk in a room with John and James. The twins and other girls would get the big bed room.

There was a bigger Barn and numerous other out buildings.

Jonas felt much more at peace here on Indian Creek, and so did the family. Jonas still had only a half a heart; Susannah took the other half with her to Heaven.

James and Nancy were only about a quarter of a mile away. They had offered their services to help with the children. Already Crockett and Hannah had been visiting, while the older children helped move in to the new place. Nancy hoped to keep the children often.

Jonas was glad to have the help but warned Nancy, "Please don't spoil them," he said.

"These are the best children I ever saw, how could my love for them spoil them?" she asked.

"I know women, and you will let them get by with everything," Jonas said.

"They will be fine," answered James, in his wife's defense.

"I know and thanks," replied Jonas.

The house on Indian Creek farm was a solidly built structure. It was built of hued logs. It was one story with a floored loft. It had more rooms all on one floor than the old house. The loft was high enough to stand up in and made a good bed room for Jonas and the boys.

There was not a fire place in the loft area, but the heat from below was adequate to warm it. There was a big fire place and oven in the kitchen. Another fire place in the sitting room and big bedroom. The sitting room was on the side facing Indian Creek, and had a nice glass window. It was the only window in the cabin.

There was a strong door at both the front and back. One in the sitting room, and one in the kitchen. It had a large front porch all the way across the front, and a small one at the kitchen door. Both porches were covered with a roof.

Jonas brought almost all of the furniture out of the old place, but left the bed that Susannah passed on in.

They had room for the large table and chairs in the kitchen. Everything seemed a bit jumbled up, because the floor space was less than the old place. But everyone seemed to be happy with the move.

The sitting room of course now had the big bear rug spread on the floor. Little Crockett still loved to sit on it and play. It was always his preferred place to nap.

Hannah did not share the same attraction for the rug.

David Crockett Whitt was now about two years and ten months old. He was tall and lanky for his age. His hair was a dirty blond and his eyes were gray and speckled. Some folks might say they were hazel. He had an enormous amount of energy. He followed Jonas around all day long and handled the tools when Jonas was working on a project. He also loved the animals.

Crockett would play with the youngest little bull, that he had named Purty Boy. Purty Boy would play back with Crockett. One day the calf got a little rambunctious and knocked Crockett to the ground. He got up and gave Purty Boy a direct hit on the nose. Purty Boy shook his head and waddled over by the fence to pout at his little boy friend.

Crockett went over and petted Purty Boy! This game went on from day to day.

Jonas told him. "do not to wrestle around with Purty Boy, he is getting to be a big bull he is liable to hurt you so stay out of his pen, but you can pet him through the fence," Jonas instructed.

Crockett didn't like it but he obeyed his Paw.

John Bunyon, Rachel, and Rhoda begin to spend more time with their sweethearts. Sunday afternoon, was the best time for visiting.

It was getting the time of year to have a corn shucking, but Jonas was not for it this year. He told the children they could have a small one, only inviting eight or ten people to help shuck the corn.

John Bunyon, Rachel, and Rhoda thought that would be just fine. They were only concerned with having their sweet hearts come anyway.

Jonas said that each one of them could invite someone.

That would be about the end of September 1839.

Jonas and the boys had cleared back a lot of brush and cleaned up the farm in short order. The wood cutting was began, and the fall plowing was also going on.

Between Rachel, Rhoda, James and Nancy, baby Hannah was doing fine.

Crockett ate good, but stayed lean. Jonas had said that he runs it off as fast as he puts it on.

"That boy is right in my hip pocket, no matter what I'm doing, he is right there," Jonas said.

Jonas really enjoyed the attention from Crockett, even though he was in the way a lot. Jonas was a patient man when it concerned his children. Jonas was not an emotional man about his children, but he loved each and every one of them.

Jonas was not at complete peace about his loss of Susannah, and he thought of her everyday. He had to divert his thoughts so that he would not fall back into depression. He kept busy and tried to keep the family going in a positive direction.

Jonas told the children one evening as they sat on the front porch, "You all are my hero's," he said.

"Everyone of you have stepped up and acted like mature adults," Jonas added.

"Rachel, and Rhoda you all have done the cooking, cleaning, and took care of your little brother and sister," Jonas continued.

"John, and James you all have done the work of grown men, and Elizabeth and Emma you have helped like little women, with everything that needed doing," Jonas Praised.

Little Crockett looked up at his Paw and said, "What about me?" he asked.

Jonas answered him with sincere love, "You have been my best little helper."

David Crockett grinned from ear to ear.

Each one of the children smiled and thanked Jonas for the uplifting complement.

"Paw things had to be taken care of, and we are able and willing to help," John Bunyon exclaimed.

Everyone hugged each other and sat down to watch the road for travelers.

Jonas and Crockett got up and walked over the hill to the Cemetery to visit with Susannah, as they often did.

On the way back they stopped to see Hezekiah, and Rachel. They were doing fine for their ages, but time was starting to catch up with them.

School started again, this year James Griffith would drive the wagon. John Bunyon, Rachel and Rhoda would not go to school. They were grown-ups and had a good handle on the three R's. James Griffith was not crazy about going back to school, but felt big, by driving the wagon.

The trip up the valley was much shorter since they moved to Indian Creek. Emma was a little older than James but driving a team was mans work. Elizabeth was glad to get back to school to see her friends. Emma would have a beau before long, the way she is growing.

Time was passing so fast since the move to the waters of Indian Creek.

The younger children loved to go the eighth of a mile, to visit Uncle James and Aunt Nancy. They always had fun over there. Nancy would make clothes and little gifts for the children. Sometimes they would eat supper with them. Nancy loved every minute the children were there.

God had chosen not to give Nancy and James any children. Now Nancy had an idea why. God in his wisdom knew that Jonas would need help with the children, after He called Susannah home.

Here it was the spring of 1840 already. Winter was not too bad and didn't seem to hold on that long. Thoughts of planting and farm work were in everyone's heads.

Rachel however, had a problem with the love bug. Mister Adam Beavers had caught the same bug. They were seeing each other often. Adam talked to Jonas about asking Rachel to marry him.

Jonas had agreed to it if they would wait until June of 1841.

"Why so long?" Adam asked.

"It will give both of you time to really consider what you are getting into," Jonas told him.

Jonas talked to both Adam and Rachel, and they reluctantly agreed to wait until June 1841.

John Bunyon and Miss Catherine Beavers were also doing some courting, but had said nothing about getting married.

Jonas was well aware of the courtships. He also knew that many people the ages of John, Rachel, and Rhoda were already married and had children. He was truly thankful that his children had not rushed into anything.

A few folks had tried to play match maker for Jonas.

He insisted to everyone, I am not ready to think about even seeing another woman. I still love my Susannah and will probably never marry again.

Jonas kept himself busy with the farm and his family. He did however like to talk to other men about current events.

The country was still in recession. Martin Van Buren was still president. His policies on inflation kept the country in recession. Also he was a Northerner with Northern ideas.

The South was not too happy with mister Van Buren. Wages were low, and jobs were not findable except for farm work. Jonas was a fine carpenter and mill right but had not worked much besides his own farm work. It was the policy that land had to be paid for by Gold or Silver. Many banks had failed.

Jonas did some work for his parents, but did not charge them.

Hezekiah had some fine Black Walnut trees on his farm. He asked Jonas to trim out the inside of his house with it.

Jonas worked from time to time on the project. Hezekiah's house was built from great cedar logs. The walnut trim really dressed up the inside. The banister to the second floor, the window frames, the door frames, and around the fireplaces were all trimmed out in the Black Walnut lumber.

Also Jonas built a second floor porch and added great columns on the front. The Hezekiah Whitt house was a truly Colonial Mansion for the time in Tazewell, county.

Anytime Jonas got his tools together, little Crockett would be on his heels. Jonas would let him hold a tool or even help sometimes by holding a board in place. He also taught him to sand the boards and rub in bee's wax. Jonas was surprised by the attention the three year old showed to work.

"That boy will be a fine carpenter some day," Hezekiah said.

"I agree," said Jonas.

Living on Indian Creek and the Kentucky Turnpike was interesting. Travelers were seen on the road quite often, most were local travelers going and coming from the village of Indian. Every now and then travelers were headed to the Commonwealth of Kentucky.

Jonas had two brothers living there now. John B. Whitt lived in Floyd County. Richard (Devil Dick) Nelson Whitt lived further west in Carter County Kentucky.

Sometimes the travelers would stop and talk, get directions, or just get a drink of good cool water from the Whitt well. It was interesting talking to the strangers. The Whitts were always anxious to hear news from other parts of the country.

Jonas warned the children not to be too trusting of strangers. All kinds of people are traveling, good and bad.

Some of the news learned from the travelers who sometimes carried old news papers was about an antislavery convention in London. The women abolitionist were turned away. Some men walked out in protest.

Some other news was that this great new country now had reached a population of over seventeen million souls.

William Henry Harrison was running against Martin Van Buren for President. He had a slogan that was catchy, "Tippecanoe and Tyler too!" Tippecanoe referred back to when Harrison attacked the Indian Federation in Indiana territory in the absence of Chief Tecumseh. It made the territory Governor Harrison look good and added to his fame.

"Tyler too" meant that the Vice President would be John Tyler if elected. As far as most of the South was concerned, anybody would be better than Van Buren.

Some folks passing through did not have any news but loved to stop and have casual conversation with the Whitts.

The three year old David Crockett was always front and center when anyone stopped. Crockett would always say, "Where you all going?"

The next thing was, "Where have you all been?"

Crockett had no idea where Kentucky was or even where Richmond, Virginia is. He knew Indian and Jeffersonville, because he had been there. He just wanted to be in the center of things. People would talk to him like he was a grown up, and that made him feel big.

The summer had come and was almost gone. It had been a good planting season and looked to be a good harvest year!

Hezekiah had been in to Jeffersonville a lot this summer. He was talking to everyone about the up coming election. We got to get that Yankee thinking President out of office he would say.

He did not meet much opposition. One reason was that Hezekiah's opinion was greatly respected in Tazewell County. Another reason was that everyone in the county was tired to death of Van Buren's policies.

Jonas liked to listen to folks, but liked to make up his own mind about all matters. Jonas remembered one thing that Susannah would say if he didn't agree with her.

She would say that Whitts are the most stubborn people on earth, even though she had to include herself in that quote! There were very few disagreements between Jonas and Susannah as he remembered. I would just let her have her way, he would say.

Jonas went to the cemetery most every day to visit with his beloved Susannah.

Crockett went most of the time with his Paw. Sometimes Jonas would talk out loud to Susannah, as he stood by her grave.

Little Crockett would look up at Jonas and say. "Does Maw hear you Paw?"

"Well son, she is in Heaven, and I think she hears us," Jonas said.

Crockett would speak out in a loud voice to his Maw.

Jonas told him he didn't have to speak so loud.

"Your Maw is in heaven but can hear you whisper," Jonas said.

Then Crockett would speak in a low voice saying, "Maw I sure do miss you!"

Sometimes a tear would roll down Jonas's weathered face.

"I miss you Susannah, you are the love of my life," Jonas said.

Little Crockett said the same thing in a whispering voice, "Maw you are the love of my life."

Usually on the way home they would stop and see Hezekiah and Rachel.

Grand Maw Rachel most likely had a cake or cobbler to share.

Crockett didn't want to miss stopping at Grand Maw Rachel's.

Hezekiah organized a shooting match in Jeffersonville to raise money to help William Henry Harrison become president. It was expensive to enter, but paid twenty dollars in gold to the winner. Most of the men and older boys that could get a dollar and thought they had a chance to win had entered.

James Griffith, and John Bunyon both entered.

Jonas did not enter.

He said, "I couldn't see good enough to beat my boys, let alone some of the fine shooters in the county."

The day of the contest came on the first Saturday in October.

James Griffith had been going out and doing a little practice shooting. Jonas knew James was really good.

John Bunyon was also, after all John made a hard shot when it counted. He had dropped a running bear at over fifty yards.

The contest had simple rules, the best shot at 50 yards, 100 yards, and 150 yards would take the twenty dollar gold piece. Each shooter shot at the 50 yard target, all bulls eyes moved to the second round, and so on.

Hezekiah collected one hundred fifty four dollars for the contest.

After the first round James Griffth, John Bunyon, and Adam Beavers, Rachel's beau were moving up with fifty six other contestants.

Now the targets were set at the 100 yard mark. The bulls eye was a one half inch black circle on a six by six inch piece of paper.

Some of the shooters were saying, "I can't even see the target."

The shooters took turns, after all fifty nine had shot, the targets were checked!

Only nine had hit the bulls eye. James Griffith was one of them. John Bunyon and Adam Beavers were just off the bulls eye.

The targets were set at one hundred and fifty yards.

Hezekiah told the nine contestants to get ready.

Hezekiah said, "In case of a tie, there will be a shoot off until someone wins."

Jonas and John both went over and wished James Griffith luck.

Jonas told him not to get nervous.

"I know you can make the shot," Jonas said.

Now some of the earlier contestants were saying, "Who can even see the targets?"

The nine final round shooters loaded their guns and waited their turn. There was eight under the age of twenty five, the oldest was thirty nine. The youngest was only fifteen, that was James Griffith Whitt.

It came time for James Griffith to step up and take his shot. He had practiced a few long shots this week and felt ready. He had put in a little more powder in his Brown Betsy, he primed the flash pan, wiped off the end site with a little spit.

James took aim, held his breath, and squeezed the trigger.

The old rifle flashed, cracked, and smoke rose from the barrel.

James backed up with a smile on his face.

He moved out of the way of the other shooters.

He whispered to Jonas, "I got it!"

The targets were all examined and two shooters recorded bull eyes. James Griffith and Tom Whitten the thirty nine year old. They were to have a shoot off to settle the tie.

"Now if by chance you have a misfire you will be allowed to prime the pan again," said Hezekiah.

"Are you ready gentlemen?" Hezekiah asked.

They both said they were.

Now Mister Whitten would shoot first at the one hundred fifty yard target, then James would have his time. Both men loaded their rifles and primed the pans.

Hezekiah motioned for Mister Whitten to take his shot. A hush came over the crowd when Whitten prepared to shoot.

Out of the silence the rifle cracked and smoke rose into the air. Whitten backed off to give James Griffith his turn.

James took perfect aim just like before, held his breath, and squeezed the trigger.

The crack broke the silence, James jumped to his feet, and he turned with a big smile on his face.

Tom Whitten turned to James and said, "I think you beat me Mister Whitt."

Hezekiah interrupted saying, "The targets have to be judged before the winner can be determined."

"Yes sir," said James Griffith.

The targets were brought back for all to see, Tom Whitten caught the bulls eye on the edge. The shot was half in and half out.

James Griffith Whitt's was a clean shot through the bulls eye. Hezekiah held up the arm of James Griffith and said, "Here is your winner!"

Mister James Whitt has won the prize and Hezekiah handed him the shiny Twenty Dollar Gold Piece. Every one present roared with praise for the grand shooting exhibition that James Griffith Whitt had just given.

Tom Whitten was the first to congratulate James.

"Fine shooting young man", he said.

"Thanks Mister Whitten," said James Griffith.

"Call me Tom from now on Mister Whitt," he said with a smile.

James Griffith Whitt was some where in the clouds. He was so pleased to have won the contest. All the men old and young shook his hand.

Jonas said to Hezekiah, "Paw I hope this don't ruin him!"

"Don't worry son, he may have a swelled head for a day or two, but he will be just fine," Hezekiah said.

"He is a fine Whitt man, and is made of good stuff," added Hezekiah.

Hezekiah related that when he was seventeen, and marching with the militia against the Indians he did quiet well.

"I got a lot of praise, and it didn't do permanent damage," Hezekiah said.

"Let him celebrate a little, he just out shot every man in Tazewell county," Hezekiah added.

"You are right he did, didn't he!" replied Jonas.

"That's right, and I have a hundred thirty four dollars to spend for William Henry Harrison's election," Hezekiah exclaimed.

Jonas was proud as punch of his sons. John Bunyon killed a bear, and young James Griffith out shot every marksman in Tazewell County.

Jonas was thinking about the competition. James had competed against the best.

The men in Tazewell County were ranked with the best shooters in the country.

Hezekiah was strutting around with a big smile on his face. Many of the men made it a point to shake hands with Hezekiah and also Jonas.

John Bunyon and Adam Beavers were also delighted with the results. Both would have loved to have won themselves, but they both knew they were beat by the best.

Adam told John, "I could barely see the target, it looked like a pin head from one hundred and fifty yards."

John agreed!

James Griffith had gotten the bulls eye two times at 150 yards.

That Tom Whitten is counted as the best shot around.

"Not any more, Mister James Griffith Whitt is now the undisputed champion in this county," Adam Beavers said.

The election was the big talk all fall in the country.

The election was held and the votes counted.

William Henry Harrison had unseated Martin Van Burin. The South had hopes that things would be different. The recession would recover and people would spend money again. Texas may be accepted into the Union now. The Indians left in the hills of North Carolina and Tennessee would be better treated. There should not be another trail of tears for the first Americans.

Hezekiah and Jonas were both optimistic for the future with new leadership.

Even David Crockett Whitt went about saying, "Tippecanoe and Tyler too!"

Jonas would gain a son or lose a daughter.

James and Rachel would not wait for June to get married. They had come to Jonas and told him , we have waited almost a year. We love each other, why do you want us to wait longer?

Jonas now agreed to give Rachel's hand in marriage to Mister Adam Beavers.

The wedding was performed by Justice Hezekiah Whitt at his home in Baptist Valley on Sunday afternoon, January 6, 1841.

They were so happy, even Jonas felt the happiness! They would reside with the Adams family temporary.

Rhoda and aunt Nancy would take on the job of caring for baby Hannah.

Jonas and the family missed Rachel, but she came to visit as much as possible.

The weather would keep everyone indoors for the bigger part of January and February 1841.The winter was a bad one in 1840-1841. The snow stayed on the ground for two solid months.

The hay and fodder feed was getting low. The livestock started to look thin. There was some reports of wolves attacking people's animals.

"It is pretty bad, the animals will do what ever they can to eat, this is the worst winter I can recollect," said Jonas. Finally the thaw came at the end of February 1841.

There was a new President to inaugurate. People gathered in Washington D.C. on the fourth of March to usher in the new President. The weather was cold and blustery, and William Henry Harrison rose to speak in the outdoor ceremony.

He had prepared a lengthy speech and held the audience for hours in the chilly air. President Harrison was sixty eight years old and wanted to prove to the people he was fit.

After the ceremony Harrison was chilled to the bone. The President had weathered Indians, politics, and enemies, but now he faced a new foe.

William Henry Harrison had come down with pneumonia. This would be one battle he would not win. After being President for about one month, he died April 4, 1841.

The new Vice President John Tyler was sworn in as the new president.

CHAPTER 12

WHAT'S NEXT FOR THE
JONAS WHITT FAMILY

Tazewell county is in shock when they get the word, that William Henry Harrison is dead. John Tyler is the new President. Some folks are saying that John Tyler is a good southern thinking man. After all he served two terms as Governor of Virginia. He believes in each state having rights. At this time in history Virginia looked on itself as a small country. Most southern and a few northern states felt this way.

Hezekiah was loyal to the Old Dominion, yet he believed in the states being in one union. Hezekiah knew that southern people thought differently about things than did the northerner's. The South could feel power shifting to the north.

"We have to hold on or the Yankees will make all of our decisions for us," replied Jonas.

"I think John Tyler will make us a good president," answered Hezekiah.

Rachel (daughter) was back visiting her family every time she could get Adam to bring her. John Bunyon was also over at the Beavers home often. He and Catherine were quiet struck with the love bug.

Little Hannah was growing like a weed, she was two years old and quite mobile. Jonas told her that she was into more stuff, than all the other children combined. She just gave him a beautiful smile and went about her business of investigating everything that caught her big hazel eyes. Jonas could see Susannah in those beautiful eyes.

David Crockett Whitt was quite the little man. He would be five in December.

The twins Rachel and Rhoda have done a wonderful job of taking care of these two motherless children. Nancy, James's wife has invested much time and effort helping them also.

Little Crockett follows Jonas wherever he goes. Jonas loved the attention Crockett gave him, even though it took extra patience.

Now little Hannah was really attracted to her Paw. She would always run to him any time he came in. She was learning to talk, but still did a lot of jabbering.

Little Crockett was just a little bit green eyed about his little sister. He would try to squeeze in between Jonas and little Hannah. Jonas would try to encourage Crockett to hug and kiss his little sister.

Jonas said, "Look Crockett, Hannah looks just like your Maw!"

Crockett did not see the resemblance! He just saw a pesky little girl that tried to get his Paw's attention all the time.

Some news that travelers brought in was about some slaves on the ship Creole. The slaves some how took over the ship and made it to the island of Nassau. This was a British port, so the slaves were all set free. Another tidbit of news was that forty eight wagons arrived in Sacramento California by traveling the Oregon Trail. This was the largest group to arrive at one time.

Jonas told John Bunyon, "Sometime in the future, we will be a nation from sea to sea"!

John agreed with Jonas saying, "Nothing surprises me any more."

Even in Tazewell county, they could see the influx of people.

Seemed like they saw people traveling the Kentucky Turnpike most everyday.

Time seemed to fly by day after day, month after month. Jonas was staying busy with the children and the new Indian Creek Farm. Another winter had come and gone and here it is early spring of 1842.

John Bunyon and Catherine Beavers were wanting to get married. John ask Jonas for his blessing before he talked to Mister Alexander Beavers. He had asked Catherine to marry him on Christmas but they kept it a secret. She said she wanted to be his wife, but he must talk to her Paw first. John agreed to the requirement.

"If you are sure about it I agree," Jonas said.

John went in one Sunday afternoon in March to talk to Mister Beavers. John caught him in a really good mood, after Sunday dinner.

Alexander agreed that Catherine could marry him if he promised to always love and protect his little girl.

John agreed, and burst out with a loud, "Yippee!"

Catherine come running in the room with a wide smile.

"Thanks Paw," she said, "You have made us so happy."

"When is the big doings going to take place?" Alexander asked.

"We thought next month if you agreed Sir", John said.

"Thursday the 14th of April will be set for our wedding day," said Catherine.

"We will move in with the Whitt's until we can find us a place," Catherine continued.

"Did you talk to Jonas about this?" he asked.

"Yes sir," John answered.

"I asked Paw about this, when I asked for his blessing in our marriage," John said.

"Sounds like you all got it all worked out," replied Alexander.

"Almost everything, we had to wait for your blessing before we could decide anything else," answered John Bunyon Whitt.

Next thing John and Catherine did was to pay a visit to Hezekiah Whitt.

"Grand Paw, me and Catherine want to get married do you think you could marry us?" John asked.

"Reckon so, John if you have Mister Beavers permission," Hezekiah answered.

"We do sir, and Paw gave us his blessing too," John said.

"Miss Catherine are you sure you are ready to marry John?" Asked the old Justice.

"Yes Sir," I love him so much!" she answered.

"Well that settles it, all but a license and a date," exclaimed Hezekiah.

"Well Sir, we want to get married on Thursday April the fourteenth," said John.

Jonas took John Bunyon out in the field and said, "Look over there in the edge of the woods."

"What do you see Paw?" he asked.

"I see a cabin built there for you and Catherine," replied Jonas.

"Right now it is only in my mind," he added.

"Now can you see it John?" Jonas asked.

"Yes Paw I am beginning to get the picture," John said.

"When do we start building it?" John asked.

"How about today, we can go up there and lay it out," Jonas said.

"Your wedding is only about three weeks away, you won't be much help then," laughed Jonas!

"We will build it in the edge of the woods, it will be cool in summer, protected from wind in winter, and the logs are right there," explained Jonas.

"Makes sense to me," exclaimed John.

"That is a really a good idea Paw," John said.

"It will get crowded when I bring Catherine to live with us in your house," John added.

"Well a cabin will give you privacy, and me more room," Jonas answered.

Jonas took a hatchet, and a long measuring tape and they went up to look at the spot.

Of course David Crockett went also. Wherever Jonas went little Crockett wanted to go.

"Paw you sure have a good eye about picking a place to build," said John.

"Don't know son, in this case I think it is a good one," Jonas replied.

"What do you think Crockett, is this a good place for James and Catherine to have a cabin?" Jonas asked.

He looked about, turned to James and said, "Do it right there!"

Jonas laughed!

They walked the area, looking it over, and planned.

"What about there where the five trees are standing, the five tulip poplars?" John asked.

"Looks good to me," replied Jonas.

"First light we will come up here and down the five poplars, and clear out the area," Jonas said.

"Then we can use some of the field rocks for foundation," Jonas added.

"James Griffith can help, what about Adam Beavers, do you think he might lend a hand?" ask Jonas.

"James will be glad to help, and I bet Adam will help also," said John Bunyon.

"The only draw back I see is the well is a little far, but you and Catherine are both young and strong," surmised Jonas.

"What do you think about that?" Jonas asked.

"I don't see it as a problem Paw!" John exclaimed.

"Some day we will have our own place, or we can dig another well," John continued.

"Alright son," Jonas said.

"John, it's settled, we will start tomorrow morning," Jonas added.

"Fine with me, I will ride over and talk to Adam this evening," John said.

"Catherine being there doesn't have any thing to do with it does it son?" Jonas asked.

John looked up at Jonas and gave him a big grin.

The cabin work went real well. Jonas, John, Adam Beavers, and James Griffith did most of the work. Hezekiah came by to watch and give pointers. James Whitt the brother of Jonas also worked several hours on the new home place of John Bunyon and his bride to be Catherine Beavers.

It was the Thirteenth of April, the cabin was built, and some used furniture had been put in the cabin. The most needed items had been provided by friends and family. The cabin was a beautiful little home in the edge of the woods.

Tomorrow John and Catherine would meet at the home of Justice Hezekiah Whitt and exchange marriage vows.

Jonas Whitt has stayed busy, lived his life in a routine since April 1839! He was living but he was not alive all the time. Jonas knew things were not what they should be. He kept thinking any day now I will be alright. Life did not have much meaning, even though he had a wonderful family.

Did he hold a grudge against God for taking his beloved Susannah? He didn't even know the answer to that.

Jonas went out into the barn to be alone. He had to slip off from Crockett and Hannah! He sat down on a milking stool, put his face in his hands and spoke out loud.

"Lord, Lord do you hear me, I need your help," Jonas prayed.

"Lord I have been traveling this road through life, and I am not going nowhere."

"Since you took Susannah home I am a weary pilgrim."

"I have no direction in my life, where am I heading?"

"I know Lord, I have not been close to you like I used to be."

"Please hear me this day, and forgive me for my sin."

"Give me purpose in my life once again."

"Thank you for your loving kindness."

"Thank you for being with me and my family, even though I have not been with you the past three years."

"Thank you for the years that you let me have Susannah."

"Thank you for my family, Father God!"

"Lord help me to walk with you as you walk with me."

"Give me direction Lord, make my life mean something to others, and to me, once again."

"Holy Spirit, Comforter, abide with me."

"Give me peace and happiness once again!," Jonas prayed.

Jonas felt an unusual warmth come over him. He felt a load lift from his shoulders. Jonas felt peace flood his soul. Jonas felt the Lord!

"Thank you almighty God, thank you for showing me the way back to you." Jonas prayed.

"Help me to never leave you again, Amen," Jonas prayed.

Jonas rose with a smile on his face, he was once again a man of peace. He would be the Old Paw to the children he once was. Now he could put Susannah in Heaven, and not try to keep her tied down to this world. He could go about life once again. He might even be able to love another woman some where down the road.

"Now I can get back to living!" he said out loud.

Jonas went back in the house a different man.

Jonas went in the house and hugged each one of his children.

They all could see a difference in Jonas. He was smiling from ear to ear and jolly as he could be.

"We got to get ready for a wedding," he yelled out gleefully.

It is Thursday, April 14, 1842, and the wedding party has gathered in the front yard of Hezekiah and Rachel Whitt's home.

Those attending were mostly family of John Bunyon Whitt and Catherine Beavers.

Hezekiah takes center stage and opens his Bible. On his left is John Bunyon Whitt and James Griffith Whitt the best man.

Alexander Beavers escorts his daughter Catherine up to the waiting groom.

John and Catherine take hands and face the grand old Justice, Hezekiah Whitt.

Jonas stands a distant ten feet to the right of John Bunyon.

Hezekiah does his duty in a very professional manner. He uses several scriptures from his old worn Bible as he instructs the young couple into the Holy Bonds of Matrimony. The service was not so long, but very serious.

Finally Hezekiah finished with I pronounce you Husband and Wife.

Adam Beavers speaks up saying, "Kiss her John!"

John Bunyon didn't waste time, he gave her a really long kiss.

Someone yelled out, "Come up for air before you croak!"

Everyone had a good laugh.

Hezekiah announced the new couple as Mr. and Mrs. John Bunyon Whitt.

Catherine turned her back on the spectators and threw her bouquet over her shoulder toward the single girls.

Emma jumped into the air and retrieved the prize.

Elizabeth hollered out saying, "You will be next Emma!"

Everyone cheered!

The Fiddler stepped up and started to play some music and the newly married couple lead in a waltz around the yard.

Some home made wine was brought out and a toast to the couple was given by Jonas Whitt.

"Here, Here," could be heard round about.

Adam Beavers followed with the next toast, and more "Here, Heres," were sounded.

It was a beautiful time for all concerned. John and Catherine were in marital bliss. finally the couple got into the borrowed buggy of Grand Paw Hezekiah and headed for the brand new cabin in the back section of Indian Creek Farm. Everyone followed for a short distance cheering the newly weds on their way.

James Griffith came up to Jonas, with a big smile on his face.

"Paw are we going to have a chivalree?" he asked.

Jonas smiled back.

"I think that would be in order, long as we don't go too far," Jonas announced.

"What you got in mind, James?" Jonas asked.

"Sneak around after dark and make some noise I guess," replied James Griffith.

"It might be more proper if we get a crowd and sing to them, just keep them on their toes for a bit," Jonas said.

"Pass the word, we will meet at our house in the front yard about 8:30 PM," Jonas said.

"Then we will all sneak up to the cabin about nine and sing real loud, we wouldn't brother them too long, just keep them guessing," said Jonas.

About 8:30 a couple dozen folks, mostly young men and women gathered in the front yard of Indian Creek Farm.

Jonas told everyone to be real quiet as we sneak up on them.

Jonas let little Crockett come along also.

Now be real quiet, he told the five year old.

"I will Paw," Crockett answered.

James and Nancy kept baby Hannah at the house so Rhoda, Emma, and Elizabeth could go.

We will circle the cabin and make a few little noise's like birds and critters. Then on my signal we will all sing out real loud "Froggy went a courting, and he did ride"

The plan went fine, the cabin was circled and little woodsy noise's begin. First one side then the other. Finally a candle was lit in the cabin. The door was cracked open and two shadowy forms could be seen peaking out.

Jonas gave the signal and a loud course of "Froggy" rang out, and folks beat on pots and pans, rang cow bells, and made noise any way they could.

The door was open and John and Catherine stepped out the door wrapped in blankets.

"Hold it down people, we have been found!" John said.

Everyone laughed and said good night to the newlyweds. A few funny things were said, and the pot and pan band headed back to the main house.

Rhoda ask, "Did you see the looks on their faces?"

Everyone was in a really jolly mood. The chivalree was a lot of fun, and the newlyweds will remember this for the rest of their lives.

Little Crockett was the biggest duck in the pond. He laughed and enjoyed the chivalree more then anyone else.

Jonas brought out some spirits and gave all the grown ups a little swig.

Everyone begin to disperse back to their own homes. Some were still laughing and singing as they went.

Jonas had a new outlook on life. Every day had a new meaning, God healed Jonas of his depression ,Jonas and his family enjoyed life now!

Crockett and Hannah enjoyed their Paw. Time was going on, and life was worthwhile to the entire Whitt family.

James Husk Lowe and his wife Rebecca lived down the Baptist Valley road a little way from Jonas's Indian Creek Farm.

Their son John Bunyon Lowe had a sparkle in his eye caused by Rhoda Whitt.

Rhoda also was catching the love bug.

Mister John B. Lowe came to Jonas and ask if he could call on Miss Rhoda?

"All right with me, if Rhoda don't mind," Jonas answered.

Rhoda didn't mind one bit! The courtship of John B. Lowe and Rhoda Whitt had begun.

All my babies are growing up and getting married, thought Jonas.

David Crockett will be six in December, and Hannah is three. The rest of the children are grown ups are almost.

I wish Susannah could see the children now, well maybe she can, Jonas thought.

Crockett is a fine little man, and Hannah looks just like her Maw.

Crockett didn't spend quite as much time over with Aunt Nancy and Uncle James as he did. He was on Jonas's heels wherever he went. Hannah spent much time over there.

Rhoda didn't have quite as much time now as she had a new interest, Mister John B. Lowe.

Elder David Young came by one day. He stopped to get a drink of cool water from the well on Indian Creek Farm. Of course he came to visit with the Whitts also.

Jonas and he had a good conservation. Jonas told him of his experience with God that day in the barn!

"Praise the Lord", replied Brother Young.

He told Jonas that he could see a visible difference in him.

Jonas told him that he finally had closure after three years, but he will never forget Susannah, nor quit loving her.

Another theme of their talk was the preaching at the Tazewell county court house. He told Jonas, about the passing of the county order a couple years ago, several preachers were taking advantage of preaching in the court house. The order read that the various religious denominations have leave to preach in the court house, provided the meetings do not interfere with the transaction of public business. Elder Young had held several meetings since the ruling of 1840. He said that the Methodist's had also had several meetings.

"That's good, now when I go to the court house I can listen to some preaching too," Jonas said.

"Not everyday," brother Young replied.

"A couple going to get their marriage license may be lucky and find a marrying preacher awaiting," Jonas replied.

"Could happen," laughed brother Young.

Another item of news was that a new county was formed from Grayson county to the south of Tazewell county.

"What is it's name?" Jonas inquired.

"Carroll is the name, they set up the county seat in the town of Hillsville," the Elder replied.

"When did they do that, this year, 1842?" Jonas asked.

Brother Young replied, "Yes, I don't know the exact day."

"Aren't you from Montgomery county Jonas?" asked Elder Young.

"Yes I sure am," he answered!

"What about old Montgomery?" Jonas asked.

"They have been slicing it up and making other counties for years, this year they gave part of Pulaski county back to Montgomery county," Elder Young stated.

"They should leave her alone now, Montgomery used to be very large," Jonas replied.

"I guess they will cut them all down to about the same size in time," replied the Elder.

"I guess," replied Jonas.

"Remember at one time way back, Kentucky was a county in Virginia!" exclaimed brother Young.

"Yes I do remember, Virginia used to go from the Atlantic all the way to the Mississippi River," Jones said.

"Ever been to Kentucky?" asked Jonas.

"No but I hear that you can get good land real cheap over there," replied the Elder.

"My two brothers live there, but I have never seen it," replied Jonas.

"Maybe someday," he added.

"Better get on old Buttercup and head up the valley," Elder Young announced.

"That old yeller hoss has served you well Elder," Jonas commented.

"Still does", answered brother Young as he mounted up.

"Peace be with you brother Whitt, and your family," the Elder said.

"Peace be with you brother Young," replied Jonas.

Crockett spoke up as he seen the minister leaving saying, "Goodbye, Preacher."

Brother Young turned and answered, "Goodbye Master Crockett."

He headed up the valley on his old horse, Buttercup.

Crockett turned to Jonas, "Why did he call me master," he asked?

"That is what people call young men when they want to be proper," answered Jonas.

"Well paw, am I a proper boy?" Crockett asked.

"You sure are son, you are my proper boy," Jonas exclaimed.

Crockett grinned from ear to ear!

Jonas goes over to check on his Paw and Maw every day. Both of them are getting up in years and have slowed down as of late. Even the grand old gentleman Hezekiah has started spending much time at home. Jonas and his brother James have been talking about the situation. They are staying abreast of the changes old age is causing Hezekiah and Rachel Whitt.

Jonas told Hezekiah of some news he has heard from some

travelers.

"Paw there is a new religion springing up here in the United States," he said.

"What are you talking about son?" he asked.

Jonas tells him about A man by the name of Joseph Smith who swears God gave him tablets, like Moses got. He says that all the churches have become too cold. God is setting him up as a leader, like God did Moses. And listen to this, Smith says, God told him that every man in this Mormon Church could and should have more than one wife!

"How could a fellow keep up with more than one wife?" asked Hezekiah.

Jonas laughed.

"I know what you mean Paw," he answered.

Rachel entered the room and wanted to know what they were laughing about?

"Some Smith feller is starting a new church and says he is the leader," replied Hezekiah.

"Well What's wrong with that, Elder Young is in charge of our little church," she asked?

"No Maw, I mean he thinks he is another Moses, and wants all the men to have more than one wife," Hezekiah explained.

"That would never work, the women would kill him," she said.

"We agree Maw," said Jonas laughingly.

Hezekiah said in a more serious tone, "People better be careful, God said not to be adding to or taking away from His word!"

Jonas said, "I understand Paw, I don't believe in such goings on!"

"Plumb queer ideas!" Rachel added.

Jonas kept notice of his parents condition. Old age was beginning to take toll. Hezekiah was not in Jeffersonville very much any more. He hobbled around somewhat. Rachel was bent over in the back and used her cane much more now.

James the oldest son and Jonas had several talks about their parents. Neither one of them thought their parents would move in with them.

"It looks like someone will have to move in and help them," James said.

The likely son would be James. James and Nancy had no children, and Jonas had his hands full with his own family.

"If you are willing, I think that will be grand," Jonas said.

"We will not have to worry about them if you and Nancy are under the same roof with them," Jonas added.

"We will go and talk with them soon and get it worked out," James said.

"Do you think Nancy will have a problem with it?" asked Jonas.

"No Jonas, Nancy and I have already been talking about it," James answered.

"Paw is so proud, I hope he is willing for me to move in," said James.

"I think he will once we talk to him about it, he will have the freedom to do whatever he feels like," James said.

"I can take him to Jeffersonville every now and then if he needs to go," said Jonas.

James, Nancy and Jonas went to visit Hezekiah and Rachel Whitt in the spring of 1843. After a cup of tea James started the conversation on the matter of him moving in to help take care of Hezekiah and Rachel. Nancy and Jonas both pointed out the benefits of James and Nancy moving in and living with the elder Parents.

It surprised them that Hezekiah was for it, but Rachel was not sure she liked the idea.

"I got my things I do everyday, I ain't up to cooking for a crowd", Rachel announced.

"No, no, Maw you don't understand," James said.

"You can do your things, Nancy will be here to help with the cooking, I will be here to help with the heavy work," James explained.

"About time somebody is going to spoil us old folks a bit!" Mother Rachel exclaimed.

Hezekiah and Rachel laughed together.

"Well that's settled," said James.

"We will make plans to move in," Nancy said.

They changed the subject to current times. Everyone was talking about a large migration west. Large wagon trains were going plumb to California and Oregon and every place in between.

"I wish I was young, I would go out and have a look at this great country," said Hezekiah.

Only last year Fremont lead an expedition to the Rocky Mountains to explore. What great stories are coming back east from all these happenings.

"We are living in exciting times", exclaimed Jonas.

Another thing in the news was the Seminole Indian wars were ended, way to the south in Florida.

President John Tyler was having much opposition from the northern states as he pressed for states rights. Governor James McDowell was doing what he could to support the President. Virginia had strong feelings about states rights as did all the southern states.

"I hope and pray that this country will come together some day," stated Hezekiah.

"I am afraid the North wants to divide this nation," James said.

Jonas had comments also, he told them we all have to work toward being one nation or there will be a great division some day.

"The North and the South squabble and everyone else is heading out west," Hezekiah said.

George Washington would turn over in his grave if he could see how the leaders in his city are acting. He always said that we all have to stick together, to ward off our enemies.

"Only thing Paw, we have so many enemies in our own country", said Jonas.

"Sad but true," replied a solemn Hezekiah.

Jonas told them he heard that the northern people called President Tyler, "Your Accidentcy."

"That is awful, let's talk about something of a better nature," Rachel requested.

"How is Rhoda and John B. Lowe's courting a coming along?" asked Rachel.

"Well they see each other most everyday, if that tells you any thing," replied Jonas.

"I expect a wedding before too long," Jonas added.

Rachel and her husband Adam Beavers were still with his folks. They came by most every week, and everyone had seen each other on the Sabbath at the Baptist Church.

John Bunyon and his bride Catherine were down to the Jonas Whitt's everyday as they shared the well and also worked the same fields.

James Griffith was the leader of the children still at home. Elizabeth, Emma, Crockett, and Hannah kept Jonas busy.

Rhoda was a blessing, she did most of the cooking, and washing. All the children were good to pitch in on the chores.

Jonas had an idea that he may want to travel and see Kentucky someday, but had no idea when.

The letters Hezekiah gets from Richard and John B. Whitt paints a wonderful picture of the Blue Grass State. Still what could be better than this wonderful land of Tazewell County, Virginia? Maybe someday Jonas will go and take a look at Kentucky.

For now we have plenty of living to do right here, he thought. I have my family, Maw and Paw are living right here. I have work on the mills when they need me, and the carpenter work neighbors call on me for, all keep me busy. Why do I even think of moving anyplace else? I guess it is just the times I live in, thought Jonas.

Monday morning January 8th 1844, Indian Creek Farm is awakened to a foot of wet snow. It had rained yesterday, and overnight it changed to this beautiful white wonderland.. The snow was so heavy the sound of timber breaking from the nearby woods could be heard.

Rhoda got up and looked out!

"Well Paw, guess this is not a good day to do the washing," she said.

"Guess you are right about that," replied Jonas.

James Griffith had built up the fire and went out to clear a path to the Johnny, to the wood pile, and to the well.

Way across the field a distant voice could be heard. John Bunyon was shoveling snow around his cabin and saw James Griffith!

"Some snow huh?" hollered James Griffith.

"Brother you all alright?" shouted John Bunyon.

"Yeah we are fine down here," James shouted back.

"You and Catherine alright up there in the woods?" asked James Griffith.

"Good, we are doing good!" John shouted back.

Seven year old Crockett comes out all bundled up.

"Where is the other shovel John?" he asked.

"Little brother, how about getting some more wood in the house and then draw a bucket of water?" asked James Griffith.

"Alright James but I wanted to shovel the snow," he replied.

"There will be plenty of snow left for you little brother," answered James Griffith.

"Oh! Alright," replied Crockett as he headed for the wood pile.

Rhoda had some pork frying, dough mixed for the biscuits, and the table set.

Emma came in to the kitchen and said, "Good morning Rhoda what do you need for me to do?"

"Sister we need to milk Ol Jersey, you mind going to the barn and milking her?" asked Rhoda.

"No, but where is James Griffith?" Emma asked.

"He is making roads to the places we have to go to," answered Rhoda.

"What do you mean Rhoda?" Emma asked.

"Have you looked outside sister?" Rhoda asked.

Emma went over to the window and pulls back the curtain.

"Wow! What a big snow," she exclaimed.

"I see James out there shoveling, looks like he is almost to the barn," she added.

"I will get my coat and go to see Miss Jersey," replied Emma.

Everything moved a little slower this Monday morning. breakfast was enjoyed, Elizabeth, Emma, and little Hannah cleaned up the kitchen.

"This will be a good day for some lessons," Rhoda announced.

James answered quickly saying, "I thought if it was alright with Paw, I would take Crockett out for a little hunt."

"We might round up some rabbits, or a grouse or two," James added.

"Guess that would be alright, hunting is something Crockett needs to learn too," Jonas said.

"Well us girls will work on some arithmetic, and ABC's," replied Rhoda.

"Hannah needs some practice, Crockett could use some to," added Rhoda.

Crockett spoke up saying, "I will do that later, we got to track stuff in the snow!

"Some rabbit and grouse would be a welcome change for dinner," Jonas exclaimed.

"You boys go ahead, I will take care of feeding and watering the stock," Jonas said.

"James be real careful, Crockett is still learning about guns," Jonas cautioned.

"Paw would it be alright if we took your shot gun, we will be more apt to bring back some birds?" asked James Griffith.

"Yes, just be careful with it," he answered.

The boys trudged off toward the woods.

Jonas hollered out one more time, "Be careful, and watch out for breaking limbs!"

"We will," James and Crockett answered in unison.

Jonas took care of the animals, and brought some material and tools back to the house. Guess I will do a few repairs, and maybe make something, he thought.

The girls sat around the fire while Rhoda went over some ciphering and penmanship. Hannah was a fast learner, she already knew her alphabet, and numbers.

Jonas watched the girls as he worked, he could not help but see Susannah in the actions and expressions of little Hannah. She even looks like her Maw he thought. Long as that girl lives, Susannah also lives on in her.

Jonas had finally reached a point that he did not grieve so much over Susannah. He would never forget her, or even stop loving her, but he could move on in his life now!

James Griffith and Crockett came back in the late afternoon with two rabbits, and a pair of grouse. Crockett could not be quiet about the hunt.

"James let me shoot this big rabbit," he exclaimed.

James chuckled.

"He did it Paw, Crockett is now a hunter," he said.

Jonas took the rabbit and held it up for everyone to see.

"This is some fine Hare," said Jonas.

"Hair," Crockett said, "What do you mean Paw?"

Rhoda spoke up saying, "See I told you, Crockett needs

schooling."

"Paw what is going on, this rabbit has a lot of hair, I thought we called it fur," Crockett stated.

Jonas laughed, as did the rest of the family.

"Crockett this is a lesson for you, a rabbit is also called a "Hare," Jonas explained.

"Alright Paw, I understand now," Crockett said.

"I learned about hunting and also a new word today," Crockett added.

"Do we eat Mister Hare for supper, Paw?" Crockett asked.

"Well you need some practice on skinning the fur off them critters," said James Griffith.

Jonas turned to Crockett and said, "You know the rule of hunting don't you son?"

Crockett answered, "Yes sir, You catch it you clean it!"

"Right," answered Jonas, "That goes for fishing and hunting."

"James will help you, don't get hair all over your Hare meat," Jonas said.

"Hare, Hare, Hare," said Crockett.

Everyone laughed!

"Crockett wouldn't be forgetting that word too soon," Rhoda exclaimed.

After a fine supper of wild game, Jonas said, "I enjoyed that so much."

"We used to have to eat a lot of wild meat, now we are almost citified," he exclaimed.

A knock was heard at the door. Hannah ran towards the door. "Wait," said Jonas.

"Let a grownup answer the door, you never know who is there," Jonas instructed.

Jonas opened the door slowly.

Good evening sir was heard by all.

"Well hello to you Mister Lowe," Jonas said.

"Come in out of the cold," Jonas added.

Rhoda ran to her room to straighten herself up, for she did not expect her beau to come calling in this snow.

Jonas put his coat on.

"Think I will walk over and see Maw and Paw," he announced.

John B. Lowe went over to sit in the sitting room.

Hannah ran in to entertain the guest.

I never know what is going to happen around here Jonas thought as he headed for the Hezekiah Whitt house. I have a wonderful family and they keep me guessing as to what's next?

Rhoda came out in a better dress, and her long black hair, back in place.

"Good evening Mister Lowe," she said as she curtsied.

John B. Lowe stood and took her hand, bent over and kissed it.

"You are so romantic," she exclaimed!

"I didn't think you would come calling today with this snow and all," she said.

"Just a little snow, I wanted to see you real bad," John exclaimed.

"You just seen me two days ago," replied Rhoda.

"Don't matter, I wanted to come and see you today also.," John answered.

"Well I'm glad you did," replied Rhoda as she took a seat beside him.

After Hannah found something else to get into the pair had some privacy.

John looked into her hazel eyes and said, "I want to ask you something today."

He slipped off the love seat to one knee.

"Oh my God," she said.

"That's right dear, will you marry me," he asked softly?

She squeezed his hand cutting of the flow of blood, "yes I will," Rhoda answered.

He stood up and pulled her up and they embraced for a kiss.

Hannah noticed this and ran around saying, "Kissy, Kissy Kissy!"

"Rhoda and John are kissing," she said.

John turned to the little girl and said, "It's alright we are engaged now."

Emma and Elizabeth came running in and ask, "When?"

"Well we have to talk to Paw and then we will set a date," she explained.

CHAPTER 13

ANOTHER WEDDING IN THE VALLEY

Jonas returns home from his visit with Hezekiah, Rachel, James, and Nancy. John B. Lowe and Rhoda are still sitting in the sitting room.

"How is Grand Maw and Grand Paw?"' Rhoda asks.

"About the same, Paw seems weaker here lately," Jonas replied.

James told me they are doing alright, except Paw misses going into Jeffersonville.

"He feels like he is falling out of the loop," Jonas added.

"Paw we have something to talk to you about," replied Rhoda!

"I bet I know what this is about," said Jonas with a smile.

"Mister Whitt," John said, "We would like your blessing to be married."

"Well John, and Rhoda, I see no reason why you can't get married, you have had a long courtship, and should know your minds by now," Jonas stated.

"When do you all want to get married?" Jonas asked.

"Thank you Sir, we were waiting for your blessing before setting a date," said John.

Rhoda got up and went to the kitchen, returning quickly with the calendar.

Rachel sat by John B., and leafed through the calendar.

"I want it to be summer time so we can have it out doors," she said.

She turned through June, then to July.

"So many people get married in June, I want to be different," she said.

Then she pointed to Tuesday July 2, 1844.

"That is when I want to get married," she said.

"That is fine with me, but why on Tuesday?" John asked.

"Don't know, just a feeling I have," Rhoda replied.

"Good, if you have a feeling about something it is better to follow it, besides that Thursday is the 4th of July, our countries birthday," Jonas said.

"You children have my blessing!" Jonas said after a pause.

"What about James and Rebecca, and the other Lowe's have you discussed this with them?" asked Jonas.

"Yes sir, well with my Maw anyway," replied John. B.

"She felt about the same as you Mister Whitt, I am sure Paw will be pleased also," said John B. Lowe.

"Well Mister Lowe let's get one thing straight, I am Jonas and you are John," Jonas said.

"You are practically in the family and have been for some time," added Jonas.

"Do you all intend to have Paw marry you?" Jonas asked.

"If Justice Hezekiah would do it, I would feel honored," answered John B. Lowe.

"I want him to do it too," replied Rhoda.

Hannah could not hold it any longer, "Paw" she blurted out, "John kissed Rhoda!"

"Well honey that is alright," he explained.

"John and Rhoda are going to be husband and wife this summer," Jonas explained.

She wilted, she thought Jonas would get after them!

"Don't worry honey, they are in love and a kiss here and there is acceptable,"

Jonas said.

Rhoda blushed, and John smiled.

Hanna went running through the house yelling, "Rhoda's getting married."

"Yes we know," answered Emma, and Elizabeth.

James and Crockett had no comment as they were working on tanning some rabbit skins.

Crockett asked James Griffith, "When you going to get married big brother?"

"Don't know, I guess when I let some pretty little thing catch me," James Griffith said.

Crockett thought that to be so funny, he laughed out loud.

Finally winter was over, Jonas and James Griffith were getting the fields ready to plant.

Potatoe's were already in the ground. Emma, Elizabeth and Crockett planted most of the potatoe's.

Hannah was following along after Crockett as he dropped the sliced potato seed into the rows.

"What you doing Crockett?" she asked.

"Silly girl, can't you see I'm planting potatoe's," he said.

"Why do it?" she asked.

Crockett stopped to explain the whole process. We cut the potato up with an eye on each slice.

"Can the tators see us?" Hannah asked.

"No, No, he went on, then we bury them in the ground, and the little baby tators will come up and be big potatoe's," he explained.

"Do you understand, Hannah?" Crockett asked.

"No," she exclaimed, "Look none has come up yet!"

Crockett put his hands over his ears and shut his eyes in disbelief.

"Hannah, they don't jump right up, they take all summer to grow," he exclaimed "next fall at harvest time we will have big one's.

"You just wait and see," he said!

This satisfied her for now.

The older girls had a good laugh about this. They couldn't wait to tell Paw.

John Bunyon and Catherine were out working their plot that Jonas shared with them. The crows could be heard as they talked to each other with their Caw, Caw. The mules digging their hoofs into the earth as they pulled the plow, had a sound of it's own. The men behind the plows added to the sounds with the commands, Gee, Haw, Whoa, and Gitty- up. The newly turned earth gave out an aroma of new birth. The Robins were back and following the teams at a safe distance. The fishing worms were exposed to the hunting birds. Yes it was spring once again in Tazewell county. The grass was already green, and the flowering trees were starting to show their new colors.

Rhoda rang the dinner bell, she had worked all morning in the house. She had a nice dinner ready for the big appetites coming in from the fields.

Crockett said to Jonas as they were coming to eat, "Paw, I bet we could catch some of them fishing worms and go fishing."

"When we get caught up with the planting we will," he answered.

"I bet them Horny Heads are biting, and the Red Eyes too," said James Griffith as he caught up with them.

"Paw when do you think we will be caught up?" asked young Crockett.

"Soon," he said, "We can't plant corn and beans until the tenth of May."

"After we get out the early crops out we will have a day or two to wet a line," Jonas answered.

An Adkins family traveling the Turnpike stopped for some water and conversation at The Indian Creek Farm. Jonas and most of the family gathered around for what ever news they might hear. The family was given water to drink and filled their containers from the well. They talked about the migration westward, President Tyler, and other current events.

One thing of interest was a new invention. Something that would give instant communication. A man by the name of Samuel Morse was using electricity to send messages on wires. He had a code of longs and shorts that could be converted into letters and words. This was done by using a key, A telegraph key. The operator would click out shorts, and longs of electric pulses. They are spending Thirty Thousand Dollars to run wire and set up the Telegraph system from Washington to Baltimore. The Telegraph message was received at the same instant it was sent.

"Good Grief," exclaimed Jonas.

"You mean you don't have to wait an hour, or day to get an answer?" Jonas asked.

"That is right, instant messages will be sent and received," said Mister Adkins.

"They will charge by the letter, so people will have to write short messages," he added.

"Well, It will take years before it gets out here," replied Jonas!

"Not too many years, they have plans to construct lines to all major cities, then to spread out to smaller towns," answered Mister Adkins.

"That is something, we never know what to expect any more do we?" asked Jonas.

Mister Adkins' said, "It seems that most anything is possible, except flying."

"I don't think people will ever make a workable flying machine," he added.

Jonas agreed with the man. Young David Crockett Whitt took all of this news in. He thought to himself, people might just invent a flying machine one of these days.

The Adkins family was heading to Kentucky, to start a new life. They said that they had kin folks in Morgan county, that would assist them in getting settled.

Jonas wished them good luck as they got on their way. They shook hands with the Whitts and gave them a big thanks for the good cool well water.

I would like to visit Kentucky sometime Jonas thought!

My goodness, it is the last of June already. The wedding of Rhoda and John B. Lowe will be day after tomorrow July 2nd, 1844.

July is starting off to be a hot and humid month in Baptist Valley. All the plans are made, and are in motion for a grand wedding.

Everyone has their best Sunday clothes cleaned and ready.

Justice Hezekiah is ready as he can be to do the marrying. He is not the spry and exuberant man he once was! He is already at the ripe old age of eighty three.

Everyone was worried that Hezekiah may not be able to stand on his feet to do the ceremony.

Hezekiah says what's the fuss, he told them he had his cane and the Lord will give him strength to do this for his Grand Baby.

The wedding will be held in the front yard of the elder Whitt's house, under the big oak. Everyone has been pitching in, setting up tables and benches. The decorations will be put up in the morning.

The grass has been trimmed, and things are just about ready for tomorrow.

There was a quick and loud thunder storm yesterday, everyone hopes that will not happen tomorrow at the appointed hour of 6:00 PM.

All of the James Lowe family, the Jonas Whitt family, and the many friends of both bride and groom have been invited.

It should be a grand Southern Wedding, with celebration and dancing to follow. Everyone is looking forward to tomorrow.

John B. Lowe has already rented a cabin, and took over a small farm on the halves, in preparation for his bride. He has lived in the cabin for only one day, trying to get things ready for a wife. The cabin is about a mile up the valley from Jonas's Indian Creek Farm.

John Bunyon Whitt, Adam Beavers, James Griffith Whitt, and young David Crockett Whitt all went over and helped John B. Lowe clean the cabin, and set up furniture.

Crockett will not be eight years old until December, but he thinks he is one of the men.

Young Crockett asked John B. Lowe, where Rhoda would sleep? He pointed out that he only had one bed.

John turned a little pink and the others roared with laughter.

"What's so funny?" asked Crockett.

"When you get a little older you will understand," Adam replied.

The morning of July 2nd, 1844 has arrived. The day looks to be a great one, weather wise.

James, Nancy, Rachel, Emma, and Elizabeth meet for breakfast at Hezekiah's house. After a leisurely meal and conversation they will go out and make the final preparations for the evening wedding.

Hezekiah and Rachel were up and about, talking about the wedding.

Grand Maw Rachel said, "Me and Paw may take us a little nap after dinner."

"We want to be pert for the wedding," she added.

"Pert," replied Hezekiah, "I ain't been pert for a spell now, he said laughing.

"Old man," replied Rachel, "You know what I mean."

"May I have another cup of that coffee?" Hezekiah asked changing the subject.

"Sure Grand Paw, I will get you one," answered Elizabeth.

"You are a good girl," replied Hezekiah.

"If you don't mind bring me my Bible and that little book beside it also," Hezekiah added.

Elizabeth went for the coffee, Emma got his Bible and book.

"Thanks girls," he said with a big smile.

Hezekiah went over his Bible and marrying book one final time.

"I don't want to make no mistakes," he said as he looked everything over.

Rachel took his hand.

"Don't worry Love, you have married a bunch of couples over the years," she said.

"Thanks Rachel," he said as he squeezed her hand.

"This is one time that is special, Rhoda is getting married," Hezekiah exclaimed.

The hour is at hand, no storm, no problems. It looks to be a grand affair. Rhoda is in the bedroom of the Hezekiah house, starting to get ready.

The tables have brilliant white clothes spread on them. Flowers are every where. Red, white, and blue banners are tied to the porch banisters. The American flag is hanging down from the upper porch in a grand manner. People are starting to arrive and take seats. It is quite hot and humid, but there are no complaints. The shade of the great oak is doing it's best to cool the lovely dressed gentlemen and ladies sitting under it's big limbs.

Young David Crockett Whitt has arrived with Jonas. The precocious boy marveled at all of the decorations.

"This sure is something," he said to Jonas.

"Yes it is," Jonas replied.

"Seems like each wedding tries to out do the last," Jonas added.

"Look Paw, here comes John B. in his wagon," Crockett said.

"Well he has to be here, if there is going to be a wedding," replied Jonas.

"Well Paw, I know that," said Crockett.

"You acted surprised that he would show up today," Jonas said laughing.

"Did you think he would back out?" asked Jonas.

"Naw, he just looks different all dressed up in that suit and tie," replied Crockett.

"Now Crockett, you be on your best behavior today, don't get in the way, and don't be asking so many questions," Jonas instructed.

"Alright Paw," he answered as he headed into Grand Paws house.

James helps Hezekiah, and Jonas helps Rachel down the steps to their places. Rachel sits on the front row, and Hezekiah goes to the front under the arch way.

Hezekiah motions for John B. Lowe and Adam Beavers the best man to come to his left. Then Hezekiah lifted his arms as a signal for everyone to rise.

Little Hannah came down the aisle dropping rose petals. Following her came Rachel Whitt Beavers, Catherine Beavers Whitt, Emma, and Elizabeth to stand on the right of Justice Hezekiah.

Next he sent a big smile to Rhoda and Jonas her escort. That was the signal for the bride to come forth. It was 6:00 PM according to Hezekiah's pocket watch. He wanted to be sure the hands were going down, as was the custom.

They had set up a small table for his books and a chair behind him if he needed it.

Jonas brought Rhoda before Hezekiah with a slow deliberate walk.

As they stood in front of the stately old justice, He asked , "Who gives this woman to be wed?"

"I do, her father," Jonas said.

Then Jonas went to the vacant seat between mother Rachel, and Crockett.

Hezekiah went through the ceremony with out a problem. Finally after he prayed a beautiful prayer over the kneeling couple, he had them rise and said the awaiting words, "I now pronounce you man and wife."

"You may kiss the bride!" he added.

After a rather long kiss, Hezekiah presented them as Mr. and Mrs. John Bunyon Lowe. Cheers went up and the crowd was ready for some fun.

The newly married couple were escorted to the table holding the wedding cake. After giving each other a bite of cake, and getting it all over their faces, everyone enjoyed the humor of the moment.

Everyone filled their cups and Jonas rose to offer the first toast. He wished the best for the newly married couple, and all drink to them.

"Here, Here," could be heard between each toast offered.

The drinks varied from coffee, tea, to home made wine to the powerful beverage, corn liquor.

After the toasts were completed the fiddler was summoned to start the dancing. Then Mr. and Mrs. John Bunyon Lowe had the first dance. Everyone cheered them on. Next all the guests took to the dance floor (yard) and everyone was having a great time.

James Griffith got some of the younger boys together, and decorated the Lowe wagon. They made a sign and hung it on the back saying, "Just Hitched!"

They put ribbons around the sides and around the spokes of the wheels. They got some old shoes, and rope and tied them to the back. They even found some rusted out pans and an old wash tub and tied them to the back. They set all of these up under the wagon out of sight.

About 8:00 PM, the couple started making their way to the wagon to head up the valley.

Someone had even put a sign over their cabin door saying, "Grand Entrance" which embraced Rhoda, and John B. as they drove up. John carried Rhoda across the threshold, gave her a big kiss and hurried to remove the sign and unhitch the team!

Back at the Hezekiah house the party went on for a spell. James Griffith was talking up a chivalree. Everyone was for it. Plans were made to be at the cabin by dark, bringing with them some noise making devices. Pots and pans, cow bells and even a drum was gathered.

Jonas took Hezekiah's wagon and loaded up everyone who wanted to have some fun. Some other folks that lived in that direction drove their own buggy's and wagons.

Young David Crockett was ready for this, as he had participated in John Bunyon Whitt and Catherine Beavers Whitt's chivalree. He was an old hand at it you might say.

When the folks got close to the cabin, everyone got quiet, and sneaked all around the cabin. Jonas would give the signal with a bang on his pot. Everyone joined in and made enough noise to awake the dead.

They stopped abruptly, and listened for reaction from inside the cabin.

Lamps were lit and a commotion to put on some clothes were heard. The door was cracked open and the couple peeked out.

Everyone cheered!

Some one started singing the Froggy song. Everyone joined in.

Much laugher and merriment was had by all the chivalree participants.

After a few more minuets everyone loaded up and headed toward home, beating on the noise makers and laughing.

Young Crockett didn't really understand the whole concept, none the less he was enjoying the ruckus.

James Griffith kept saying, "Did you see the look on John's face?"

John Bunyon Whitt and Catherine took part in the chivalree, as they were the brunt of the last one.

"It is much more blessed to give than to receive!" Catherine exclaimed.

Especially when it comes to a chivalree," replied John Bunyon.

Jonas chuckled!

Jonas went over the next day to see how Hezekiah and Rachel were doing after the big wedding. They were both tired, but none the worse for having everything at their home.

Jonas told them all about the chivalree, and the fun that was had.

"I used to just love being in the excitement of a chivalree!" Rachel said.

Hezekiah stated that he too, had been in on some of the fun.

"I know Paw, you embarrassed Susannah and me to death on our wedding night," Jonas said.

"That was fun, you looked so sheepish looking out of that door," Hezekiah said.

"That has been many a year ago Paw," Jonas replied.

"Paw you know tomorrow is the 4th of July, I was wondering if you and Maw wanted to go into Jeffersonville and see some of the festivities?" Jonas asked.

"There will be a band playing music, some speeches by the local officials, I think some games, like sack racing, horse racing, pole climbing and pig catching," Jonas continued.

"There will be a cake dance too, any way plenty of food and fun," Jonas said.

"Do you want me to drive you into town?" Jonas asked.

Hezekiah looked at Rachel, and back to Jonas.

"No son, I don't think we can handle a full day like that," exclaimed

Hezekiah.

"I miss these things, but the years have taken a toll on us," he said.

"You go ahead and take your family, you can tell us all about it when you get back," he said.

"We will enjoy the day swinging on the porch," added Hezekiah.

"Alright Paw, I just don't want you and Maw to miss out on things," Jonas said.

"I know son," Hezekiah answered.

"But we will be better off here," he added.

"What about James and Nancy, do they have plans for the day," Jonas asked?

"They might want to go in to town and celebrate Independence day," said Hezekiah.

"This always makes me think of the war, some of it I just as soon to forget", said the Veteran.

"We beat the Kings Army and the Indians that were raised up against us," exclaimed Hezekiah.

"I know Paw, we are all grateful for what you men did for this country," replied Jonas.

"Thanks Son", Hezekiah replied.

Rachel changed the subject.

"Did you notice Emma and that young man John Madden Stephenson?" she asked.

"There seemed to be some flames sparking between them," she added.

"Yes I did, but she has not spoken of it this morning," Jonas answered.

"I half way expect him to show up in the near future," Jonas added.

"Young love, Oh my," replied Hezekiah.

"Hope they get married before I get too old," he said.

"Paw, lets not rush them into anything, they haven't even done any courting yet," Jonas said.

"Oh, I know, I'm just thinking of my self," said Hezekiah.

"Well Paw, I'm going home and see who wants to go to Jeffersonville tomorrow, if they want to go I will go, if not I might just sit on the porch with you all," Jonas said.

"Now son you take them into town, it will be good for them," said Rachel.

"Alright Maw," Jonas answered as he walked toward home.

That evening Jonas told the children, after our chores are done in the morning we will ride into Jeffersonville for the Forth of July celebration. Everyone was looking forward to it.

James Griffith already had plans to be there. He was a grown man, his nineteenth birthday would be only a week away on the tenth of July 1844.

John Madden Stephenson was waiting at the edge of town for Emma and the Whitt party. Old Jeffersonville was well decorated for the nations birthday, and the people came from all ends of Tazewell County. The day had the makings of being one to remember.

When Emma saw John M. Stephenson, she turned to Jonas and said, "Paw would it be alright if I walked around town with Mister Stephenson?" she asked.

"Well I reckon, I don't see why not," replied Jonas.

"Meet us at the court house by 5:30 PM, if not before," replied Jonas.

Jonas had five year old Hannah and seven year old Crockett with him. Hannah wanted to play with the other little girls.

Crockett wanted to be in the pig chase, and maybe in the pie eating contest. Jonas told him he could try the pig chase, but not the pie eating contest.

"How come Paw?" Crockett asked.

"Well for one thing, some big fellers will be eating the pie, another thing, I don't want you throwing up all night," Jonas explained.

A number of little girls had gathered under a big shade tree to skip rope. Jonas told Hannah to go and play, but stay in sight of the wagon.

"I will tie the team here by the watering trough," Jonas said.

Emma and John M. Stephenson walked on down the street.

James Griffith Whitt came in on his horse earlier, he was involved in a horse shoe pitching contest, and waved to the Whitts when they arrived.

Jeffersonville was in a festive mood, everyone had a smile it seemed. The old smooth bore cannon in the Court yard would be fired at 6:00 PM.

After that music and dancing would begin.

The day was enjoyed by everyone, except some boys that had eaten too much pie.

They were over behind a fence taking turns throwing up.

Jonas pointed them out to Crockett.

"Now see there son, you might have been one of those fellows," Jonas said.

Crockett acknowledged Jonas with a nod!

Crockett had given a great effort at catching a greased pig, but did not succeed.

About 8:00 PM Jonas gathered his brood and got started back to Indian Creek Farm.

Everyone took turns telling about their adventures of the day.

Crockett especially enjoyed the firing of the old smooth bore cannon at the court yard.

"That old gun sure did BOOM, didn't it paw?" Crockett asked.

"It hurt my ears!" exclaimed Hannah!

"Mine too," said Jonas.

"I hope none of you never have to see something like that in a real war," Jonas added.

"Me too Paw, even though I would mow down the enemy when they come a calling," exclaimed young Crockett.

"It is alright to pretend in play, but the real thing is not one bit fun," Jonas said in a serious tone.

"Your Grand Paw Hezekiah seen action more than once, he said there is no fun in it, seeing people hurt and dieing," Jonas said.

Emma was being very quiet on the ride home.

"Emma, did you and Mister Stephenson have a nice day?" asked Jonas.

"Yes sir," she answered.

"He is a real nice young man," she added.

"The Stephenson family seem nice," answered Jonas.

"I seen Mr. and Mrs. Stephenson at the celebration, and talked with them for a few minutes," Jonas said.

"Paw," exclaimed Emma, "John is coming over and ask you if it would be alright to spend time with me!

"You mean court, don't you honey?" answered Jonas.

"Well I guess it might lead to that," said Emma.

"Well I will talk to the young man when he comes to visit," said Jonas.

"I will give him a positive answer after I tell him the rules," Jonas said.

"You know I laid down rules for all the children when they start sparking," Jonas said.

"Yes sir, thank you Paw," answered Emma.

She was a little embarrassed by the conversation.

Jonas went over to check on Hezekiah and Rachel after they got home. Hezekiah said they did just fine spending the Fourth, sitting under the big oak in the front yard.

"How did things go in Jeffersonville?" Hezekiah asked.

"Several folks ask about you Paw, you have many friends in the county," Jonas stated.

"Not as many as I used to, they keep dieing off, the older I get the more friends I have to give up," exclaimed Hezekiah.

Jonas changed the subject back to the celebration.

"Things went just fine Paw, they had all kinds of things going on, it was a nice celebration, replied Jonas.

"Did the young-uns have a good time?" ask Rachel.

"Think so, Hannah played with a group of little girls about her age, and Crockett tried to catch the pig, but only got dirty," Jonas exclaimed.

"James Griffith won a ribbon at pitching horse shoes," Jonas continued.

"Elizabeth found some young ladies to spend time with, I have no idea what they talked about," Jonas said.

"She just don't seem to be in any hurry to start courting, and I am glad for that," Jonas said.

"Emma got her a beau?" asked Rachel.

"Looks like it," Jonas said.

"Is the beau that young feller, Stephenson?" she asked.

"Yes Maw, you got that one right," replied Jonas.

"I hope it all works out for her and him, if it be Gods will," answered

Rachel.

"Amen to that", said Hezekiah.

Next day James Griffith is talking to Jonas

"It seems that fall comes real soon after the passing of the Fourth," said James Griffith.

"It is harvest time already, time flies by," answered Jonas, it seems the older you get the quicker time goes by," Jonas said.

James Griffith answered saying, "I guess so Paw but I can't seem to ever get to twenty one."

Crockett was listening to all of this and replied, "I will be glad to get old enough to quit school."

Jonas replied to him, "you better learn all you can, I don't want to have any ignorant children, you have to learn the three R's just to get along now days!"

Before Jonas could turn around it was, December. Time truly passes fast when a man is busy on a farm.

Crockett would be eight years old and very mature for his age. Jonas had a nice jack knife laid away at the general store, for a birthday present.

Crockett always said that his birthday was too close to Christmas, it seemed that everything happened in December for him!

Jonas gave Crockett his new knife on the thirteenth of December, his birthday.

Emma and Elizabeth fixed a special birthday meal and cake for him. Mashed potatoes and ham were served this special day. David Crockett Whitt had a birthday to remember. The weather was mild this day, so Grand Paw Hezekiah, and Grand Maw Rachel got to come for the celebration. James and Nancy were there also as they brought the elder Whitts over. Nancy had a new shirt of calico for him. She had measured him one day as if playing a game. Crockett was surprised and really liked it. Hezekiah and Rachel brought him some candy.

Hannah was a little jealous of her big brother. Crockett consoled her, April will be here before you know it, and you can have your day then. This seemed to satisfy her for now, at least she could eat the good meal and have cake with Crockett.

Emma had also invited John M. Stephenson over to enjoy the meal with young Crockett. The courtship had blossomed and a date for a wedding was set. Tuesday April 15, 1845. Jonas and John's family had given their blessing.

"Emma you know that is the day your Maw passed away, and Hannah was born don't you?" asked Jonas.

"Yes Paw, that is why I picked it, to remember Maw and always remember Hannah coming into the world," she explained.

"Well I guess we should remember it in a positive way," answered Jonas.

Hannah was pleased, she kept saying, "Emma is getting married on my birthday!"

Emma and John decided not to have a big wedding. They wanted to have Grand Paw Hezekiah do the honors, if he was able.

"I sure will try, long as it is not a long drawn out thing, I just can't stand for very long anymore," Hezekiah said.

"Grand Paw, we don't mind if you do it sitting down, long as you can marry us," answered Emma.

Both Hezekiah and Rachel were getting quite old, but both were quite alert as far as their minds go. Crockett and Hannah were over there most every day, listening to old stories of Indian fighting, and exploring Tazewell county long before it was a county. He always talked of the beauty of these mountains and the Clinch river. He told the children of seeing elk, bear, panthers, and even Indians passing through in the early years.

"This place was a wilderness back then, a wonderful wilderness!" he exclaimed!

Crockett reminded Grand Paw of the bear that John Bunyon killed the first weekend they were here in Tazewell County!

"Yes I know," said Hezekiah.

"That old bear has always been your buddy," Hezekiah said.

"Has he still got his ears?" Hezekiah asked laughingly.

"Yes Grand Paw, he still has them," replied Crockett.

"It is a wonder he still has his ears, the way you always pulled on them," said Hezekiah.

"They are a bit tattered but he still has them Grand Paw," answered Crockett.

CHAPTER 14

MORE WEDDINGS IN THE VALLEY

Spring has come to Tazewell County once again. The hills are white with Dogwood blossoms. The farmers are busy in the preparation for planting. Most folks already have their potatoes in the ground, and are plowing for the corn and tobacco crops.

The wedding of John Madden Stephenson and Emma Whitt has been set for Tuesday the 15th of April 1845. It would be a simple wedding without all the commotion of the former weddings of the Whitt family. The day was chosen for two reasons; the remembrance of Mother Susannah Whitt's passing. The other reason was to celebrate the birth of little sister Hannah Whitt.

Grand Paw Hezekiah Whitt was to preside over the wedding service at the age of eighty five, if he could do it. He was still very alert, but his legs were weakened by the years. He was a prominent Justice and Statesman of the County of Tazewell County.

Some current news of 1845, Jonas hears of a Potato famine in Ireland, thousands of these poor, but proud people head to America. What will we do with so many foreigners, everyone is saying? John Tyler is defeated in his reelection bid. James K. Polk wins handily, running on the promise to annex Texas into the Union. In 1845 Texas becomes a state. Henry Clay the famous Kentuckian ran against Polk, and Tyler. James K. Polk would run the Executive Branch for awhile.

The wedding goes good; John M. Stephenson and Emma Whitt stand before the grand old gentleman Justice of the Peace Hezekiah Whitt for their Vows. Hezekiah mustered his strength and did not have to sit down for the service. He went through it without a problem. The Wedding was not grand in size, but a good ceremony. Only the Whitts and Stephensons were in attendance!

Aunt Nancy had baked a cake, and the Whitt twins cooked a nice meal to serve after the wedding. It was just a great time of bonding for the two families.

The newly married Mr. And Mrs. Stephenson would live in a little cabin on the Stephenson Farm near Jeffersonville. As all young men John hoped to have his own piece of land some day. He had a large tract of land leased from his father to produce a cash crop. He and Emma would work it and try to put back money for their own farm some day.

After the meal and cake, the Stephenson's headed down the road toward their new little home. It was about 6:00 PM, before they got started across Green Mountain. They were so in love, they kissed all the way home.

The wagon had some old shoes, and rusted up tin canisters tied to the back of the wagon on heavy strings. They paid them no mind. Emma was carried across the threshold and placed on the bed.

John started to undress.

"Wait, you got to unhitch the horse and take care of him; I will get into something special for you while you are outside," said Emma.

John and Emma exercised their marital rights in a heavily anticipated union.

"Just at dark a great noise surrounded the cabin, it's the chivalree" said Emma.

"Let's just ignore them and they will go away," said John.

The noise got louder and even knocks could be heard on the door.

"Guess we will have to get up and give them a wave before they will leave, said Emma.

"Yes you are right" replied John.

They put on some night clothes, cracked open the door and waved to the noise makers.

After taking a peak Emma said, "there is Paw, James Griffith, the Beavers, and several other neighbors and kin".

David Crockett Whitt was right in the middle of things.

The noise subsided, and some funny singing followed. Finally the folks started leaving, talking loudly and laughing.

Emma closed the door slowly, and took John Madden Stephenson back to the bed. "Come on" Mr. Stephenson!, " said Emma.

"Alright, Mrs. Stephenson, John replied.

Once again they were in their marital bliss, thankful for the day, the cabin, and the love of their families.

"John I love you so much," Emma said.

"Emma you are the love of my life," John responded.

Jonas told Hezekiah, "It seems all my children are growing up and getting married."

Hezekiah replied; "Son that is what they do, the same thing happens to everyone if they live long enough.

"Looks like Elizabeth will be next, she has been seeing Bige Baldwin, and I'm not sure I like it," said Jonas.

"Bige," replied Hezekiah.

"Do you mean Abijah Baldwin with all those children?" he asked.

"I didn't know his wife died!" added Hezekiah.

"His youngest is about five or six years old," answered Jonas.

"Well, have you tried to talk some sense into her son," replied Hezekiah?

"Of course Paw, she says that she loves him and nothing else matters," answered Jonas.

"He must be fifteen to twenty years older than her; she is taking on way too much," said Hezekiah.

"I know Paw, she will be stuck with an old man to care for in a few years," replied Jonas.

"I don't know what to do, she will not listen to a thing when it comes to Bige," Jonas said.

"Reckon me or your Maw could talk to her?" asked Hezekiah.

"Well you are welcome to give it a try Paw, it can't hurt, better do it real soon, before they get hitched," responded Jonas.

"I expect them to run off instead of standing before the family, because of all the protest we have shown," added Jonas.

"Even Rachel and Rhoda have talked to her," said Jonas.

"Elizabeth is such a pretty young woman, I think Bige is looking for a play thing and baby sitter," said Jonas.

"Maybe we are talking to the wrong one, have you talked to him?" Hezekiah asked.

"Yes paw, both of them together, but not alone; they know how we all feel about them getting married," said Jonas.

"Well I will try to talk to her, just as soon as I see her again," replied

Hezekiah.

"Maw has a way with the grand children, she may be able to convince her of the mistake," said Jonas.

"She needs to marry some young man about her age, said Hezekiah.

"I agree with you Paw," answered Jonas.

The summer had come, and Elizabeth was still seeing Abijah. She had not said anything about getting married, but you could see she was under his spell. Everyone in the family had talked to her and even Abijah, to know avail. Jonas watched closely for signs of an elopement.

Elizabeth talked about how great Bige and his children are. She is in love with them thought Jonas. It might be just fine long as she is happy, Jonas was beginning to get used to the idea!

There was a lull in the farm work, between planting and harvest, so Jonas took a day here and there to take Crockett and Hannah fishing. They went to their "honey hole" that Grand Paw Hezekiah showed them years before. That long deep pool in the Clinch always produces fish for bragging and eating.

Crockett caught several nice Red Eyes, and a few Small Mouth bass, but that little Hannah was the luckiest fisher girl I ever saw," said Jonas!

"No matter where she throws her worm, a big fish is waiting with its mouth open," exclaimed Crockett.

"Seems that way, don't it?" replied Jonas.

Hannah just laughed, and kept catching fish; she kept Jonas busy stringing the fish and putting on more worms.

Crockett told Jonas, "we will have to leave her home next time, she makes us look bad."

Jonas laughed!

"We couldn't do her that way, now could we?" he asked.

"Guess not," mumbled Crockett.

James Griffith was still the main farm hand. He had taught Crockett so much about farming and also the ways of the woods. He taught Crockett the theory of marksmanship, and Crockett was beginning to be an excellent shooter.

The theory behind good shooting is of course, "aim small, hit small" and hold your breath while squeezing the trigger.

He taught Hannah the basic stuff about shooting even though she is only six years old.

She told James Griffith she could teach him how to fish.

"From what I hear you could do just that," laughed James Griffith.

One cool October morning after breakfast, Elizabeth brought out her carpet bag all packed for a trip. She sat it down by the door and told everyone Abijah Baldwin would be along soon to get her. She told them that they were going to be married and all the plans were made.

Jonas asked Elizabeth, "why don't you let the family stand up with you and be part of your wedding?"

"Paw you know how everyone of you have been against Bige, I think after a while you will accept him as my husband," said Elizabeth.

"I think it is best this way for now," she said quietly.

In a matter of minutes a horse and buggy could be heard outside.

"That is him I would guess," said Jonas.

A loud knock could be heard on the door.

James Griffith jumped up; "Want me to run him off Paw"?

"No," answered Jonas, "open the door and invite Mister Baldwin in, he is going to be our new kin."

"Elizabeth has made up her mind, we have to abide by it," Jonas stated.

James Griffith opened the door.

Bige Baldwin was standing there waiting for his new bride.

"Come in sir," James Griffith spoke boldly.

Jonas, Crockett, and Hannah went over and hugged Elizabeth goodbye.

James Griffith did the same, and turned to Bige and said, "Mister Baldwin if I ever hear of you mistreating my sister, you will find yourself dead."

"Hear now," James Griffith asked?

Bige spoke with a low voice, "never fear, I love Elizabeth, and I will never hurt her in any way; I just want you folks to accept me as her loving husband."

"Elizabeth, you and Bige are welcome to come and visit any time, we will try to be benevolent in every way," said Jonas.

"And we would like to be welcome to visit you in your home," added James Griffith.

Abijah spoke up, "Mister Whitt, you and your family will always be welcome in my house."

With that Bige picked up the carpet bag and headed for the buggy. Elizabeth gave all them one last hug and headed toward the door. Her eyes were filled with tears as she was helped up in the awaiting buggy.

Jonas and Hannah walked over to Hezekiah's home later in the day. Hezekiah was much weaker. He was almost eighty six years old.

First thing he wanted to know was the status of Elizabeth.

"I saw old Bige heading toward your place, is my little grand baby gone with him?" asked Hezekiah.

"Yes, I am afraid so Paw, we made the best of a bad situation!" answered Jonas.

"James Griffith wanted to run him off, I thought it best that we should try and have a peaceable solution," said Jonas.

James told him in no uncertain terms, he was a dead man if he hurt Elizabeth in any way.

"I would have shot him," said the elderly Hezekiah!

"I'm glad you weren't there Paw, let's give it some time for Elizabeth's sake," responded Jonas.

Grand Maw Rachel went to the bed room to weep!

This whole thing was a strain on the Whitt family.

Nancy spoke up quietly, "Maybe this will all work out for the best."

"If Elizabeth and Bige are truly in love it will be fine; just pray for them is my suggestion," said brother James.

Hezekiah with tears in his eyes said, "You are right, we all need to lift them up in prayer."

The winter of 1845 was especially hard for Hezekiah and Rachel. It seemed that one or the other was sick all winter.

James and Nancy were a real blessing to them. Jonas was also over there almost every day to help in some way.

David Crockett was almost nine years old, and doing the work of a man! Hannah was only six, and had become a big help in the kitchen. This was the way of good country families in 1845.

Jonas and James were helping the elderly Hezekiah and Rachel.

James Griffith, Crockett, and Hannah were helping their Paw, Jonas Whitt.

Winter would soon be over in Tazewell county 1846!

Hezekiah was so weak by the end of February that he hardly ever got out of bed.

Rachel was also sickly, but able to get up and stir around.

Jonas and James kept hoping with the spring their Paw would spring back to better health.

On Sunday the 28th of March 1846 at 8:06 A.M., God called the stately old Gentleman Hezekiah Whitt home.

What would the Whitt family do with out their beloved grand leader? Everyone gathered at the Hezekiah House that day in disbelief! Rachel was so sad, even though she knew this day was coming. She tried to be brave in front of the entire family.

"You all know this is his birthday, don't you?" said Rachel.

"He lived a good life serving his family, his state and his country all the days of his life; bless his heart, he is eighty six today," stated Rachel.

"He turned over this morning and held me tight and kissed me goodbye," she said sobbing.

"Paw always said if I make it through March I always live another year!" I never knew what he meant, "He did not quiet make it through March this time," said James.

"I have heard him say that for years," replied Jonas.

"We have to get letters off to all the other children." Nancy interjected.

"They will not be able to get here for the funeral, but they will want to come home as soon as possible," James responded.

"Got to get word to town and to Elder David Young," James announced.

"I hate having to make plans like this," replied Jonas. "I know what you mean," said James.

"Paw had lived a long good life, he is with Jesus now," Jones said.

"He would not come back here to all his aches and pains, even if he could," Jonas added.

"He loved his family dearly, but now he is in the love of Christ," said James.

James Griffith, Crockett, and Hannah were at Church this morning. They will be in shock when they get back and hear the sad news!

All the children and their families gathered that afternoon at the Hezekiah Whitt house. The house was full of Hezekiah's off spring. He was loved by all, except a few political foes! Even they respected him.

James Griffith saddled his horse and headed out to share the sad news. He was headed to find Elder David Young first, and to let any one else he seen, know about the great loss of the Whitt family.

There would be a church service in the evening at most of the churches, so an announcement could be given then.

James Griffith made a long ride around Tazewell County that day. He carried the sad news far and wide. Everyone in Tazewell County knew or at least had heard of Hezekiah Whitt and would want to know about his demise.

James, Jonas, and all of the other local children of Hezekiah decided to have a meeting in the morning when things would be settled down. Funeral arrangements, had to be made, and many other things to consider. Letters would have to be written to all the kin that did not live near by. Even the will would have to go to probate, but that would not be mentioned for some time. Rachel was not well, and her health had to be considered.

James and Jonas went to the barn to find the coffin; Hezekiah had it made several years before. Jonas had done most of the work on it and put it in storage in the barn loft under heavy canvas. The sons of Hezekiah climbed into the loft with tear filled eyes.

Jonas went right to it.

"It is right here," Jonas replied to James.

"This thing has been waiting here for about six or seven years, hope nothing has disturbed it," replied James.

They dragged it out into the open. They uncovered the fine coffin with care.

"It looks great", exclaimed Jonas.

The coffin was made of oak and trimmed out in walnut; it shined brightly under the rubbed in bee wax.

James committed, "Jonas I think this is some of your best work, it still looks brand new!"

"It was stored to last for years, I hoped I would never have to go and get it out," said Jonas.

"Paw wanted it ready, so no one would have to do hurry up job when he passed," said James.

"I remember him looking over his coffin," Jonas said.

"This is the nicest coffin I ever seen, it is fit for a King or President," Paw had related.

"We told him he was worthy of such a fine coffin," remember Jonas.

"Yes I do, he really liked it, I think he would come out and look at it from time to time, because I see it has been tampered with," replied Jonas.

"I heard him mention it every now and then, so he probably did," said James.

Jonas had his sons, John Bunyon, and James Griffith to help lower it down out of the loft. The four carried it to the house and set it up to lay their beloved Hezekiah in it.

Rachel and the women dressed Hezekiah in his finest suit, put on some rouge and good smelling perfume.

Jonas, James, and others lifted Hezekiah into his coffin.

Rachel broke down in loud lamentations.

James and Jonas held her tightly and the tears flowed like little rivers. The whole family fell into deep grieving! Wailing and weeping went on for some time.

The coffin was displayed in the sitting room so that the friends and family could visit with Hezekiah. The wake would be on the night of the March 29th. As was the custom many folks came to sit with the family, bringing plates of food and drinks. It seemed that the whole State of Virginia came by. So many people knew Hezekiah and wanted to pay their last respect.

Rachel was worn down and had to find seclusion in an upstairs bed room. Each one of the family grieved in a different way. Some tried to stay busy and not think on the matter, while others give into it and went to bed in depression. Yet others went through sessions of weeping.

David Crockett had a hard time accepting the fact that Grand Paw

Hezekiah would not be around to talk with him. Hannah was busy playing, trying to ignore the realization of what occurred. Jonas sat down and talked to both of them, explaining that Grand Paw went to Heaven to live with Jesus!

Crockett understood some what, but Hannah kept saying, "He is in there in the coffin."

Jonas tried to explain that when people die their body stays here but their spirit leaves and goes to Heaven or Hell. Don't worry about Grand Paw going to Hell. He was a devoted Christian so he is in Heaven with Jesus.

Jonas explained, "Grand Paw is up there walking around Heaven with no pain, and is real happy, he can run and jump like you do!"

"He is waiting for Grand Maw and the rest of us to join him some day, so we have to prepare ourselves to go there by living a Christian life," Jonas added.

The morning of March 30th came and Jonas got some pine tar. He spread some all around the edge of the lid on the coffin. The Coffin was sealed and secured, not to be opened again.

A big breakfast was cooked that morning for all that were there, and the procession would start at 11:00 A.M. There was some scripture reading, and remembrance by the different friends and family.

At about 10:45 A.M., Jonas told Crockett to get Hezekiah's flag and go out in the yard to start the line.

Six strong men were chosen to carry Hezekiah to the top of the hill where he would be laid to rest. James and Jonas took Rachel out to follow behind the coffin. Next followed every family member, then the friends of Hezekiah would join the sad procession.

Jonas motioned to David Crockett to start the trek to the grave site. Jonas had already given him instruction to walk slowly and hold the flag high and proud.

Crockett took the first step, and the men carrying Hezekiah followed suit.

On top of the little hill a grave had been dug, and benches erected for the family. Elder David Young and a choir from the church were waiting.

Almost seven years has past since another sad line of people climbed this little hill. Jonas and his children could not help but think of that day they lay Susannah to rest.

David Crockett Whitt led the procession with honor! He held the old flag high for his grand paw. He walked slowly allowing everyone to keep up. Hezekiah would be so proud of his grand son, as he looked down on this celebration of his life. Rachel did not tire as Jonas, and James helped her along.

Many people were waiting at the Green Mountain road to join in the march. The whole hill was covered when everyone closed in to hear the minister preach the funeral.

The lay of the land for the trip from the house to the grave yard was down a slight hill, cross the Green Mountain Road and up the top of the Cemetery hill. The distance was a little more than an eighth of a mile.

Elder David Young stepped up to address the family and friends of Hezekiah Whitt.

Crockett had taken the flag off the pole and draped it over the beautiful coffin and taken a seat beside of Jonas and the family.

The Elder spoke loud so that every ear could hear. He opened with the Lords Prayer, read scripture from Revelation, and sat down. The choir stood and sang a couple of hymns. Once again the Elder David Young stood, he was going to give the Eulogy of Hezekiah Whitt.

Gentleman Justice of the Peace Hezekiah Whitt has been a model for us all to follow. At the young age of seventeen, he along with his father Reverend Richard Whitt took the Patriot's Oath on September 13th 1777. Hezekiah saw action several times in the defense of Virginia and this United States. He laid his life on the line time after time so that we could enjoy the freedoms this country stands for.

After the war was won, Hezekiah was appointed along with eight other gentlemen by Governor Patrick Henry to serve as Gentleman Justices of the Peace to establish this great county of Tazewell.

Hezekiah was chosen because he was trustworthy, loyal, and brave. Hezekiah has been a servant to the people of the United States, The State of Virginia, and the County of Tazewell most of his life.

He was also a servant of the Lord Jesus Christ.

He has been a faithful Husband and Father to his family.

Hezekiah will be missed by his loving wife Rachel, by his seven children, all of his grand children and great grand children. I dare say

Hezekiah will be missed many years into the future by the off spring of his seed, if the world still stands.

He is lifted high and respected by all who know him. He will be missed by his associates and neighbors.

Today we lay to rest the body of a great man. We as believers in Christ know that Hezekiah is in the presence of Jesus Christ. Hezekiah wishes that we cry no more, but rejoice for him. He has fought the good fight, he has run the good race, and now he has found rest with the Lord.

After the Elder had finished the service, the old Betsy Ross type flag was folded and given to Rachel. Hezekiah had this flag since early in the war, almost seventy years.

CHAPTER 15

HEZEKIAH IS GONE
BUT NOT FORGOTTEN

After the Funeral, most of the people shook hands with the family and started making their way toward their respective homes. It looked like the whole County of Tazewell was at the gathering to honor the late Hezekiah and his family.

It began to rain. The ladies began to bring out their umbrellas.

Jonas quoted the old saying; "Happy the dead the rain falls upon, happy the bride the sun shines upon."

The next few days things did not get back to normal, how could they? Hezekiah Whitt was dead, and Rachel was not adjusting! She was over on the other side of the mental river.

She kept talking like Hezekiah was still living in the house with her. She said that he was still there, she had seen him all around the house. Rachel was not afraid of her life long friend, lover, and companion. She would go about her day, talking to the deceased Hezekiah.

James and Nancy almost believed that Hezekiah was there also. Jonas was over to see his Maw everyday, but did not believe what seemed to be true. Could it be that Hezekiah was waiting around for something before he moved on to the realm of glory?

Elder Young was sent for. When he arrived James and Nancy had a talk with him before he went in to see Rachel. He said that he had heard of things like this, but never dealt with it personally. He read a few passages in his Bible and prayed before he went in to visit Rachel.

Elder Young went in alone to visit with Rachel.

Good morning Elder, "she spoke in greeting!"

"Good morning to you Rachel, I thought I would stop by and see you this morning on my rounds."

"Well come on in I will get you a nice cup of tea and something sweet, I have some apple cobbler, and some cookies, "Rachel said.

"Which would you like?" she asked while getting the tea.

"A cookie would be nice," he answered.

As she sat down with him at the kitchen table, he asked how she was doing since the funeral.

"Well just fine I reckon, Hezekiah is still here with me." she answered.

The hair on the back of the Elder's neck stood up. He thought she would try to hide the fact that she was seeing things.

"What do you mean Rachel?" Elder Young asked.

"You saw him in that beautiful coffin." added the Elder.

"You followed him all the way to the cemetery; you know he is buried over on cemetery hill, don't you?" asked Elder Young.

"Well Elder, I ain't crazy, I seen all of that, but my dear Hezekiah come back home with me," exclaimed Rachel.

"He is sitting over there in that chair, I can see him smiling at me right now," Rachel stated..

Goose bumps rose up all over the Elder.

"Rachel, I can not see Hezekiah, you know he is gone on to be with the Lord." said the Elder.

"Well not yet he ain't, he told me he was waiting for me!" replied Rachel.

"What do you mean Rachel, waiting for you?" asked Elder Young.

"Well waiting!; You know!; I will be going with him real soon!" said Rachel.

Elder David Young was in shock, he had never seen anything like it. Rachel was completely calm, and normal it seemed! Yet Rachel talked to Hezekiah right in front of the Elder.

"Rachel, does Hezekiah answer you?" said Elder Young.

"Sure he does, I can't understand why no one else sees him" replied Rachel.

He is so happy, and has no pain.

"He told me I would be going with him soon, he told me it is wonderful, no pain, no tears, and he is young again," said Rachel in a most serious tone.

"How does he look to you Rachel, you say young?" asked the Elder.

"He appears to be young like he was when I fell in love with him,"

Grave of Hezekiah Whitt. Baptist Valley, Tazewell County, Virginia.

she replied.

"Hezekiah thinks it is funny that you are asking me all these questions." she added.

"I think He wants to be alone with me," she added.

"Please Elder, do you mind to leave us alone, and go about your work?" Rachel asked.

"Yes Ma-am, I do have things I need to do, if you want to talk again, just let me know," said Elder Young.

"I will." replied Rachel!

Rachel said, "Elder you be ready to have my funeral, It wouldn't be to far off," and she smiled!

"Now Rachel, you don't know that," Elder Young replied.

"You can count on it," Hezekiah doesn't know what day, but said "I would be coming with him to see Jesus real soon!"

The Elder was a bit shaken inside, but tried not to show it.

"Well Rachel, if I am still around, I will give you a good funeral," Elder Young assured her.

"I will be back to see you in a few days," he said.

The Elder went out to the yard to speak with James, Nancy, and Jonas.

"Well Elder, what did you find out?" asked James.

"I hate to admit it but I think the spirit of Hezekiah is with your mother," he said.

"She seems just fine, and is quite convincing about seeing Hezekiah, I sense no evil in the house, She told me to be ready to have her funeral real soon," stated the Elder.

"Brother have you gone around the bin," Jonas asked the Elder?

"No Jonas, I am telling you what I think after being in there with Rachel, sometimes Indian folk know things" the Elder replied.

"If I were you I would prepare for, well what she says," he added.

"She said that she would be going with Hezekiah soon, have you sent letters out to the other children yet?" asked Elder Young.

"No, we put that off until things settled down some," said James.

"I would do it today, the other children may be able to see Rachel before she goes on.," he answered.

Jonas was a little angry inside, because the Elder was talking like this. Elder Young sensed this, and explained to Jonas.

"I am sorry Jonas, I am only telling you what I believe, there is no evil in it," said the Elder.

"Rachel wants to go to her beloved husband, she wants to go and meet the Lord Jesus," Elder Young said.

Jonas nodded, "Thanks Elder Young, I know you mean no harm."

"What do you suggest we do, when Maw is talking to Paw?" James asked.

"Go along with her, it will be pleasing to her and maybe Hezekiah too," the Elder said.

With that the Elder prayed for the family, mounted his horse and headed across Green Mountain.

Young David Crockett Whitt has been about, listening to all the talk about Rachel. He thought to himself, I bet Grand Paw Hezekiah is here waiting for Grand Maw Rachel. I know if Grand Paw is still here, he wouldn't hurt any body. I hope he will let me see him, like he does Grand Maw. Young Crockett was like everyone else, he could not understand what was going on with Grand Maw Rachel. Why did Grand Paw have to die? Why is Grand Maw wanting to die? Some things are not meant for us to understand, was his conclusion. David Crockett never seen the spirit of Hezekiah, even though he believed Grand Maw Rachel did.

Letters to Richard Nelson, John Bunyon, Rebecca, and Susannah were written and mailed out. The other children were already contacted.

Richard (Devil Dick) Nelson Whitt lived in Carter County Kentucky. John Bunyon lived in Floyd County Kentucky. Rebecca and Susannah lived in the far west side of Tazewell county. (present McDowell County West Virginia). Griffie Whitt lived clean across the waters of the Mississippi River in Missouri.

Crockett is anxious to meet his Uncles from that famous place called Kentucky. He hoped to hear stories of Daniel Boone and Simon Kenton. He wanted to hear about the Indian Wars that took place there only a few years past.

Grand Maw Rachel never changed, as far as the relationship she had with the spirit of Hezekiah. Each day Rachel seemed to get weaker, and spent her days in bed or in the sitting room. Crockett spent much time visiting with Grand Maw Rachel. She told him many stories of the old days, and continued to speak to the invisible Hezekiah.

James, Nancy, and Jonas were all worried about her. Her mind seemed sharp and crisp except for the continued talking to the deceased Hezekiah. The Elder David Young came by every day or two to pray with the family and visit Rachel. Any word from the sons in Kentucky he would ask?

"No not yet, we pray they will get to see Maw before she passes," answered James.

"Maw gets weaker each day it seems," said Jonas.

Elder Young had an idea, what if you put Rachel in the buggy and take her to visit Hezekiah's grave? Reckon that might turn her back around? Jonas looked at James, James looked at Nancy. It is worth a try, we will do it. James went in and talked to Rachel.

"Maw let's get you ready and take a buggy ride," said James.

"Why son," she asked?

"I am doing just fine here with your Paw," Rachel added.

It made James and the other children so sad to see her this way.

"Maw please do this for me," James said.

"Well I reckon I can, where are we going," she asked?

"I want to take you over to the cemetery so you can visit Paws grave," James said.

"If it is that important to you I will go," she said.

"It makes no sense to me, when Hezekiah is right here," she added.

The family got Rachel up and dressed. They carried her out to the buggy. All the children went with her except those from Kentucky as they had not got home yet. They talked about the nice coffin, the great crowd that attended the funeral, and the good sermon the Elder preached that day. Rachel went along with everything the children were trying to do.

"I remember all of this Children," Rachel confirmed.

"Your Paw really enjoyed all that you done for him, He was impressed with the crowd that day," she said.

The children all looked at each other in disbelief!

Well, Jonas was thinking, nothing ventured, nothing gained! I am beginning to believe Paw is still here with Maw.

They took her home and put her back to bed because she told them,

"I am bone tired children."

It was about the end of May 1846, and finally two riders rode up to the Hezekiah Whitt House.

James spoke up, "Glory be, there is John and Richard."

Crockett was there, so James sent him over to get Jonas and the rest of the family. After Crockett shook hands with these two famous uncles he headed home to fetch Jonas.

John and Richard were famous to Crockett because of all the stories he had heard about them. John and Richard were both big strong men. They both looked like Hezekiah, except they were both much more massive. They were tall like Hezekiah, and well filled out with muscle. Crockett thought to himself, I am glad I don't have to fight these big men. I am glad they are my uncles.

"Paw, Paw," Crockett hollered as he ran in the door.

"What is it son?"

"Uncle John and Richard are over to Grand Maw's," said the excited Crockett.

James Griffith, son of Jonas was in the house at the time.

"Let's get over there, I barely remember them," said James.

"Take your horse James Griffith, after you meet them, would you mind to make a ride and inform the rest of the family?" Jonas asked.

"I will be glad to, I do want to see them first," replied James Griffith.

James and Nancy explained the situation to Richard and John Bunyon, before they went in to see their Maw.

Richard looked at James, "you mean Maw thinks Paw is still alive?"

"No!" James answered, "She sees his spirit and says he is waiting for her!"

Richard looks at John in disbelief.

"Can you understand this brother," asked Richard.

"No" answered John!

"Let's go see what they are talking about," John added.

Richard and John went in to see Mother Rachel.

She looked at them and said, "there is my babies from Canetuck."

"You are a sight for sore eyes," she said as she raised up to hug them.

She looked over at an empty chair, "look Hezekiah, John Bunyon and Richard are here from Kentucky."

They both looked at the empty chair and back at each other.

Rachel seen their disbelief, "Oh don't worry boys, for some reason I am the only one that can see your paw."

Rachel asked, "Have you heard from your brother Griffy?"

No maw," we wondered if he had got the word about Paw passing."

"I am so sorry Maw that we didn't get home in time to see Paw," said Richard.

"Don't fret son, your Paw understands, he is smiling at you right now," said Rachel.

Richard just didn't know what to say.

John changes the subject, "Maw, you look good, how have you been?"

"Well I am bone tired boys," Rachel responded.

"I will be a leaving you before long." she added.

"Now Maw you don't know that;" exclaimed Richard.

"Well honey I can't live forever," she said, and let it go at that.

John Bunyon Whitt and Richard (Devil Dick) Whitt had a lot of catching up to do. They had many stories to tell and many to hear. They both came by horse back, leaving the wives and families back in Kentucky because of the time. They did not want to miss seeing Rachel, before it was too late. She seemed to be very mentally alert, except for the Hezekiah thing. Richard and John had not ruled out that their paw Hezekiah was visiting in the spirit.

Brother Griffy and his wife Patty from Missouri, show up the very next day. They came in a hurry on horse back also. They get in to Tazewell county about an hour before dark.

John and Richard are sitting around talking about Kentucky, and their trips coming home. Jonas and David Crockett seem really interested. The family has been visiting all day. Rachel is tired but has sit up most of the day. She still looks to an empty chair and speaks to the invisible Hezekiah. The sound of riders is heard out back. James gets up and heads to the back door. I wonder who that could be this time of day, he said.

He opens the door and there is Griffith Whitt and his wife Patty.

It's brother Griffy, James exclaimed. Everyone arose to greet their brother from way out in Missouri.

Rachel heard all the commotion, "Did I hear you say Griffiy?" she said.

"Yes Maw, that's right, Griffy and Patty just rode up," said Nancy. Griffy and Patty tied up their horses and were in the house in an instant.

Jonas was thinking, we didn't get to tell them about Maw seeing Paw all the time.

Griffy and Patty hugged their way through the crowd on the way to see Rachel. As Griffy came into the bedroom, Rachel praised the Lord for seeing her son from so far away.

"Yes Maw, It is me and Patty, we have come as fast as we could to see you," said Griffy.

Rachel turns to the empty chair, and says, "look Hezekiah, Griffy and Patty are here."

Griffy looks in the direction of the empty chair and back to his Maw.

Rachel sees the confusion on Griffy's face and speaks up," Don't worry son, I know it may seem strange to you but Hezekiah is here waiting for me!"

Griffy is dumbfounded!

"Maw I thought Paw was buried at the end of March," said Griffy.

"Well son, his body is over on the hill, but your Paw come back home with me," answered Rachel.

"Nothing to be alarmed about, He is such a handsome man, looks like he did when we got married," she continued.

Griffy thinks it is time to change the subject, "How are you doing Maw?" he asked.

"Not too good honey, I am getting weaker each day it seems," she said.

"I thought I would be gone with your Paw to meet Jesus by now," she said.

"Well we never know when we will get the call," said Griffy, "You might out live all of us"

"No son, Hezekiah would not be here waiting if that was so," she answered.

"I wish you all could see him, he is so pleased to see all of you here with me," said Rachel.

Nancy opens up with another line of talk, "bet you all are starved to death," she said.

Griffy and Patty answered, "we could eat, we have not eaten a good meal since we left home."

"Well we have a pan of fried up fish, and I can get you some good grub to go with it in a couple of shakes," Nancy said.

"If you don't want the fish we can slice you off some good old Virginia Ham," she added.

"Now don't go to no trouble, anything will be good, "Patty answered.

Griffy turns back to Mother Rachel.

"Maw and Paw, we are going to take care of our horses and get some vittles," he said.

"Then we will spend some time with you, If you need to sleep, we will be here tomorrow to catch up on all the news," Griffy added.

Rachel smiles, she is glad that Griffy acknowledged that his Paw was present.

"Alright Griffy, take care of the horses, eat and get some rest; we will visit all day tomorrow," said Rachel.

Griffy and Patty both go over and give Rachel a kiss.

Griffy and Jonas go out to take care of their mounts.

"What is going on with Maw?" he asks Jonas.

"We are not sure, she is sharp as a tack, except that she insists that Paw is waiting for her, sorry we didn't get to warn you before you walked into that, you handled it real well brother," said Jonas.

Griffy looks at the young straight boy with Jonas.

"Now who is this young man?" Griffy asked.

"Griffy this is my youngest son David Crockett Whitt," replied Jonas.

Griffy stuck out his hand to Crockett. Crockett clasped the big hand of uncle Griffy Whitt.

"Glad to meet you sir," said Crockett.

"Glad to meet you, You know you have a famous name don't you son?" asked Griffy.

"Yes sir, a lot to live up to I guess," said Crockett.

Griffy laughed.

Jonas helped Griffy unload the horses, and instructed Crockett to take them to the barn.

"Now son water Uncle Griffy's horses and give them a good feeding of corn and oats," Jonas instructed.

"Yes sir," was the answer as Crockett led the tired horses to the barn. He did all that Jonas had said and also dried the horses down and ran a curry comb over them.

Crockett was thinking, the horses of Uncle John, Richard, and Griffy are of the best stock. I think they must be thoroughbreds. Kentucky is famous for their horses. Jake was one of the few that compared.

Crockett was also thinking that Griffy looked like Richard and John, but was much leaner. He is more like Grand Paw Hezekiah and Paw.

The Whitts talked about an hour past dark. In June that is late for farming people.

Jonas was the first to say, "We better get in bed, tomorrow is another day, and we can visit most of it.

"Maw will be fresh in the morning I hope, so she can visit all she wants," said Griffy.

Jonas and Crockett headed back to Indian Creek Farm, after he offered a bed to any who might want to go with him.

Nancy spoke up, "thanks Jonas, we will be able to bed everyone down here."

"See you all on the morrow, and Good night all," Jonas said as they disappeared into the night.

Next day the 2nd day of June, the Whitts had a full blown reunion. By now every Whitt in the Valley had heard the news of Griffy, John, and Richard coming in to visit. The women got together and cooked up a great feast for the family to eat. Rachel was quite pert at least for the first half of the day. Each brother took turns telling story after story. Crockett listened intently, wishing that all of these stories were written down in a book.

After all the brothers talked, the children of Jonas told of some happenings in their own lives. The trip from Montgomery County and the bandit episode was told by James Griffith (son of Jonas). John Bunyon (son of Jonas) told the story of killing the bear on the first weekend in Tazewell County.

Even Crockett spoke up, he told of the great shooting match, and his big brother James Griffith beat every one in Tazewell county.

Stories of rolling hills, the Ohio river, and the Mississippi river were told. Even stories that were told to them about Kentucky's early days were rekindled. Stories of Blue Jacket, Little Turtle, and Tecumseh, and the Indian escapades were retold with exaggeration! Names like Daniel Boone, Simon Kenton, and John Logan were also mentioned.

Kentucky was once the great hunting ground of many Indian nations. This great state was worth fighting for. It is now a tame peaceful land with rich soil, and great grazing for cattle and horses. At one time the rolling blue grass lands teemed with Elk, Buffalo and wolf packs that followed them.

Young David Crockett Whitt asked about his namesake, "What about old Davy Crockett?"

"Was he a big name in Kentucky?" asked Crockett.

"Not really" Uncle Richard answered, "he was in Tennessee mostly, and moved on to Texas."

"He did about the same in Tennessee as Boone did in Kentucky," Richard said.

"I don't know if they ever met or not, Boone would be older than Crockett" he surmised.

Uncle Griffy spoke up, "I know that Daniel Boone moved to Missouri after he got closed in on, in Kentucky." "Boone had said, "when he saw the smoke of his neighbors chimney, he don't have enough elbow room."

"He is buried in Missouri not too far from where we live," Griffy added.

Also mention of the great earthquake of 1811 was told. It was said that the great Chief Tecumseh predicted it. Tecumseh said, "when I stomp my foot it will be felt for hundreds of miles." "That would be the sign for all Indians to come together and run the pale face's back across the mountains," said Griffy.

Everyone had a chance to tell stories.

Jonas said, "I wish Paw was here to add to the stories."

"He had a bunch of them, and he was not bad to exaggerate," said Richard.

"Yes," answered James, "Paw was not one to brag."

After a week of visiting with Rachel and the entire family, the three brothers decided they better start back home. Richard had brought a letter with him from Doctor Samuel Truitt, of Greenup County Kentucky. It was sent to Jonas because Richard had told him about the skills he had. Jonas was an expert mill right and house builder. Doctor Truitt was wanting to build two grist mills up in Greenup County, Kentucky.

"I thought you lived in Carter county," Jonas said.

"I do, but Greenup county is the next county over, It borders on the Ohio River; I met Doctor Truitt by chance when I made a trip up that way," said Richard.

He talked about the need for a grist mill, and one thing led to another.

I told him, I would bring you a letter and see what you think about it.

"Well for now, I will say no, I ain't about to move off long as Maw is sick," Jonas said.

"Some day in the future I may entertain that idea, you can tell Truitt that I am considering the idea, " Jonas continued.

The three brothers decided to travel together on their journey back to Kentucky. You can't be too careful, bad people are still watching for an easy target. They were to travel the Kentucky Turnpike to Floyd County. Then Richard and Griffy would follow the Big Sandy a way further before heading into Carter county. Then of course Griffy and Patty would ride west and cross the Mississippi in western Kentucky.

The three sons were reluctant to leave Rachel, but they had to get back to families and farms. Rachel understood, she kissed each one on that cool morning in June before they started back. Crockett hated to see his uncles depart as well as the whole Whitt family did.

Crockett and Jonas both had a hankering to see Kentucky some day.

CHAPTER 16

RACHEL PASSES, CROCKETT WILL SEE KENTUCKY

Rachel seems about the same, she still speaks to Hezekiah as if he never died. She missed her children after they left.

The 20th of June Rachel did not eat a thing. She was so weak she could hardly turn over.

As evening came to Hezekiah Whitt House, Rachel summoned her family around her. She spoke in whispers, and eye gestures, portraying her love for each family member. She said that she could see a beautiful river and Hezekiah and Jesus was waiting for her. There were so many beautiful trees and flowers. Angels were abounding!

"Children, I am going home!" she said.

Rachel slipped off into a coma. Her body was shutting down, and her legs and arms were as cold as winter.

Nancy ask us to gather around and sing some hymns.

"Rachel will be able to hear us," she said.

James got a song book, and lined each verse, then the whole family sang the song verse by verse. This went on for about an hour, then Rachel smiled and gave up the ghost. Jonas went to the clock and stopped it at 11:11 PM.

The family made tentative plans. Different ones would set up with their beloved mother through the night, Word would go out early in the morning so that final plans could be made. Jonas and James would take the first three hours of watch. Later others would be awaken to come and sit with the beloved Rachel. First light the ladies would come and bath Rachel and put her in a favorite dress. A coffin was already prepared, because of recent events. Jonas, and James had worked on the coffin with love.

As Jonas and James sat and talked in the bedroom. They had reflected on all that had went on since their Paw died. They begin to talk about Rachel seeing Hezekiah, and seeing the realms of glory.

"I think it is because of the Indian blood that flowed through her veins," James said.

"That would explain a lot, I have always heard that Indians have an inside line to the spirit world." Jonas said.

"Me too," replied James.

"Bless her heart, she and Paw can go on to glory now," exclaimed Jonas.

Jonas described how they both lived long, productive lives. They were great examples of how we should live and treat our fellowmen. They both had great faith in Jesus, and the promise of heaven.

Next morning James Griffith and David Crockett rode out in different directions to let the folks know that Rachel had passed. In a short time people started showing up with food and offering to help in any way possible.

Elder David Young was one of the first to show up. He wanted to get there to offer spiritual guidance and console the family. Five more men showed up with picks and shovels to prepare the grave. One of the men made a mistake by asking where she would be buried?

Jonas rose up in anger, "what do you mean?"

"Sorry Jonas, but your mother was Indian wasn't she?"

"She will be buried beside her life long friend and husband," commanded Jonas.

"Do not come in here with that Indian race stuff," Jonas said.

"Sorry Jonas I was only going with what folks sometimes do," answered the neighbor.

Jonas patted him on the back, "thanks Frank for coming over to help," Jonas said.

"Maw will be buried right beside of Paw, any one comes to stop you, you send them to me," said Jonas.

"Yes sir, I understand," answered Frank.

There would be a wake the night of the 21st. and the funeral would be at noon on the 22nd. This has been a hard year for the Whitts with both Hezekiah and Rachel passing away. People in Tazewell county are so kind and caring in these times, Jonas thought.

Hezekiah was well known and so was his loving wife, Rachel Whitt. Hezekiah was always ready to extend a hand to any one that needed help. Hezekiah was especially helpful in legal matters and in politics. Rachel was just a grand neighbor to everyone.

Large crowds came to pay honor to Rachel at her wake. Some came only to have a short visit, while others would sit out the night with the Whitt family. Some folks didn't even know Rachel personally, but knew of her good deeds and of her prominent husband.

Some of the family would hide out for a nap. Some of the family were always vigil for the entire wake. There was much conversation and well wishing to the family. Many stories were told about Rachel, and of course Hezekiah.

Crockett stayed around the wake until Jonas sent him to bed. Jonas told him that the family wanted him to lead the procession tomorrow. I think it will be fine to carry the old flag one more time, since it belonged to Grand Maw now.

The coffin was really nice. The sons had fashioned it out of wild cherry wood. Crockett had helped with the sanding and rubbing in of the bee wax. It was a fitting coffin for any high ranking person. Rachel was the highest ranking Matriarch of the Whitt clan. When Hezekiah and Rachel passed away a whole social and historic realm passed from existence. They would be sorely missed by family and friends.

At about 11:40 A.M., Jonas instructed Crockett to take the old war flag and start the line. The coffin carried by six strong friends was next, followed by James and Nancy. The rest of the brothers and sisters were next; followed by all the remaining family. Then the many friends followed up the procession in the rear. As the line moved down the hill and crossed Green Mountain Road, many other people joined in at the rear. Many people showed up for the funeral, but not quite the crowd that honored Hezekiah a couple months back.

Like before Crockett carried the old flag high and proud at a slow respectful pace.

At the top of the hill the Elder David Young and most of the Baptist congregation were waiting. Crockett stepped aside as the men set the coffin on timbers that lay across the open grave. The family came around and took a seat on the benches in front of the grave. Crockett draped the flag across the cherry wood coffin, and took a seat beside his Paw.

The Elder took over the service, and preached a great sermon, many hymns were sung. The Elder also told of recent events of Rachel seeing Hezekiah and Jesus waiting for her. She had no dread of death because she knew beyond a shadow doubt that heaven was hers.

"This even in death, was a great witness for the Lord Jesus Christ," The Elder added.

After, the funeral people came by to shake hands with the family and offer one last condolence. The skies had been gray all morning. Now the rain began with a mist at first. In a short period the rain became heavy. The grave was almost covered by the time the heavy rain came.

Crockett quoted the saying he heard Jonas say about two months back, "Happy the dead the rains falls up on, happy the bride the sun shines up on"

Jonas heard this and turned to Crockett and said, "that is a good saying son."

"It seems to always rain on the funeral of good folks," James said.

The family gathered in at the Hezekiah Whitt House. After more eating and visiting, the family began to disperse.

Every one knew the wishes of Hezekiah and Rachel as to the house and farm. It was to go to the oldest son James. James and Nancy had moved in over a year ago to care for the elderly parents. No one would object to this. There was several other farms and acreage's to be dispersed at a later time.

Late that evening, as Jonas, James Griffith, and Crockett sat and reflected on the days events. Jonas right out of the blue said, "I am going to Kentucky, you fellers in favor?"

Crockett spoke right up, "I am Paw."

"I don't want to right now, Me and Nancy Webb are getting close, I will stay and take care of the farm if that is alright," James Griffith stated.

Jonas answered James, "You are a man now son and I respect your decision."

"We will start planning tomorrow, Hannah has pretty much adopted James and Nancy, she is too young to go off on a sashay like this, she will be better off with Nancy," Jonas said.

"We will go and build Sam a mill or two, if we would decide to stay we will come back and get the little darling," Jonas continued..

"Looks like just you and me Crockett, do you want to build some mills in Greenup County, Kentucky," asked Jonas?

"Yes sir, I will be a big help Paw," replied Crockett.

The very next morning Jonas wrote out a letter to Doctor Samuel Truitt, Truittville, Greenup County, Kentucky. He stated that he would be available to come and build the two mills on contract. Jonas stated that he would leave the next day after a reply. He also stated what compensation he would expect including room and board for him and his ten year old son.

"Crockett," Jonas called out, "here son, watch for the postman and get this in the out going mail."

"Do not lose it if you want to go to Kentucky," Jonas added.

"I won't Paw, I will put it in the Postman's hand," answered Crockett.

Crockett headed out on this very important errand.

"Wonder how long we will have to wait for an answer Paw?" Crockett asked as soon as he got back.

"I figure around the end of August, now Crockett don't get disappointed if the Truitt's don't need us any more," said Jonas.

"He may have found a mill-right by now," added Jonas.

"Alright Paw, I bet we get a reply in August ," exclaimed Crockett.

"Hope you are right son," answered Jonas.

"In the mean time we have much to do, we got crops to take care of, and animals , and equipment to make ready," said Jonas.

"We will take a wagon, and all my tools, we will have to do some planning, for the harvest, and sell some things," Jonas continued.

"We have plenty to do, but plenty of time to do it, I think," said Jonas.

Things got back to almost normal. Jonas made plans to wait until the spring of 1847 to head to Kentucky, if Doctor Samuel Truitt confirmed the agreement. This way there would be no haste in getting ready. The crops could be harvested, and everyone could have ample time to say their good bye's.

Crockett was a little disappointed, He wanted to head right out.

The whole country was excited about the western lands. James Polk was President during this time, and he pushed for expansion of the United States. He had settled a dispute with Great Britain, and established the border on the 49th parallel between Canada and the United States. Also, he offered to buy California and New Mexico from Mexico for Twenty Million Dollars. The Mexican government did not have power to sell off half of it's lands so nothing was settled.

General Zachary Taylor was sent to the Rio Grande with troops. The Mexicans attacked which started a shooting war. The United States soon defeated the Mexicans in several battles. The United States took over California and New Mexico and gave the Mexican Government Fifteen Million Dollars for damages. New territories brought on a new problem with the state of slavery. Another thing for the North and South to disagree about. Expansion was in the air and many people picked up and headed toward the west. It is no wonder that Jonas got itchy feet.

The first week of September, a letter arrived for Jonas Whitt. Crockett got the mail that day. He saw the return address and was filled with excitement.

He ran to Jonas with the letter saying, "It's here Paw."

Jonas took the letter and with his pocket knife, slowly opened the envelope. Crockett was about to pass out with anticipation. Finally Jonas removed the letter, unfolded it's pages and begin to read.

Dear Mister Jonas Whitt, I received your letter and am delighted that you are available to come and do my mill work. I do approve your statement of compensation and room and board. I have an Inn, and you and your son will be quiet comfortable for your extended stay in Kentucky.

Please send me a conformation as to when you may arrive here in Greenup County, Kentucky. Your Humble Servant, Doctor Samuel Truitt.

"Yea, Yea," shouted Crockett, "we are going to Kentucky!"

"Looks that way," replied Jonas.

I will write him a letter today and mail it tomorrow. We will leave about the end of March (1847), and we will need detailed directions to Big White Oak Creek in Greenup County.

"Why can't we go now Paw?" asked Crockett.

"It is so long until next March!" Crockett added.

Jonas explained that it would be better not to be hasty, a well planed trip will be much better. We have a lot of things to finish here. March will be here before you know it. Our tools will have to be cleaned and oiled. The wagon will have to be put in top notch shape. Axles will have to be greased and all the harness gear will have to be gone over. Kentucky is a long hard trip. We sure don't want to have a break down on the trail.

Jonas went on explaining about how much there was to do here on the farm. We will have time to sell the tobacco and other crops.

You have wood to chop for the winter, and plenty of other things to keep you busy. We may even have time to go fishing a time or two before it turns cold.

"What about hunting this winter," ask Crockett?

"We should be able to get out and maybe get a deer or turkey for the table," answered Jonas.

Jonas and Crockett take almost daily walks to the cemetery to visit with Susannah, Hezekiah, and Rachel. Crockett can hardly remember his Maw, but he loves her very much because of all the stories about her. He has been making trips with Jonas to the cemetery for six or seven years. He remembers Grand Paw and Grand Maw very vividly, since he spent so much time with them.

Jonas and Crockett would always stop at the old Hezekiah Whitt house on the way home. Jonas told Crockett that they would have to start calling the old house the James Whitt house.

Hannah loved her Paw but stayed with James and Nancy most of the time. Nancy had a way with children, even though she had none of her own.

James Griffith was still living with Crockett and their Paw Jonas. James Griffith was a full grown man now at twenty one years old. He was the main work hand on the Indian Creek farm, but spends much time in Jeffersonville.

He has become very popular with the young ladies of Tazewell county. He has one young lady that is the object of his affection, Nancy Webb. She is still too young to have a full time beau; at least her Paw Joseph Webb has confirmed to James Griffith Whitt.

When Jonas and Crockett leave in the spring, James Griffith will stay and run the Indian Creek Farm. Hannah will stay with James and Nancy while Jonas is away in Kentucky. If by chance Jonas and Crockett decide to stay in Kentucky, Jonas will come for Hannah, and the farm will be sold. But that is a long time off, and "we live here for now," said Jonas to Crockett.

"Paw do you think we may stay in Kentucky?" asked Crockett.

"Don't know son, but we will be there for a long time building two mills," replied Jonas.

"Who knows we may get even more work to do after we get there," Jonas added.

All through the fall and winter Jonas kept his sons busy with the farm work and preparation for the Spring trip. Jonas also made visits to all of his children on every opportunity. Also the children spent time with them at the Indian Creek Farm. Good memories were made and would have to last until Jonas and Crockett returned from Kentucky.

Just before Christmas, the thirteenth of December, Crockett's eleventh birthday a letter arrived from Kentucky. It was the letter they had been waiting for. It was from Doctor Samuel Truitt, with detailed directions to the Truitt property in Greenup County.

This was as good a Christmas and birthday present to Crockett as he could wish for. He had never been on a long trip since the family came from Montgomery County back in 1837. It really seems true now that this letter has arrived.

James Griffith and Crockett went on several hunting trips that winter. Crockett had sharpened up his hunting and shooting skills. He was tall for his age and quiet strong. Jonas told them if they didn't quit carrying in game there would be too much to handle. And besides that they better leave a few critters in the woods for the future. James Griffith and Crockett had a good laugh over that.

It was the first of March 1847 and final plans were made for the trip. Jonas wanted to stop and see his brother John Bunyon in Floyd County, on the way. They would be able to have a short visit and get some rest. By then a good home cooked meal will be a good diversion from the trail cuisine.

Getting there they would follow the Kentucky Turnpike that runs by Indian Creek Farm. They would follow the road through Indian, (now Cedar Bluff) north west to a bottom called Rich Lands. Then they would continue to a place now called (Raven). Here they would leave the Clinch Valley to climb to the top of a long ridge. (now Road Ridge) They would ramble along this ridge for several miles and finally descend to a little valley.

The ridge is a divide for the water shed. Water on one end takes a southern flow. Water on the other end takes a north western flow. This little valley had a small creek winding north west beginning at the bottom of the ridge. This creek is a fork of the Big Sandy River. The Creek is called Louisa Creek (now Levisa) Some folks call this area "Head of the River". The terrain would change drastically.

The mountains close in on the trail. They would follow the Levisa Fork to the Big Sandy River which begins at the confluence of The Tugg Fork. The valley is very narrow.

Finally the end of March arrived, and the trip would begin. April is unpredictable in this part of the country, so heavy coats and light coats would both be on hand.

"I just hope we don't get caught in a snow storm," Jonas said.

One thing about it, they don't usually last long in April," Jonas added.

"I remember a few years back we got a foot of snow, remember Paw," exclaimed James Griffith?

"Yes I do, we have a good tent and provisions, so we can weather a snow for a day or two," Jonas said.

The wagon was packed with care and everything tied down and covered. The best team of Mules was hitched to the wagon. Jonas' saddle horse Jake was tied to the back of the wagon. He would be a spare if something happened to one the mules. After their arrival Jake would be the transportation around Greenup County. A rifle, shotgun, and Jonas' cap and ball pistol would be handy as well. The basket of fried chicken and other food items prepared by the women was sat on the floor under the seat. A small barrel of water was also part of the load.

Every one of Jonas' children was on hand that morning to see them off. Jonas and Crockett hugged each loved one, and got up in the wagon. This day was the twenty eighth of March 1847. Jonas and Crockett pulled out on the Kentucky Turnpike and headed toward Kentucky. It was about twenty minutes past eight A.M.

Jonas and Crockett bounced along the road toward Indian. (now

Cedar Bluff) Crockett said to Jonas, "I didn't think we would ever finally get started to Kentucky."

"Well son" replied Jonas, "you are starting to learn patience."

"Now you have an adventure ahead of you, but a long hard trip also," Jonas said.

Jonas explained that they need to take their time, because they have a heavy load, and the road down Levisa Fork is rough and narrow.

"I was over that way awhile back," Jonas said.

"I was over there checking on the farm for Paw; He had it rented out," said Jonas.

"It is located on Dismal Creek and Levisa Fork; and that is as far as I have been in that direction," Jonas added.

"I remember Paw, you stayed over night and you were riding Jake," Crockett replied.

"That is right, and you know Jake makes good time," Jonas said.

"We may get a third way there today with this wagon," Jonas added.

"Well where we get is where we get," answered Crockett.

"That's right son, be patient," Jonas said.

As Crockett drove the wagon through the village of Indian, Jonas waved to the folks.

"We know most of these people don't we Paw?" asked Crockett.

"Yes and most of them know we are heading for Kentucky," Jonas exclaimed.

The weather was not bad, but the March wind had not gone away. The grass was green, and the trees were wanting to burst out in bloom. Jonas was whistling a tune and the two were quite happy. They followed the Turnpike south west along the Clinch River. Before long the valley widened out into a big bottom. The ground was rich and folks had a big portion plowed under in anticipation of spring planting.

There was a village here also, some folks called it Town Hill. Some folks called it the most likely name, Rich-lands.

"Paw," asked Crockett, "why do folks call this place Town Hill?" asked Crockett.

Jonas gets out a piece of chicken and a biscuit nods to Crockett, chicken son? Crockett nods back with a yes answer. Jonas looks to the right at a knoll over looking the valley.

"Up there son, they say the Indians had a town there once up on a time," Jonas said.

At the western end of this beautiful valley they stopped at a creek.

"This is Hill Creek son, we better water our mules and Jake," Jonas instructed.

"We can stretch our legs a bit too," Jonas added.

Crockett drove the wagon into the creek, stopping with the mules standing in the water. Jonas untied Jake and took him to water also. After watering the animals the trip was resumed.

They followed the old Turn Pike hugging the North side of the hills. "We will be getting to where we start our climb up the Turnpike Ridge before long," Jonas said.

Jonas explained that the Turnpike traveled the ridge for a number of miles, and hopefully we will get a good start on it today.

They stopped at another creek (now Coal Creek) and watered the mules again. Jonas explained that the mules don't need watered very bad, but it may be the last they get for a while." (This place is the present town of Raven.)

The basket was a joy for the two to snack on as they traveled.

"We will not have to do any cooking this evening will we Paw?" Crockett asked.

"Not much," answered Jonas.

"It is a pity we will not have a full basket fixed for us every day," Crockett said.

"Yes," said Jonas, "we could head back to Indian Creek and get one for tomorrow."

Crockett laughed, "that's alright Paw, we can do with out it."

"Now get ready to do some climbing son, head right up this grade, we are starting the climb up Turnpike Ridge," Jonas said. (now Road Ridge)

Crockett headed the mules up the grade at a nice slow pace.

"That's right son, don't push them too hard," Jonas said.

Jonas mentioned that they were going to leave the Clinch Valley. Right down the river from here is a creek called Mill Creek. There is a Grist Mill up the creek a-ways, at a beautiful falls.

"I worked over there a day or two for the folks doing some repairs, sometime back," explained Jonas.

"Who was it that owned it Paw," asked Crockett?

"Don't remember, but it was something like Stinson," Jonas replied.

At the top of the first hill the road continued on up the Ridge. The road took a westerly direction. The two looked back over the Clinch Valley. They could see a big mountain that followed the river, and ran for miles.

"Look son this will be the last time you see Clinch Mountain for a spell," said Jonas.

"It is a beautiful place ain't it Paw!" said Crockett.

"Yes it is son, but we will see some beautiful grounds in the Kentucky lands, exclaimed Jonas.

"Want me to drive for a while son?" asked Jonas.

"No Paw I got it, unless you are getting a little afraid going up this steep ridge," answered Crockett.

"You are doing fine, just let the mules make their own pace," instructed Jonas.

"I will Paw," Crockett responded.

"Thank goodness this road levels off ever now and then, to give the team a little break," Crockett said.

"Yes son," agreed Jonas "we will get to the summit and stop a little early for the night"

"The mules will need some rest after this pull," Jonas added.

About five that evening Jonas saw a good place to pull off and set up for the night.

They un-hitched the team and scotched the wagon so it would not run off.

Jonas said to Crockett, "gather fire wood son, I am going to scout around for some water, I will be back dreckly."

"Alright Paw, I will, and I will start a fire." replied Crockett.

Jonas pointed to a rock house (overhanging cliff), "over there will be a good place," he said.

Crockett nodded, and Jonas was over the hill and out of site.

In about an hours time Jonas was back to camp.

Found some water, "I will take Jake, and the mules to water them," said Jonas.

"It is not far from here, you go ahead and start setting up camp," added Jonas.

"I will Paw," answered Crockett, "that rock house will feel good tonight against this wind."

"Yelp, it is pretty breezy up here on this ridge," answered Jonas as he led the animals to water.

About an hour passed before Jonas was back.

"What took so long Paw, thought you said the water was close?" asked Crockett.

Jonas explained that it was close, but it is a small spring, they had to drink one at a time. Jonas put the feed bags on the animals, which held Oats. After supper we can hobble them and let them graze. This new grass will finish filling them up.

"The oats really give them energy, don't they Paw?" replied Crockett.

"Yes son, you have to take good care of your horses and mules, if you want them to take care of you!" replied Jonas.

After supper the two sit back by the fire and talked about the trip and many other things. Jonas told Crockett to keep the shotgun loaded and handy the rest of the way. There are bad men that prey upon the travelers in the Kentucky hills. Some of these bad men are here because they are wanted in the east or in central Kentucky. There is an old saying about this. If the law gets after you "head for the hills."

"We are in those hills son," said Jonas.

Jonas told Crockett about the trip from Montgomery County to Tazewell county. His older brothers and sisters helped him hold off three bad men over in Rocky Gap.

"I remember that story," replied Crockett.

"I was a baby and you all made the robbers back down with the old Brown Betsy's," replied Crockett.

"That is right, and I had a new 44 cap and ball revolver at that time, it is this same old pistol I carry when I'm out like this," said Jonas.

"Hope none of those bad fellers try to brother us Paw," said Crockett.

"Most likely they wouldn't son, just the same we will not let any one get the jump on us," said Jonas.

"They would take every thing we have and maybe even kill us," replied Jonas.

Next morning the wind had laid down, but the temperature had dropped to an unpleasant level. Jonas got out from under his heavy quilts first and got the fire going. The rock house and fire made a pleasant place to sleep. Crockett got up and helped Jonas make ready for the days travel. After some hot breakfast, the two packed their gear back on the wagon. The mules were brought back and hitched to the wagon. Jake was tied to the back of the wagon and they were moving toward Kentucky once again.

They wore their heavy coats today, the temperature was slow to rise and the wind begin to pick up again. As they rode along, Jonas told Crockett that they may make it over to Grand Paw's property on Dismal Creek and Levisa Fork today.

"Who lives there Paw," asked Crockett?

"A Mister James Thompson, rents the place," replied Jonas.

"He seemed interested in buying it the last time I talked to him," said Jonas.

"When your Uncle James probates the will for your Grand Paw and Grand Maw, it will be sold; Mister Thompson may buy it;" said Jonas.

"How much land is it Paw," Crockett asked?

"It is pretty good size, about 245 acres I think," said Jonas.

"Well at any rate that will be a good place to stop and water the team and take a rest, said Jonas.

"We might even be able to mooch a meal from the Thompson's," added Jonas.

"When will we get there Paw?" asked Crockett.

"Don't know, but it will be quite some time, we have to travel this ridge for several miles, then we have to go slow back down the other side of this ridge," explained Jonas.

As they rode along they passed, a wagon headed toward Tazewell County. A Mister Blankenship was taking a load of coal to the Perry family. They talked for a few minutes, and both wagons resumed their journey. Crockett wanted to know what the Perry's would do with coal?

"Burn it son," replied Jonas.

"It is much slower burning and puts out more heat then wood,"

Jonas said.

"The Perry's are rich ain't they Paw?" asked Crockett.

"Well to do, you could say," Jonas replied.

Jonas and Crockett passed another wagon heading toward Kentucky, There was a whole family on this wagon and it was pulled by two yoke of oxen.

"The oxen are very strong, but not very fast," replied Jonas.

They talked with these folks for a few minutes also. They were out of Russell County, heading to a place called Lexington, Kentucky. This family was the Holbrook's.

"They wanted to start a new life in the blue grass lands," Mister Holbrook said.

Crockett said, "they have blue grass in Tazewell county."

Yes we heard that, but we want the flatter lands we have heard of in Kentucky," replied Mister Holbrook.

"We better get a going, we may see you later, take care!" said Jonas.

"You do the same," answered Mister Holbrook.

Crockett told Jonas, "that is the biggest wagon I ever seen."

"I know," Jonas replied, "they are going pretty slow because of the big load and size."

"That is the kind of wagons they use going across the prairie to Oregon," said Jonas.

"Tough going in this country," said Crockett.

Yes nodded Jonas, and they moved on leaving the giant wagon behind.

CHAPTER 17

HEAD OF THE RIVER

Jonas and Crockett continue out the ridge on the Kentucky Turnpike. They are getting close to the descent, and they will have to apply the brakes. A runaway wagon can bring death and destruction in a hurry. Jonas warned Crockett about the steep grade ahead!

"I am ready for the steep grade, I got my big foot right here on the brake Paw," said Crockett.

"Alright son, I just want you to be prepared," exclaimed Jonas.

As they went down the winding road Crockett said; "Paw my ears keep popping."

"That is normal son, we have gone downhill a long way; I think your ears have to adapt to the elevation," Jonas answered.

"Well ain't that something; I never thought of that," exclaimed Crockett.

Jonas started telling Crockett about the divide up on the ridge. He explained that the water shed is different over here on this side of the ridge.

"What do you mean Paw, asked Crockett?

"The Clinch River runs mostly south, and over here the water will run toward the northwest," Jonas said.

"When we get down to where we are beside the creek you will see what I mean," Jonas added.

Crockett drove the wagon like a teamster, he drove down that steep curvy road with out any mishap. Before long they were riding on a slight downhill grade, almost level. The creek was on their right as the road meandered along beside it.

"Look at the creek, it is heading toward the north," Jonas said.

"Yes Paw, is that Levisa Fork, asked Crockett?

"It sure is, we are at the head of the river," Jonas answered.

"We can follow this water all the way to the Ohio River," replied

Jonas.

"Wow Paw, this will help to keep us from getting lost." said Crockett.

Jonas laughingly said, "you are right about that!"

It is little right here, but the further we go the bigger it will become," said Jonas.

"The Russell Fork will hook up with it on down the river, right Paw," asked Crockett?

"That is right, it will become a river, even though it is a mere creek right here," said Jonas.

"Then way on down the Tug Fork will join in, from that point it is the Big Sandy River," Jonas added.

"Paw I know about the Tug, it is not too far from where we live in Tazewell County," answered Crockett.

"That's right son, over a few ridges and you are there at it's head water," Jonas said.

"Why didn't we go that way to Kentucky, Paw?" Crockett asked.

"Well we could have, but it is too rough and a poor road; we could never get our wagon through that a way," exclaimed Jonas.

"We could have even went on down southwest to Lee County, and from there, turn northwest through the Cumberland Gap, and went that way," Jonas said.

"Do they have a good road that way Paw?" asked Crockett.

Think so, only thing, it is much further that way from Indian Creek Farm," said Jonas.

"Probably add a month to the trip," added Jonas. "There is even another way, through Wise county, you go through Pound Gap, but that is also far and rough," Jonas stated.

"Better water the team and take a little rest son, they didn't get much water yesterday," said Jonas.

"Alright Paw; do you see somewhere to pull into the creek?" asked Crockett.

"No son, just stop here and we will lead them to the water," Jonas answered.

"Paw," Crockett said.

"Yes son," answered Jonas.

"Reckon the mules and Jake are a wondering where we are headed?"

Crockett asked.

"Don't know son, you think of the dangest things," Jonas said.

As Jonas and Crockett proceed down the little bumpy, and rutty road Jonas pulls out a plug of tobacco. Jonas cuts himself a jaw filling hunk and puts it back on the right side of his jaw. Crockett looked as Jonas meticulously loaded his mouth with an enjoyable chew of home grown tobacco.

"Paw, how about me trying a little chew?" Crockett asked.

"Well son, you will get sick, do you want to get sick?" asked Jonas.

"No I don't want to get sick, but that stuff looks good," answered Crockett.

"It don't make you sick, Paw," Crockett added.

"Well I will give you a little bit, if you start getting sick spit it out, and do not swallow any of the juice," explained Jonas.

"Alright Paw," Crockett said excitedly!

Jonas handed him a small portion of the juicy stuff. Crockett shoved it back into his jaw like he had seen Jonas do.

"What now paw?" Crocked asked.

"Just hold it in your mouth, when you get juice spit it out," said Jonas.

It was not long until the whole bit of it spewed from Crockett's mouth. Jonas gave out a big Hee-Haw! Crockett looked at his Paw, as if to say how do you chew that stuff?

The little narrow valley was damp, and the road had sections of deep ruts.

Jonas laughed as he said sarcastically; "Choose your rut well, as you will be in it for several miles."

"Ain't it the truth Paw?" Crockett said laughing.

Jonas was looking at the land marks and trying to remember where the Dismal Creek was.

"I think the farm is just ahead around the next bend," said Jonas.

"Paw there ain't many folks live over this way," replied Crockett.

"That is right, they are spread out pretty thin," answered Jonas.

"People are isolated over in this country, you have to like it or you would get lonesome," Jonas said.

"Does Mister Thompson have a large family?" asked Crockett.

"Well I think I remember five or six children, they are all ages," Jonas answered.

As the wagon rounded the bend in the road, they could see a steady stream of smoke flowing towards the heavens.

"That smoke just beyond those trees has to be the cabin of the Thompson's," said Jonas.

Crockett became a little excited at the thought of meeting this family, way out here!

In another one hundred yards voices could be heard and motion were detected from the Thompson family. Mister Thompson and an older son was using a cross cut saw, and another son was chopping up the sawed pieces. A small boy was running around chasing the chickens.

Mister Thompson turned to the child and said, "Willie, stop that or them chickens will never start laying."

A small girl was gliding around the yard in a graceful dance in her imaginary world.

The little dancing girl looked up and hollered, "Paw, wagon's coming."

Mister Thompson looked quickly in the direction of Jonas and Crockett.

Jonas immediately raised his hand and waved to the Thompson's.

"Hello there Mister Thompson," he shouted out.

This put James Thompson at ease, and he waved back. Crockett pulled the wagon off to the side of the road and locked the brake. They both got down and walked toward the house as James Thompson met them with a hand shake.

"Jonas isn't it, Jonas Whitt?" asked James.

"Yes and you are James Thompson," said Jonas.

"That's right," James answered.

Jonas introduced David Crockett to James and the children that were out in the yard. By now Mandy the wife of James and her two teen aged daughters came out on the porch to see what was going on.

"Jonas and Crockett, this here is my wife Mandy, and my girls Mary Jane, and Virginia," said James.

Jonas stepped up and tipped his hat to the ladies. Crockett did likewise.

Virginia seemed to be about Crockett's age and her dark eyes sparkled like stars toward Crockett.

Crockett was instantly "twitter patted!"

James asked right off, "how is your Paw and Maw doing?"

Jonas was taken back a little?

"I guess you haven't heard, both Hezekiah and Rachel have passed on to glory," said Jonas.

"Oh! I'm so sorry to hear that, We only communicate about once a year when we send the rent," replied James.

"We sent it by our friend Bill McGraw last fall and never heard any thing back," James said.

"Bill had to go to Jeffersonville on business so we had him take it," said James.

"I got a receipt signed by James Whitt I think, I wondered about that at the time," added James.

"He is the administrator of the estate, so that would be right," Jonas replied.

"Is this place going up for sale?" James asked right off.

"Most likely when the will is probated," answered Jonas.

"You still interested in buying it," Jonas asked?

"Sure am if the price is right," replied James.

"Well if I were you, I would write a letter to James and let him know that you are interested," Jonas said.

"I will do just that, I'm sorry to talk business before we have fed you and young David, exclaimed James.

"By the way what are you all doing way out on this end of the county," James asked?

Crockett spoke up, "going to Kentucky to build a mill!"

Jonas turned and looked at Crockett as if to say, you are speaking out of turn.

"Well you fellers are on the right road!" James said.

Virginia was still there gawking at Crockett!

James looked at her and said, "girl go tell your Maw to set two more plates for supper!"

"Yes Paw," answered the young lady.

"David would you like to go with me?" Virginia asked.

Crockett looked at Jonas asking?, "well I guess it will be alright if James don't mind."

"It's alright I reckon, they may put him to work in there, I try to stay out of the females way," James said.

"I know what you mean," replied Jonas.

"I think I will unhitch my team and let them do a little grazing while we eat supper with you kind folks," said Jonas.

"That will be fine, the grass is getting up purty good," said James.

"I guess tomorrow is April, if I looked at the calendar right;" replied James Thompson.

"Yelp," exclaimed Jonas, "Spring is trying to spring."

After supper Jonas and James talked about the current events, and the subject of Kentucky came up. James told Jonas that several folks have come by here lately on their way to Kentucky.

I heard of some mischief a happening over where Levisa goes by Grapevine Mountain. That is close to where she runs into the Russell fork.

James told Jonas to be extra careful from here on out. People have been beat and robbed. Some were shot outright cause they would not give up their stuff.

"How big a gang is it?" asked Jonas.

"I heard it was different little gangs of two to four un-Godly men," said James.

"They come to the mountains to get away from the law, then they go after the folks that may look like easy pickings," James added.

"Crockett and I will not be easy to get a jump on, I already trained the boy to be vigilant," said Jonas.

Crockett and Virginia were like peas and carrots, they talked and talked. Of course Crockett had to brag and look like the big man, and Virginia had to listen intently. This was Crockett's first puppy love, and it was a new feeling for Virginia.

Before long, time had slipped away.

"Would you and Crockett like to stay in the barn tonight, and get an early start in the morning?" James asked.

"Well it is late, if you don't mind I will take you up on it, besides that it looks like rain is about to set in," Jonas answered.

Crockett and Virginia were delighted to hear the news. They could spend a few more hours together.

James told Virginia she had chores to do.

"I got to take care of the team and Jake,"Crockett stated.

"I got an idea, you help me and I will help you," Virginia said.

James overheard this.

"That will be alright long as both of you get your work done," said James.

Jonas and James sat on the porch and had a smoke and a little snort of corn squeezins! They enjoyed the conversation until almost dark.

Virginia and Crockett were carrying quilts toward the barn.

"Well Jim thanks for your hospitality, think I will get ready to turn in" said Jonas.

"You are welcome Jonas, how about sending my little girl back to the house," James said.

"I will do that, and good night," answered Jonas.

When Jonas went in to the barn, Crockett and Virginia were in an embrace enjoying a big kiss!

"Hummmmm," said Jonas!

They jumped back like they had been shot.

"Virginia, your Paw said it is time to come in the house," Jonas exclaimed.

"Thank you Mister Whitt," she shyly replied.

"See you in the morning David," Virginia said.

Crockett nodded, "see you in the morning."

During the night the rain started. Jonas thought to himself, good to be in the barn on a night like this! Sleep came and morning came early. Jonas nudged Crockett.

"Want to go to Kentucky?" he asked?

"Will we be there today Paw?" asked Crockett.

"No but we will be a lot closer than we are now," and laughed!

"Not funny Paw," mumbled the sleepy Crockett.

Crockett hurriedly yanked on his bibs and ran to the family privy.

A knock was heard as the big barn door squeaked open. The young black haired Virginia came in.

"Mister Whitt, my Maw told me to go and fetch you and David for breakfast," Virginia said.

"Thank you Miss Virginia, we will be heading that way in just a few minutes," replied Jonas.

"Where is David?" she blurted out.

"He went to the little house out back," grinned Jonas.

"Ohoooo I'm sorry, never thought of that," she said quietly.

"I will run back and tell Maw you all will be a coming soon," said Virginia.

Jonas thought to himself, These young ones have got it bad! Good thing we are leaving, or we would have to sit around the clock watch them! Jonas thought, they will forget each other in a few days, he hoped!

Jonas and Crockett enjoyed a big breakfast with the Thompson's and got back on the road. The rain had subsided, but the road would be a bit mushy today. Before Crockett and Jonas got up on the wagon they shook hands with all the Thompson's. The starry eyed Virginia grabbed Crockett and gave him a bear hug! Mandy smiled as she witnessed her daughter's expression of puppy love. Jonas also noticed this!

Now the Whitts were on the move again, heading toward the Kentucky border.

Jonas and Crockett reflected on the visit with the Thompson's.

"They are nice people, I hope they can buy the farm," Jonas said.

"Me too, I want to visit them again," replied Crockett.

"Them or her?" asked Jonas.

Crockett turned his head quickly and smiled.

"All of them of course, but mostly Virginia," Crockett said.

"Ain't she great Paw?" asked Crockett.

"I reckon she is," replied Jonas.

"Now keep your eyes on the road today, the ruts will be bad, and we have to watch out for any sign of trouble," Jonas instructed.

"I will," said Crockett as he drove the sluggish wagon down the rutty Turnpike.

Time seemed to fly by this morning, but the miles were going slowly. The heavy wagon was hard to pull in the mushy road, so Crockett did not push the mules too hard. About 1:00 PM, they stopped to give the team a rest.

This gave Jonas and Crockett a chance to get down and stretch. Crockett asked Jonas if he heard any thing about the road condition ahead?

"Well, Mister Thompson said it was not too bad, far as he knew, he did say after a rain it would be soft and rutty," Jonas said.

"He was right about that," replied Crockett.

Mister Thompson told me the road would get higher on the hills as we go into Kentucky.

"They want the road out of the flood plain, the road should drain better if that is the case," Jonas said.

"I hope he is right," replied Crockett, "this is slow going in this mud."

"We have to be patient and not over work the team," said Jonas, as they boarded the wagon.

"Paw how far is it to the Russell Fork and Grapevine Mountain?" asked Crockett.

"I think about two more days the rate we are a-going," answered Jonas.

"But we have to be vigilant from here on out," said Jonas.

"Mountain outlaws can show up around the very next bend, and as I told you they will kill just to see what's under our canvas," Jonas continued.

"Paw I am trying my best to keep a sharp eye out, and the shotgun is right here between my legs," replied Crockett.

"That is what it takes," replied Jonas.

"Crockett if we are confronted, you will know the danger," said Jonas.

"If you feel that our lives are in danger, and you will know, shoot to kill," Jonas continued seriously.

The hair raised up on the back of Crockett's neck.

"I hope I will know, and I hope I can shoot," replied Crockett.

"Don't worry, Whitt men know these things, when they come," replied Jonas.

"Did you ever have to kill Paw?" asked Crockett" "No, but I came close a few times," answered Jonas.

"Grand Paw Hezekiah had to kill several men, He killed Tories, Cherokee, and Creek Indians, replied Jonas.

"Who was the Tories?" asked Crockett.

"They were people that would not sign the Patriot's Oath, they sided with the King, and killed a lot of their neighbors," answered Jonas.

"Paw had to fight against some of them as well as the Indians, he did not relish the idea of killing white men or even Indians, he hated the fact that he shed blood, even though it was them or him," said Jonas.

"He said it stays with a man, that bad feeling of taking a life," Jonas added. Crockett said seriously, "I hope I never have to let go on another man."

"I do too son, but if you and your property are threatened, by outlaw or war, you will have a duty to pay," said Jonas.

"I understand," said Crockett, "I think I could do it, if I am forced into it."

About 6:00 PM, Crockett saw a wide meadow ahead. It was rare for the valley to be this wide in this area.

"Paw that looks like a good place to camp tonight, what do you think," asked Crockett?

"Pull off the road and let's have a look around," replied Jonas.

"What about up there in the edge of the woods?" asked Crockett.

"Header on up there son," replied Jonas.

Crockett drove the team to the upper side of the meadow near the woods. He locked the brake and both got down. Crockett moved the shot gun over to the edge of the wagon so it would be handy.

Jonas noticed this, and said, "good idea son."

"I am going to get on Jake and ride up the trail a-ways," said Jonas.

"You go ahead and unhitch the team and lead them to the creek, take your shotgun with you." Jonas said.

"Are you going to scout out the road up ahead Paw?" asked Crockett.

"Yes son, I want to know what lies ahead since we will be sleeping here tonight," answered Jonas.

"Be careful Paw, I will start setting up camp after I water the mules," said Crockett.

Jonas gave him a nod, and answered with one word, "Good!"

Jonas rode off up the road after he had scanned around the entire area. Crockett watered the mules and brought them up close to the wagon, before hobbling them for the night. Next Crockett got out the things they would need for the night's camp. He set up the tent on a level knoll just ahead of the wagon. He then gathered some stones to put around the fire place just below the tent.

He walked around the edge of the woods gathering dry wood from the trees. Dead limbs still on a tree makes the best fire wood, because it is dried out. Limbs on the ground are often wet and rotting. After getting the wood back to the fire place, he gathered a little tinder from the bark of a cedar. He ruffled it up between his hands and placed it in the center of the circled rocks.

He got out his fire starting kit. It was a file, a piece of flint, and a burned piece of flannel. He lay the burned flannel over the fluffy tinder, held the file at a forty five degree angle and struck it with the flint. A shower of sparks streaked to the burned flannel and some caught as little red dots of fire.

Crockett carefully picked up the tinder with the flannel holding the little fire. He gently blew the spark into the tinder, first there was smoke then a flame appeared. He dabbed out the sparks on his burned flannel. He put little branches on the little flame. He added fuel as the fire grew. He put his flint and steel, and burned flannel back into his water proof bag for future use.

In a little while Crockett heard a horse trotting, he looked up to see Jonas coming down the turnpike. Crockett waved his hand to acknowledge that he seen Jonas coming.

Jonas gave a quick wave, and rode Jake to the water. After he watered Jake he walked him up to the camp.

As Jonas unsaddled and hobbled Jake, Crockett smiled and asked, "see anything Paw?"

"Nothing to be too alarmed about," answered Jonas.

"About five miles up the road I seen where somebody scattered out some clothes and broke up some wooden boxes, exclaimed Jonas.

"What do you make of it Paw?" asked Crockett.

"Either people threw out their trash, or bandits went through their catch," replied Jonas.

"There was several tracks, horses and men's" said Jonas, "of course wagon tracks too."

"Since this is the road to Kentucky, there would be wagon tracks," said Jonas. "I don't think we should be too alarmed," Jonas added.

"How about the road, is it any better?" asked Crockett.

"Not much, if it don't rain it will get better each day," suggested Jonas.

"Did you see them fish down in the river Paw?" asked Crockett.

"Yes I did see some, bet we could catch some for breakfast, or may be even supper," answered Jonas.

"Let's cut us a pole and give it a try," replied Jonas.

"I was hoping you would say that, I gathered some worms while getting the rocks for the fire place," replied Crockett.

"Good," answered Jonas, "I think they are bronze backs, they always give a good fight and are tasty to eat."

"That means they are Small Mouth Bass, don't it Paw," said Crockett.

"Yes," answered Jonas, "that's just a nick name I reckon!"

Jonas and Crockett cut themselves a long limber sapling and tied on a line with hook and sinker. They walked to the edge of the water cautiously not to scare the fish. They gently flipped out a wiggling hooked worm for an offering to the active fish. Almost instantly both had a flipping shaking fish on their hooks. Jonas got out a piece of cord he brought with him from the wagon. They strung up the two Bass. And sent out another offering.

In about twenty minutes they had caught six nice Small Mouth Bass.

Jonas smiled at Crockett, "looks like we will have fish for supper."

"Yes it does Paw, do you think anybody ever fished here before?" asked Crockett.

"Probable Indians, or Tice Harmon," replied Jonas.

Tice Harmon, the Frontiersman?" asked Crockett.

"Well this is his old stomping ground," replied Jonas.

"I will tell you about him after supper," said Jonas.

"We got to get these fellers fried up, it is going to get dark on us real soon," added Jonas.

After a good hot meal of fried fish, and fried corn cakes the two sat back to enjoy the moment. Jonas takes a chew from his plug. He meticulously placed it way back in the right side of his jaw. Crockett watched, but never asked for any. He was remembering the chew he tried a few days ago. Crockett was thinking how good that looked, yet it will make a fellow sick! Jonas looked at him, and smiled, as if reading his mind.

"Well now Paw, tell me about that Harmon feller," said Crockett.

"Tice Harmon is his name, he did a lot to open up this western land," Jonas said.

"I know what you are thinking when I say western land," Jonas added.

Jonas explained that this area is still more primitive than some points way out west.

Jonas told the story about Tice living up in the Abbs Valley section of Tazewell County back in the 1780's. Tice hated the Indians and the Indians feared and hated him.

Tice use to bring a hunting party back in here and up the Big Sandy most every fall. They could get all the meat and bear grease they needed in a short time. He had a camp set up and used it every winter.

A band of Indians were aiming to capture Tice, and burn down his place up in Abbs Valley, but they went to the Wiley cabin by mistake. They ran in on Jenny Wiley, her little brother, and about four young-uns. They killed all of them except Jenny and the youngest baby. Jenny was expecting at the time. They grabbed up what they could easily carry and took off with Jenny. They headed across the mountains toward Tug Fork, in the direction of the Ohio towns.

Tice found out about it, and got some men together and followed them to the Tug Fork. It was swelled up with flood waters and they could not get across, so they had to give up.

The Wiley cabin never burned down, it was wet from recent rains and the Indians were in a hurry to get away before Tice found out.

To make a long story short, Tice was back over here on the Big Sandy the next year. Guess what, Jenny got lose from the heathens and ran for days through the woods and run up on the Harmon camp. Tice and his long knives, as the Indians called them, took Jenny right back to her husband. But before that Tice set up an ambush over on Russell Fork, not far from here. They killed most of the Indians, and the rest ran off, back to the Ohio country.

I have never been there but, Tice set up a station north west of here a few miles. They call it Harmon Station. Ole Tice loved this rugged country and the bountiful supply of game. So he just moved over here.

"Is Tice still living," asked Crockett?

"Well I don't know for sure, but I would guess he has passed on, but no red skin ever got his hair," answered Jonas.

"What about Jenny Wiley, did her babies make it," asked Crockett?

"No" answered Jonas.

Jonas explained that the Indians took the baby by the heels and bashed it's brains out on a tree when they were running from Tice. The other baby was born in a Indian hunting came. The Indians tested it to see if it would be brave. The little feller cried, and it was killed also.

"Paw," asked Crockett, "how did she get away from the Indians?"

Jonas explained that they left her in camp by herself after awhile. She had a dream about running off. Something about two trails in the woods, a bird flew down on a certain trail. It was like God telling her the direction to run.

She got up and after the Indians went out to do their mischief, she quietly slipped away. The story goes that she came up on the two trails at a fork. She did not know the best one to follow. As she stood there looking, a bird flew down on the left trail. She remembered the dream, the decision was made by that little bird. She ran for several days and came up on the Big Sandy River. Low and behold, there was Tice Harmon's hunting camp. Ole Tice thought she was an Indian because she wore buck skins and had a deep tan from the sun. Finally he took her under his protection and they headed for the safer country, now Tazewell County.

Crockett sat there with his big gray eyes shining. He enjoyed each and every word of the Jenny Wiley story.

"Paw are there any Indians around here any more," asked Crockett.

"No son, they are few and far between," answered Jonas.

"Most of them are out in the western areas of this country, you remember about the trail of tears grand paw Hezekiah told you about don't you," asked Jonas.

"Was Jackson a bad president," asked Crockett?

Jonas explained that in some ways he was. A lot of folks didn't agree with him, when he rounded up all the Indians he could, and marched them to the west. One reason he done that, I heard was the discovery of gold in northern Georgia. The White men wanted the Indian lands to get the gold.

"Paw that is awful," exclaimed Crockett.

"I guess it is," answered Jonas.

"We better get ready for bed, did you put the feed bags on the mules for a while son?" Jonas asked.

"Yes I did, I took them off right after supper," Crockett said, "the mules and Jake are just enjoying the new green grass now."

"Good," said Jonas, "now I want you to lay that shotgun close to your bed so you can get it in a hurry."

"Paw do you think some bad men will attack us tonight?" asked a serious Crockett.

"No son I doubt it, but we must be ready just in case," answered Jonas.

"Now go to sleep and have a good dream," Jonas added.

"I might dream about Jenny finding her trail with the help of that bird, that God sent her," answered Crockett.

"Good night son, and don't forget to talk to God," Jonas said.

"He deserves our thanks and praise; and ask Him to look over us while we sleep," added Jonas.

"I will Paw, and good night to you, Oh! I might dream about Virginia too," said Crockett.

CHAPTER 18

KENTUCKY BORDER

Next morning Jonas woke up first. He scanned the area to make sure everything was as it should be. He put some kindling on the fire, and a piece or two of fire wood. He went up into the woods to relieve himself. He noticed that he had an audience, of squirrels, chip monks, birds and a young deer. Jonas thought to himself, How wonderful, God has made things. I would have loved to have seen the Garden of Eden!

Crockett pulls the big quilt up under his chin, and peers out at the new morning.

"You going to sleep all day," asked Jonas?

"Well Paw, it does feel good laying here in my warm bed," answered Crockett.

"Get up son, it's not too cool once you get your clothes on; I got the fire fixed up," said Jonas.

Crockett crawled out and yanked on his britches.

He looked around, and smiled, "looks to be a fine day," he exclaimed.

"Yes it does," said Jonas.

The mules and Jake were all in sight, and still grazing on the new spring grass.

The Whitts eat a hurried breakfast, and broke camp. In a short time they were moving down the pike towards Kentucky.

Jonas wanted to make good time today if the road would permit it. The last few days the mushy, rutty road slowed progress.

As they rode along Jonas started a conversation.

"Well did you have that dream last night?" asked Jonas.

"I don't know Paw," asked Crockett?

"Seems like I did but can't remember it," Crockett said.

"I do that sometimes," answered Jonas," I had a dream last night."

"What was it about?" asked Crockett.

"I dreamed we were in Kentucky, up on the Big White Oak Creek, and we were there building the mill, and Indians were sulking about watching us," Jonas said.

"Indians Paw, thought you said the Indians were gone," exclaimed Crockett.

"Well son it is a dream, not real," Jonas said.

"Do you want to hear it or not?" Jonas asked.

"Sorry Paw, yes I do," answered Crockett.

Jonas went on with the dream, explaining that he asked the Truitt's about the Indians. They said don't worry, they are just spirits. Spirits, I ask, what does it mean. The Truitt's said that once up on a time the Indians hunted and fished there on the farm. Now sometimes we see their spirits watching over the land.

"Was it scary?" asked Crockett.

"No it seemed peaceful," answered Jonas.

"Then I met a woman, she was young and beautiful, well I have to say she turned my head, ain't this a weird dream," asked Jonas?

"What else happened in your dream?" asked Crockett."I dreamed that you and me and some other folks dug a trace off the creek and built an under shot grist mill, it was working beautifully," said Jonas.

"Mister Truitt was so happy, he gave us a bonus of a piece of his land." Jonas continued.

"What does it all mean Paw?" asked Crockett.

"Probably nothing, it was just a dream," answered Jonas.

"Sometimes we just dream up a mess of stuff," Jonas said.

"There is no Indian Spirits lurking around, nor is there a young woman that would notice me," Jonas explained.

"Your Maw is the love of my life, I don't expect to settle down with another woman, especially a young one," added Jonas.

"I guess I ate too many bass," said Jonas.

Crockett, laughed!

"They were fun to catch, wasn't they Paw?" asked Crockett.

"Fun to catch and good to eat," Jonas said, "the good Lord provides for his children.

The morning passed quickly, and for once they made good time. The mules had a much easier pull in this rocky stretch of road. There were still patches of soft ground, but the going was better.

They passed the debris that Jonas seen yesterday, and the road improved. Jonas was really pleased to be making better time. He told Crockett that in another day they should be in Kentucky.

"That will be great Paw," exclaimed Crockett.

"How far do you think it will be to Floyd County where Uncle John lives?" asked Crockett.

"I think we can be there in less then two weeks, maybe in around a week," answered Jonas.

"It just depends on how many miles we cover each day; I still don't want to over work the mules," he replied.

"I think this is the most distance we have traveled in one day," said Jonas.

"It is about 6:00 PM, so lets look for a night camp," Jonas said.

Crockett saw a rock house (over hanging rocks) up ahead.

"What about there?" Crockett said, as he pointed to the rock house.

"Pull up there Paw?" Crockett asked.

"Yelp, It will be alright, I reckon," replied Jonas.

"Not much grazing here but other wise it should serve us for the night." Jonas added.

Crockett headed the wagon up on the hill close to the out crop of rock. He set the brake and they both got down while looking the area over. Jonas was looking at two things, shelter and a place for defense if it was needed. They had not seen any one coming or going since they left the James Thompson farm.

"Tomorrow I think we will be heading around Grapevine Mountain," replied Jonas.

"That is where some folks have been waylaid," Jonas said, "I don't want you to be scared, but be ready for any trouble that may come our way."

"Don't worry Paw, I am ready, if any outlaws show up, this old shotgun has become my best buddy," Crockett said.

"Well son, that is good; I am going to saddle up Jake and take a little ride up the road a piece," said Jonas.

"Go ahead and start setting us up for the night," instructed Jonas.

"Oh! and be careful raking around under that rock house, Rattlers are probably waking up from the winter," Jonas cautioned.

"That is good to know Paw," replied Crockett.

Jonas was on Jake and trotting down the road in short order. That is a great saddle horse, Crockett thought. Crockett admired Jakes beautiful gait.

Crockett got a stick about five feet long and headed to the rock house. He cautiously raked back the leaves from under the over hanging rock. He over turned anything that might be hiding a creepy crawler. After he was satisfied that there were nothing sleeping in his intended bed, he cleared out a spot for a fire in front of the rock house.

Next Crockett took care of the team. He unhitched them and took them down to the river for a drink. Then gave them their feed bags with a nice portion of oats and some shelled corn.

Then Crockett unloaded the things that they would need for the night, always keeping the old scatter gun handy. He gathered kindling and fire wood for the camp fire. He lit the fire and put on some coffee.

It wasn't long before Jonas was riding back into camp.

Crockett seen him from a distance and recognized him instantly. He threw up his hand and Jonas answered by doing the same. Jonas took Jake to the river and let him drink. Then he led him up the hill and let him have his feed bag.

Jonas had a serious look on his face, so Crockett asked, "what is it paw?"

"I seen another place that looks like some folks were robbed, furniture busted up, clothes scattered around," Jonas said.

"It looked like at least three sets of tracks," replied stated.

"What are you thinking Paw, "asked Crockett?

"Well I think we start taking turns staying on watch, and even in camp," commanded Jonas.

"One working and one holding a gun," Jonas said, "it may not be necessary but I ain't taking no chances."

"Well that will keep any outlaws from catching us off guard," answered Crockett.

"Better to be safe than sorry, you sit over there with your gun, and I will fix supper," said Jonas.

"Alright Paw, I will watch closely, no one will sneak up on us," affirmed Crockett.

Jonas rustled up some supper while Crockett sat and watched in a panoramic motion. Jonas could tell that Crockett was taking him seriously about potential danger, and was proud of him. Jonas filled both tin plates and moved over to sit with Crockett and eat.

While eating, Jonas struck up a conservation with Crockett.

"Didn't find any thing under the rock house that we would mind sleeping with did you?" asked Jonas.

"No Paw, I looked real close, and found nothing under there to be alarmed about," replied Crockett.

"Well son it pays to be sure about everything in this world, you are learning that aren't you," asked Jonas.

"Yes Paw, just like you say, better safe then sorry, I don't intend to let no bad men get a jump on us," Crockett said.

"Do you want me to take the first watch tonight?" Crockett asked?

"Why don't you hobble the horse and mules and stretch your legs, I have my pistol on," replied Jonas.

"Paw, I was thinking, reckon we should tie them up close to us, some one might try to steal them!" exclaimed Crockett.

Jonas leaned over and scratched his head.

"Son you have a point, stretch a line between those two trees and tie them up," Jonas said.

"Crockett refill their feed bags, since they can't graze tonight," added Jonas.

Crockett smiled proudly, Paw is taking my advice, he thought. I must be growing up.

And for no apparent reason as Crockett got up to tie the animals, he thought of Virginia and her beautiful shiny black eyes. That girl sure did impress me he thought.

Jonas asked in a urgent voice, "what are you doing?"

"Are you day dreaming again?" asked Jonas.

"Well I guess I was Paw, I will get them fixed up," answered Crockett.

By now it was starting to get dark, Crockett finished up with the animals and came back to sit by Jonas. They sat and talked for about an hour about one thing then another. They talked about their trip, about being ready for trouble if it came. They talked about Greenup County and the work that lay ahead. They talked about the loved ones left behind. They even talked about Hezekiah and Rachel. Then Jonas gave Crockett his orders for the night.

"Here son, you hold on to my watch, and when it gets midnight you get me up," Jonas instructed.

"You have never let me use your watch before, I will be real careful with it, and I will wake you up at exactly midnight," Crockett responded.

"Crockett you are practically a man I can trust you with a watch or even my life," answered Jonas.

Crockett's heart swelled with pride that his paw trusted him this much. Jonas smiled as he crawled into his quilts under the rock house.

"See you at midnight son," said Jonas.

"Sleep good Paw, and I will be a good watch," said Crockett.

Crockett kept the fire and stayed vigilant. He would get up and take little walks around the camp, but was real quiet not to wake Jonas. He thought about the adventure he was on, and wondered what lay ahead. We might get to the Kentucky border tomorrow or next day for sure, he thought. I will be glad to get away from this troublesome area, he reflected. Time went fast, and before he knew it was 12:05 midnight.

Crockett went over close to where Jonas slept.

"Paw, Paw, are you ready to get up?" Crockett asked.

"What is it son, is anything wrong, is it midnight?" asked the drowsy Jonas.

"Yes Paw it is midnight, I got you some coffee on the fire," said Crockett.

"Good boy," answered Jonas.

Jonas got up and pulled on his overalls. Went out behind the wagon and took care of business. He came over and sat down by the fire and poured himself a cup of hot coffee.

"Crockett go ahead and lay down, did you notice anything out of the ordinary?" asked Jonas.

"No Paw it has been quiet except for the frogs hollering, and I heard an owl, I think," answered the sleepy boy.

Jonas laughed a little.

"Them frogs are courting, or trying to find a mate to court," Jonas exclaimed.

"They do this every year in the early spring," Jonas added.

"How long ago has it been since you heard the hoot owl?" Jonas asked.

"About two hours I would think," answered Crockett.

"Did you just hear it once?" asked Jonas.

"It hooted two or three times, but there was no answer from another direction," Crockett said.

"I know what you are asking, I am sure it was the flying kind of owl," added Crockett.

"Alright son, get you some sleep, I will watch over you," said Jonas.

"Paw," Crockett said.

"What is it son?" asked Jonas?

"Nothing, I just wanted to tell you I love you," said the sleepy Crockett.

"I love you son, now go to sleep, I will see you first light," answered Jonas.

The night passed by quickly. There was nothing going on that seemed threatening, to the two travelers. Jonas built up the fire and got some coffee brewing. Then he went over and untied the mules and Jake so they could graze for a while. There was limited grass at this camp, but the animals were glad to be free for even a short time. Crockett heard the animals and Jonas moving around and raised up.

"Time to get up Paw?" he asked.

"Yelp," answered Jonas.

"You might as well get up and get ready to head out," said Jonas.

"With good luck we will be in Kentucky today," Jonas exclaimed.

"I am ready for that," answered Crockett.

"Did any thing happen while I was asleep?" asked Crockett.

"I heard your owl, and frogs, but that was about it," Jonas answered.

"Get any sleep son?" asked Jonas.

"Think I did pretty good, but it seems like I just laid down," answered Crockett. The two eat a hurried breakfast, broke camp, and were once again moving toward the Kentucky border. It looked like rain may be heading in their direction. They laid out their slickers, and kept their guns ready with a greased raw hide hoods over the hammers. They had one Brown Betsy, the shot gun, and Jonas' revolver loaded and ready.

There was not much conversation it seemed they were both in a serious state of mind. Even the mules were glad to be back on the road for some reason.

"That mountain on the right has to be Grape Vine," said Jonas.

"Why do they call it that Paw?" asked Crockett,

"Well I don't know for sure, but I would guess it is because the road is crooked," said Jonas.

"Could be there is a lot of wild grape vines growing on it," added Jonas.

"Does the road travel up on the mountain?" asked Crockett.

"Mister Thompson told me about a trail across it, but we will follow the road by the river," said Jonas.

"It will be further but safer, only thing the outlaws have struck travelers on the road," said Jonas."

"Since we have a heavy wagon the best bet is down here, not on the little trail across the mountain," exclaimed Jonas.

"We will be fine just stay alert as to what is going on around you, I want you to glance behind us ever now and then," said Jonas.

"I will, I will look in every direction, Paw," said Crockett.

"Good idea, I have to watch the mules and the road," said Jonas.

They fell into the normal routine of travel with the exception of added vigilance. Jonas tried to act as normal as possible for Crockett's benefit, while still being very watchful.

Crockett turned to Jonas and said, "it will be alright Paw, we prayed this morning before we left."

"The Lord will watch over us won't He," asked Crockett?

"He sure will, but He also wants us to look out for trouble," replied Jonas.

Before they knew it the morning was gone and the miles were being covered in good time. They stopped only once so far to stretch and take care of the mules. Jonas stood watch while Crockett watered them as they crossed a creek that fed the Levisa.

Nothing out of the ordinary occurred. They kept the wheels on the wagon turning and before they knew it, they saw a shabby road sign ahead.

"Can you read it?" Jonas asked Crockett.

"Yes Paw, all it says is KENTUCKY," exclaimed Crockett.

"You would think it would say more than that," added Crockett.

As they got closer they also saw a sign on the other side of the road. Jonas turned around as they passed the signs.

"That one says VIRGINIA, I don't know what I was expecting, but I feel disappointed!" exclaimed Crockett.

"At least they have a sign," said Jonas.

The two kept moving and being very watchful. They eat leftovers as they traveled. Jonas was anxious to get out of this area. It was almost like wilderness. They had not passed one wagon or even a traveler since they left the Thompson's.

Crockett kept watching round about! Something caught his eyes up ahead in the edge of the woods. The sun shown into the woods and a bright but small object sent a glimmer of warning to Crockett.

"Paw, I see something shinny up ahead in the woods, I think it might be a gun, whispered Crockett.

Jonas strained his eyes and saw the same thing.

"Whoa," Jonas commanded the mules.

The mules stopped, almost in their tracks.

"Crockett get that scatter gun up and point it towards them," said Jonas.

Crockett raised the gun and held it at waist level. Jonas brought out the 44 revolver and laid it between him and Crockett.

Jonas took a quick survey of the entire area, even behind them. Seeing nothing, he turned back toward the thing in the woods.

After a minute, which seemed much longer, Jonas hollered toward the woods!

"Whoever you are, come out and be recognized," yelled Jonas.

A man carrying a rifle rode out on a rough looking horse. He also looked rough. He had an untrimmed beard, and his hair was long and shaggy. He wore a slouch hat that had seen better days. His clothes were filthy buckskins, but the barrel on his gun was shining in the sun.

"Hello stranger," he shouted.

Jonas hollered again, "what is your business, why were you hiding in the woods?"

The man rode closer and answered," I am a trapper, I have been out checking my traps."

"Hold it right there, don't come any closer," commanded Jonas.

The rider stopped and glared at Jonas and Crockett.

Jonas gave instructions in a loud voice, "You turn that horse around and get away from us."

"If we see you again we will shoot first and ask questions later," yelled Jonas.

The man glared once again, then wheeled his mount around slowly. He was in no hurry to get out of sight. Instead of heading back into the woods he went toward the river.

Jonas and Crockett sat and watched the man slowly cross the Levisa and head up into the woods on the other side.

Jonas started the mules pulling the wagon again. They moved at a slow pace, and watched vigilantly all around.

"Paw, do you think he is gone away?" asked Crockett.

"It appears that way, but beware of trouble ahead, and behind," answered Jonas.

"That jasper may cross back behind us, and he could have help waiting ahead of us," said Jonas in a low voice.

Crockett's heart was pumping very fast as adrenaline filled his being. He was looking in all directions with a renewed sense of apprehension.

As they moved down the road, Crockett asked Jonas, "why are we going so slow?"

"Don't we want to get away from here?" asked Crockett.

"We are better off moving slowly, we don't want to panic and run into an ambush ahead," replied Jonas.

"Plus we look like we ain't scared of anything, just sit up straight and look like you ain't afraid of anything." Jonas instructed.

Crockett straightened, and casually looked around.

"That's it," affirmed Jonas.

"By the way your keen eyes may have saved us back there, I did not see that feller up in the woods," Jones exclaimed.

"Thanks Paw, I am trying to spy anything else that may be a danger,"

Crockett said.

Up ahead the woods came down to the road on both sides. It looked like a likely spot to be jumped. The wagon moved even slower. Jonas and Crockett strained their eyes to see any thing that may be lurking in the woods. Nothing could be seen, not even a bird.

"Something is not right, not even a bird can be seen," said Jonas.

"What do you mean by that?" asked Crockett.

"No birds or animals means their could be a man is hiding there," answered Jonas.

"Raise the scatter gun a little higher, if someone is there I want them to consider, that we are ready for them," whispered Jonas.

Crockett raised the barrel of the shot gun in a menacing manner.

Jonas also turned and reached under the canvas cover on the wagon and pulled out the old Brown Betsy. He stuck it between him and Crockett. He also kept the revolver handy with the holster cover unlatched. The wagon continued to move slowly toward the area that looked to be a danger spot.

Jonas prayed in a low voice; "Lord be with us as we go through the valley of the shadow of death. Protect me and my boy from the pestilence, and the destruction that wasteth at noonday! Be our fortress and refuge, We trust you Lord that no evil befall us, Praise be the Name of Jesus" "Amen!"

Crockett answered with ,"Amen!"

As the wagon moved into the narrow place, two riders came around the bend and rode casually toward the Whitts.

They look much better than the rider that they encountered earlier. When they got within twenty five yards, Jonas stopped them with a shout.

"Hold it right there," he said, as he held the cocked revolver toward them.

The riders stopped quickly and one of them spoke up.

"Sir, put down that gun, we mean you no harm!"

Crockett turned and looked back down the road.

"Paw," whispered Crockett, "that other jasper is back there watching, he is just sitting his horse there about two hundred yards back," whispered Crockett.

Jonas answered the rider that had spoken, "what is your business, where are you going?"

Then Jonas answered Crockett in a whisper, "keep an eye on him son, if he starts closing in on us let me know."

The riders kept their distance, while trying to figure out Jonas and Crockett. They begin to whisper.

Jonas hollered at them, "stop whispering, who are you?"

"We are on our way home, we been out visiting our sick Maw," one man answered.

"I am Isaac Fleming and this is my brother Sean," he said.

"Where do you fellers live?" asked Jonas. "We live across the mountain and up the Russell fork some folks call it Holly Creek, it feeds the Russell," said the one calling himself Isaac.

"Well then where is your sick Maw," asked Jonas.

"Down the river from here and up John's Creek," said Isaac.

"We used to live there with them, but decided we liked it over in Virginia better," he added.

"Sir I promise on the Bible, we mean you no harm," exclaimed Isaac.

"Crockett is that feller still back of us?" asked Jonas.

"Yes, but he is riding away from us now, I think he saw these other fellers and thinks they are with us," Crockett said in a whisper.

Jonas hollered again at the men he was holding at bay.

"How is your Maw doing?" Jonas asked.

"She is a tolerable, but has had a bad winter," answered the one rider calling himself Isaac.

"Alright come on ahead, but slow," Jonas said, "if either one of you make a false move, you will be paid in lead."

Jonas also said in a loud voice, "Crockett shoot to kill if they mean us any harm!"

Crockett said, "I will," in his heaviest voice.

The riders came on at a slow pace, watching Jonas and Crockett's every move.

Jonas and Crockett kept them covered with the scatter gun and revolver.

When the riders got within ten yards, Jonas hollered again.

"Hold it right there, Isaac you come on and Sean you wait," he commanded.

"Alright mister," Isaac answered.

The first rider came on by the wagon and moved on down the trail.

Then Jonas said, "Sean come on and don't try anything."

Sean nodded and rode forward.

Crockett kept Isaac covered with the shot gun, and Jonas held the pistol on Sean.

Sean passed Jonas and moved on toward his brother.

Jonas hollered back at them, "You Fleming boys keep on riding and don't look back; sorry to treat you this way, but we can't take a chance."

Isaac hollered back, "no problem, I don't blame you."

"Who are you fellers?" Isaac asked.

Jonas answered, "we are the Whitts Jonas and Crockett, take care there is a shady looking man up ahead of you," Jonas warned.

"We seen him," said Isaac.

"You be careful too," replied Isaac as they rode down the turnpike.

"Shooo weee," exclaimed Crockett," I am glad that is over."

"Me too," said Jonas.

"You did real good son, but we ain't out of the woods yet, just keep an eye out for trouble," exclaimed Jonas.

"I will," answered Crockett.

"I wonder how far it is to Uncle John's house in Floyd," asked Crockett?

"We just barely got into Kentucky and you are wondering how far to John's house," said Jonas.

"I would say another week or so," Jonas said patiently.

Jonas got the mules moving again and they were making good time. Crockett kept an eye out for trouble, looking in all directions, especially in the rear. He was afraid that some of the men may try to sneak up on them from the rear. That first encounter, the trapper, never was resolved. Crockett and Jonas both thought he was an outlaw.

The rest of the day was without incident! They calmed down and enjoyed the next few miles.

Jonas led in a prayer of Thanksgiving for the Lords protection. They both said amen together.

As the day wore on a chill filled the air! Crockett shivered, and dug under the wagon cover for their coats.

"Paw, ain't this about the ninth of April," Crockett said," It feels like Febuary this evening!"

"Yes it is the ninth, the best I can recollect," said Jonas.

"There is some winter still left in the air, I think we better start looking for a good place to camp," Jonas said.

"Paw is Kentucky a colder place than Tazewell County, or is this just a late cold spell," Crockett asked?

Jonas explained that it is about the same, the elevation in parts of Kentucky is much lower than Tazewell County, so it should be alittle warmer.

"But according to the feeling this evening, I have to wonder," Jonas said.

"I have seen late weather like this before, but it never lasts for any time," added Jonas.

"Good Grief," exclaimed Crockett," It is starting to snow!"

"I see it," said Jonas.

"I see what looks like a good rock house up ahead," said Jonas.

"I am going to check it out," added Jonas.

"Who knows we may have some real weather tonight," Jonas said.

They pulled up on the hill and locked the brake on the wagon. It was a large rock house, almost a cave.

"Crockett, you go and check for creepie crawlers, and I will start getting us some fire wood, before everything gets wet," instructed Jonas.

Crockett got himself a sturdy stick and raked the leaves around under the rock house. Then he cleared out a large area in front to make a place for a fire. Then he gathered some stones to circle the camp fire. By then Jonas came back carrying fire wood.

Crockett got his fire building stuff and lit a fire. Jonas began to unhitch the team and Jake his saddle horse. The snow began to pour.

"Can you believe this snow?" asked Crockett.

"Well I have seen a late snow like this a time or two, but it is highly unusual," Jonas answered.

"We need to get everything that we need for the night and put it in the dry," said Jonas!

"Crockett, you go ahead setting up camp, I am going to take the mules and Jake to water," Jonas said.

"I think we can tie them up over here on the left of the rock house," Jonas said, "the cliff will keep most of the snow off them!"

When Jonas led the animals back up the hill, Crockett had a good fire going. And had drug out the quilts, pots and pans and other items needed for the night.

"Good job," replied Jonas!

Crockett looked at Jonas and the animals, and burst out laughing!

"What is so funny," asked Jonas?

"You look like a snow man! And the mules look like snow mules, and poor Jake is covered too," answered Crockett.

Jonas chuckled a little!

"I guess we do look funny," Jonas replied.

"It is a wet snow, and is really coming down, hopefully it will be gone soon," replied Jonas.

Crockett had some salt bacon frying and a pot of coffee brewing in short order. Jonas strung a line to tie the animals for the night. Then he filled their feed bags with oats and corn and put them on each animal. It was a pleasure to see them enjoy their supper.

Jonas was thinking about the days events, and told Crockett, "I don't think anyone will try any thing tonight, I think we can both get a good nights sleep.""

That will be great, Paw, I am wore plumb out," replied Crockett.

"Me too, after supper we can get into some warm quilts. But I want you to keep your shotgun handy, just the same," answered Jonas.

"Me and this pistol are getting to be pretty good sleeping buddies," said Jonas.

"I know what you mean Paw," exclaimed Crockett.

"This shotgun thinks it is another one of my arms or legs," Crockett said.

Jonas chuckled!

"We must stay prepared for trouble if it comes, so far we have done well," said Jonas.

The next morning Jonas and Crockett awoke to a winter wonderland. A big six inch wet snow had fallen and hung on every little branch. Jonas crawled out of his warm bed and started putting wood on the little fire. Crockett peeped out from under his pile of quilts.

"Wow look at that snow, Paw!" exclaimed Crockett!

"I know," said Jonas, "isn't it beautiful?"

"It surely is," replied Crockett.

"Reckon we will get to travel today Paw?" Crockett asked.

"Well we will get a late start, if we do," Jonas replied.

About that time, Jonas saw two big squirrels fighting about fifteen yards away. They were either fighting over a nut or maybe territory. Jonas nodded to Crockett, as if to say, here's breakfast. Crockett raised the old scatter gun slowly and unloaded on the two unsuspecting squirrels.

"Good shot," said Jonas as he went over to get the provided meal.

He picked them up and waded back trying to step in the same tracks.

Jake whinnied, in protest at the commotion.

"It's alright boy," Jonas said to his beloved saddle horse.

Jake settled down, after hearing Jonas speak.

Crockett got his clothes and brogans pulled on and took the squirrels.

"I will get them skinned out in about two shakes of a dogs tail," said Crockett.

Jonas laughed, "We ain't got no dog!"

Crockett gave him a little grin and went to work on the furry critters.

Jonas got the fire ready for cooking by raking out some coals to the side. He got the coffee pot on and the skillet ready with some good hog lard melting.

They were really hungry and devoured every eatable piece of the meat. After a second cup of coffee, Jonas took himself a chew from his plug.

The snow was already melting as the sun climbed into the Kentucky sky.

"Looks like it will leave us soon, but I am afraid it will be sloppy the next few days," said Jonas.

"First April snow I ever saw," exclaimed Crockett.

CHAPTER 19

FOLLOW THE LEVISA
TO PRESTONSBURG

The wagon is rolling again, but not very fast! Jonas and Crockett are still being careful, watching for potential trouble from outlaws.

The snow is gone but the mud is still a problem.

They start passing a farm here and there, and this makes them feel much more at ease.

The weather is more like April now with some much wanted sunshine.

As they ride along Crockett asked questions as usual.

"Paw, what county are we in?" Crockett asked.

"Pike County," answered Jonas.

"Wonder how it got named?" asked Crockett?

"I heard someone say it was named after General Zebulon Pike," answered Jonas.

"Is it a big county, Paw?" Crockett asked?

"Yes it is, and mostly mountains, it is different than most of the rolling hills of central Kentucky," answered Jonas.

"Well Paw, I have not seen many places that would make a good farm," Crockett said.

"The ground is good, but not much flat land, I guess someday the timber and minerals will be a big thing for Pike County," Jonas said.

"What about a court house?" asked Crockett. "Piketon is the county seat, so that is where it is some folks call it pikeville," replied Jonas.

"Will it be a big city, Paw?" Crockett asked.

"I think it may be about like Jeffersonville, but I really don't know," answered Jonas.

"Don't you ever run out of questions?" asked Jonas?

"Well Paw, if I don't ask how will I find out stuff," answered Crockett.

"I guess that is right," replied Jonas.

"Paw, does Uncle John Bunyon live in Pike County?" Crockett asked.

"No he lives in Floyd County, not too far from Prestonsburg," Jonas said.

"When will we get there?" asked Crockett.

"I don't know," said Jonas.

"It depends on how far we go each day," Jonas added.

"Paw, look here comes a rider, and he is making purty good time," Crockett said.

"I see him, hold to your gun; I don't think it is trouble this time," answered Jonas.

The rider slowed up as he approached the Whitts.

The rider raised his hand as a friendly gesture.

Jonas waved back, but kept a keen eye on the traveler.

The rider was the first to speak as he stoped by the wagon.

"Have no fear, I am the post rider," he said.

"I got a load of mail to get delivered," He said."

"Where you fellers hail from?" he asked in the same breath.

Jonas spoke up after noticing the bags marked with U.S.

"We are the Whitts from Tazewell County Virginia I am Jonas Whitt," Jonas said.

"What is your name?" asked Jonas.

"Silas, Silas Johnson, that is what they call me," he said.

"I deliver the mail from Piketon toward the Virginia line," Silas said.

"Where you fellers headed?" asked Silas the Post rider?

"We are going to stop and see my brother up close to Prestonsburg, but then we aim to go to Greenup County to do some Mill work," answered Jonas.

"Who might your brother be?" asked the Silas.

"My brother is John Bunyon Whitt, he lives out on a creek called Right Beaver," answered Jonas.

"My Lord, is he a big strong feller?" asked the Post rider.

"Yes he is a big man, a Carpenter by trade," replied Jonas.

"I met him once, and have heard many stories about him," exclaimed Silas.

"What kind of stories?" asked Jonas.

"Nothing bad, but stories of his strength," Silas said," he don't take nothing off no body, I heard."

"I heard that six fellers attacked him and after the donny brook was over, only one man was standing, and that was Big John Bunyon Whitt," related Silas.

"I even heard about a bear getting a hold of him and John whipped the bear, don't know how true that story is, but it is fun to tell," said Silas the Post rider.

"Have you ever been over on Right Beaver Creek?" asked Jonas.

"I been in that vicinity, but don't know the place John lives on," said Silas.

Jonas asked Silas the distance to Pikeville?

"I figure another two days pulling that wagon," replied Silas the Post rider.

"I would love to talk longer, but I got to get moving." said the Post rider.

"Well alright, we need to do the same thing," answered Jonas.

"Jonas Whitt, you and your boy have a good trip," Silas said in parting.

"Alright Silas Johnson, you be careful, and it was good meeting you," replied Jonas.

Crockett spoke up, "good meeting you Mister Johnson, my name is Crockett."

The Post Rider smiled and nodded to Crockett, and rode away.

"Well there is your answer," replied Jonas to Crockett, "about two more days to Pikeville."

"I would guess another week or so after that to Prestonsburg," Jonas said.

"One thing about it, we know people live in Kentucky now," said Jonas.

Now Jonas and Crockett could relax a little bit. As they traveled along they began passing more homesteads, and even more travelers.

Instead of camping out in to open, some nights they were welcomed to stay in folks barns. One such time they had to leave before they could settle down. The barn was owned by a woman that had two other women living with her. When Jonas and Crockett stopped and ask if they could spend the night in their barn, they had no idea what would happen.

Jonas and Crockett unhitched the team and started to get ready for a night of rest. Next thing they knew the woman came out parading around almost naked.

"Oh my, What are you doing?" asked a befuzzled Jonas.

"Can't you see I have a child here?" asked Jonas.

One of the women curtsies, and says; "I will make a man out of him!"

Another woman was rubbing herself all over Jonas!

"Get away Jezebel!" Jonas said in a loud stern voice.

"Crockett, hitch up the team, we ain't staying here," shouted Jonas.

The sinful harlots still followed them around even when the wagon was pulling out.

"Paw I ain't never seen women like that," said Crockett.

"Me neither," replied Jonas.

"Paw that one women exposed her breast to us," whispered Crockett.

"Just put it out of your mind, we will find another place to camp," said Jonas.

"The Bible says to run from such women and that is what we are doing," added Jonas.

Fortunately there was another farm about a mile down the road.

Jonas pulled the wagon in and a man came out to meet them.

"Sir would you mind if me and the boy slept in your barn tonight?" asked Jonas.

"Who are you," asked the man?

"Jonas Whitt from Tazewell County and this is my son Crockett," answered Jonas.

"We are traveling to Greenup County, and need a place to sleep," said Jonas.

"My name is Arthur Parker," the man replied and walked over and shook hands with the Whitts.

"You are welcome to spend the night here in my barn, and do you need anything else?" asked Arthur.

"No sir," replied Jonas.

"I will build a little cooking fire outside your barn if that would be alright?" Jonas added.

"No that is not alright," answered Arthur.

"My wife has a big pot of beans and some cornbread," Arthur said, "you all come on in and eat at the table."

"Sir we don't want to impose, but that sure sounds good," replied Jonas.

"No imposition," said Arthur.

"This is awfully nice of you Arthur," Jonas said as he sat down at the family table.

"We are glad to share with folks when we have it to share," said Arthur.

"The beans are still hot and smell so good," said Jonas.

"This is my kind of meal," Crockett said.

As Jonas and Crockett enjoyed their beans, thay began a conversation with the Parkers. They talked about this and that. Finally the subject of the three women up the road came up.

"They are pure trash," said Mrs. Parker.

"It is good that you didn't stop there," she said.

"Well we did stop there, but were on the run in short order," announced Jonas.

Arthur, snickered.

Mrs. Parker said," it ain't funny, it is a disgrace."

"Them Huzzies have tried to lure my man over there," she added.

Arthur was more serious now!

"What did they do Jonas?" ask Arthur.

"They tried to, you know, seduce me and even the boy, we got out of there as fast as we could," replied Jonas.

"Even the mules got confused," said Crockett, "hitch, unhitch, hitch, unhitch."

"The mules were wondering if they were coming or going," Jonas added.

Arthur couldn't help but laugh!

"Well they can get a good rest in the barn with you fellers," replied Arthur.

The Whitts thanked the Parkers and were on the road early.

About 2:30 PM, the next day the Whitts wound along the river and see Piketon.

"Paw, I think this must be Piketon," announced Crockett.

"It's the most buildings I have seen since we left Jeffersonville," added Crockett.

"Yelp I think you are right," answered Jonas.

"It sure is cramed down in between the mountains," added Jonas.

"We better watch our step, I hear it is a wild town," Jonas said.

"There is a lot of people in town today, wonder if something is going on?" asked Crockett.

"Something is sure enough going on," surmised Jonas.

"There can't be this many folks that live in town," Crockett said.

"This might be Saturday," said Jonas.

Jonas explained that little towns like this some times fill up on Saturday. Folks come into town to shop, take care of business, or just come in looking for something to do.

"Paw did you notice about every man has a pistol strapped on?" asked Crockett.

"Yes I did, son, something is going on," answered Jonas.

"Drive the team up over there, we can go into the mercantile and pick up a few possibles," said Jonas.

"I am getting a little low on coffee and chew-bacca, any thing else we need?" asked Jonas.

"Don't know of anything Paw," Crockett answered.

"We might find out what is going on," said Jonas.

Crockett pulled off the road and got down. He walked to the front of the team and tied the mules to a hitching rail. Crockett followed Jonas into the store.

A lot of folks were standing around talking, not really shopping.

The merchant walked up to Jonas and Crockett.

"Sir may I help you?" he asked.

"Yes sir we need some coffee, and a couple plugs of chewing, and may be a few other things," Jonas answered.

"My name is Ebenezer Franklin, I run this little store," said the store keeper.

"I don't remember you all, are you traveling through," asked Ebenezer?

"I am Jonas Whitt, this here is Crockett, we are on our way to Greenup county," said Jonas.

"By the way Ebenezer, what is going on in your fair city," asked Jonas.

"Jonas, glad to meet you and young Crockett, we have a hanging here today in about an hour," said Ebenezer.

Crockett looked at his Paw, and back at Ebenezer.

"You haven't heard, have you?" asked Ebenezer.

Jonas nodded his head and said, "No sir, who is doing it, the County?"

"Our district judge ordered it and we have a hangman from Lexington here to handle it," replied Ebenezer as he set a bag of coffee on the counter.

"How many are they hanging?" asked Jonas.

Ebenezer explained, "Will Lewis and John Lewis were convicted of rape and murder, and stealing two horses. They found Mrs. Sally Belcher alone in her cabin over on Tom's creek. They had their way with her then they robbed her, and killed her with a butcher knife. That weren't enough they stole their fine riding horses."

"Poor old Tom came home to find the mess and his missus all cut up, she was able to tell him who done it, afore she passed," Ebenezer stated.

"Tom Belcher went to a neighbor and had them to fetch the high sheriff, that all happened about a year ago, and now is the day them Lewis boys pay their due," said Ebenezer.

Ebenezer explained, that is why so many folks are here today. If you and the boy want to see it, it will be in the court yard beside the court house. They have a nice big gallows built up and benches set up for the folks to sit on.

"Jonas I got your coffee, and tobacco, what else can I get you?" asked Ebenezer.

"Do you have any fresh eggs, and good country ham?" asked Jonas.

"Eggs are just starting to come in again, I got a dozen, they are a mite high though," said Ebenezer.

"How high are they Ebenezer?" asked Jonas?.

"Well since I am going to close in a few minutes, I will let them go for fifteen cents," he said.

"That is high, but I will take them, we haven't had an egg since last fall sometime," replied Jonas.

"How much ham do you want?" asked Ebenezer.

"About two pounds I reckon," replied Jonas.

"Anything else I can get you Jonas?" he asked. "Not that I can think of," said Jonas.

As Ebenezer got the eggs and ham he also got a piece of whorehound candy out of a jar and handed it to Crockett.

"Thank you," Crockett said with a grin.

"Welcome son," he answered. "I got to get these folks out of here so I can go watch the hanging," said Ebenezer.

Ebenezer turned around and spoke with a loud firm voice, "I am closing the store for now, everybody is going to have to leave."

People shuffled around and headed for the door.

Ebenezer took care of the Whitt order and escorted them to the door, then he turned the key and locked it.

"Jonas, it was nice serving you, will see you at the courthouse," he asked.

"We might be there, where is it any way?" asked Jonas.

"Just follow the crowd about a block and a half down the street," he answered.

"Thanks and nice meeting you," Jonas said.

Jonas and Crockett walked toward the wagon, Crockett slurping on his candy.

"What do you think, Crockett, do you want to witness this execution?" asked Jonas.

Crockett looked a little doubtful.

"Let me warn you it will not be pleasant watching them fellowers die, you will remember it for the rest of your life," added Jonas.

"Paw, do you think I can stand it?" asked Crockett.

"Well I do think you are man enough to stand it," said Jonas.

Jonas explained that it is part of our world to punish bad men, and it will be a learning experience for you.

The whole street was full of people gathering for the hanging. No wagons or even riders on horse back were moving.

Everyone was walking! The talking of so many people created a great roar.

Jonas pulled out his watch, and gave it a good look.

"It is suppose to happen in about fifteen minutes, we better get up there," said Jonas.

They started to walk down the crowded street, to find a place to view this awful, but just thing!

Finally Jonas and Crockett found a place to stand behind the seated people.

The Sheriff went up on the gallows and shouted out, "Quiet, Quiet!"

The Sheriff said, "this is an official execution, and there will be no talking or jesters."

"In about five minutes the deputies will bring out the Lewis brothers for their execution, I better not hear a word from any of you or you will spend a night in jail," yelled the Sheriff.

Next thing, the court house door opened, and out came the Lewis brothers. Each had a law man holding them on each side.

They were followed by a minister who kept quoting scripture. In front of them the hangman led. The hangman was dressed in black and wore a tall black hat. The deputies were wearing gray uniforms, and the minister was also wearing black. They all walked slowly toward the awaiting gallows.

Tom Belcher and the rest of the kin from his and her family were seated on the front row. The Lewis brothers were paraded right in front of Tom and up the steps to the gallows. Will, and John Lewis were escorted to the swing a way doors on the floor of the gallows.

Next the Hangman applied the noose first on Will then on John. He pulled the noose tight on each of them. Their faces showed such dread, such as Crockett had never seen.

Next the Hangman asked if either one of them wanted to say anything before they were hanged?

Will was crying and praying at the same time, John said, "shut up" to his brother.

"Die like a man!" John said.

Next Will Lewis spoke again, as he looked down at the sad family, Tom Belcher, and the rest.

"Mister Belcher, I am sorry, please forgive me," Will Lewis pleaded!

Finally John Lewis spoke in a heafty voice, "Tom Belcher, Sorry for what I done!"

The Sheriff read the sentence, and the minister prayed for the two Lewis men and for the Belcher family.

The Hangman walked up and put a sack over both of their heads, stepped back, and before anyone could expect it he pulled a lever and the two men were jolted into eternity.

A mournful sound rose from the spectators. It was nothing fun to see. At that moment the entire crowd wished they were some place else.

Jonas looked at Crockett. He had his head bowed down praying.

Jonas spoke in a low voice, "You alright?"

"Yes Paw, I don't ever want to see any one else killed," Crockett said!

"Let's get out of this place, we can get out of town, and get some distance before night," said Jonas.

"Good idea Paw," Crockett said," I just as soon forget what we just seen."

"I have seen it before, it is a necessary thing, and part of life," Jonas said.

"If the death sentence were abolished, I'm afraid the bad men would rule the earth," Jonas added.

"Just the same Paw, I ain't going to watch another hanging," said Crockett.

Jonas and Crockett got on the wagon and drove right through the crowd towards Prestonsburg. They got out of town about five good miles and begin to look for a place to spend the night.

"I just as soon spend the night out on the trail, don't know if we can find a farm any way," said Jonas.

"Me too, Paw, I have seen enough people for one day," answered Crockett.

That evening not much was said around the camp fire. Jonas and Crockett just did the usual things that had to be done without talking.

Just before they turned in for the night, Jonas prayed a prayer of Thanksgiving and asked for mercy on the two Lewis men and their families. He also lifted up Tom Belcher and his family. He prayed that he and Crockett would never have to see people's lives taken again.

He also prayed for traveling mercies and a good stay in the Kentucky lands.

Next morning a beautiful morning was theirs. The sun was shining and the birds were singing. The trees were a beautiful shade of green, with millions of little leaves revealing themselves to the world.

The dogwood trees decorated the hills with a warm white color. The temperature was warm with a slight breeze coming from the south.

Crockett sat up in his quilts, and said, "This is more like the Aprils I remember."

"It is one fine day son," replied Jonas.

"I hope to be at your uncle John's day after tomorrow," added Jonas.

"Well I guess I better roll out and get moving," replied Crockett.

"Yes, let's see if we can get some miles behind us today," replied Jonas.

The camp fire was blazing by now and Jonas had some ham and fried eggs cooking. The coffee and smell of fresh eggs and ham stirred their appetites.

"That smells so good," said Crockett.

"Yes it does," replied Jonas as he turned the nice big yellow eggs.

"I am fixing you three eggs and three for me!" exclaimed Jonas.

Crockett replied, "great, we can have the rest tomorrow morning."

"That is what I was thinking," replied Jonas.

"They were awful high but we only live once in this old world," Jonas said.

"It is the little things that make life good," Jonas added.

The two travelers, enjoyed their breakfast and broke camp. Even the mules were in a good mood it seemed. Jake was showing his fiesty side as Jonas tied him to the back of the wagon.

This was the best day of travel they have had on the entire trip. Weather was good, the road was in good shape, and the Kentucky hills were showing a whole "nother side" of splender.

They only stopped one time to water the animals and get out some trail food that could be eaten on the go. The two chewed on beef jerky and cracked parched corn as they traveled. The mules protested alittle when they only had a short rest.

The road left the river for awhile and headed up on the side of a big hill. It was a narrow, but good road.

As the road leveled out and followed the contour of the hill, they still made good time.

"Look up ahead, Paw, I see a cabin and out buildings," said Crockett.

"Yes son, must be a little mountain farm it looks like the road goes real close to it," said Jonas.

"Paw it looks like an inn or store to me, I see another wagon sitting there," said Crockett.

"Well it is starting to get late in the day," said Jonas.

"We will stop and see what it is all about," added Jonas.

"Good idea Paw, my bottom is just about worn out!" Crockett said.

Crockett drives the team close to the building to a hitching post.

About that time a tall man with a difficult walk came out to greet them.

Jonas was the first to speak. "Hello there, mister."

The man threw up his hand and waved.

"I am Douglas Adkins, I run this little establishment," he said.

"I am Jonas Whitt, and this here is my son Crockett," said Jonas.

"You fellers in need of a room and a meal this evening?" asked Mister Jones.

"Well, if you don't charge too much, we might just stay here tonight," answered Jonas.

"Come on in and have a look see, my partner is a good cook, and we ain't got bugs in our beds," Douglas stated.

Jonas and Douglas got the price out of the way.

"Crockett, you go ahead and start unhitching the team, I will be right out and help you", said Jonas.

Jonas went in and checked out the room, and asked what was for supper?

Douglas told him, they had some good stew, cornbread, and apple cobbler.

He stated to Jonas, "We got coffee, tea, and milk to drink, I also have some good shine, to settle you in for the night."

"You fellers put your animals in the barn, feel free to give them the hay and oats you will find out there," said Douglas.

"Have your boy draw some more water and fill up the watering trough, so they can get a drink," added Douglas.

"Thanks Mister Adkins, I will be back in shortly; we will be ready to eat before long," replied Jonas.

"Call me Doug, Mister Whitt," he said.

"Fine," said Jonas, "you may call me Jonas."

In a short time the animals were taken care of, and the Whitt's were in the Inn.

"Smells good," said Crockett.

Doug walked over to the fire place and got the pot of stew. He brought it over and set it on the table. Next he got a half of a pone of cornbread from another counter and set it on the table.

"You fellers sit right down and eat all you want; I will fetch you some cobbler and something to drink," said Doug.

After Jonas prayed and asked a blessing on the food, and for this house; they dug into the hot meal.

"This is a fine supper!" Jonas remarked.

Doug replied, "Thank you."

"My partner is a fine cook, she is not here right now," said Doug.

"Went to see her folks for a little spell", Doug added.

Doug explained that she just left today, and she will be sorry that she missed you fellers.

After supper Jonas took a chew and moved over by the fire place where spitting would be handy.

Crockett was still working on the tasty cobbler.

Doug got down his little brown jug and set it on a little table beside Jonas.

"Mind if I join you Jonas?" Doug asked.

"Come on and join me, we might open up a keg of something," replied Jonas.

"Keg?" asked Doug.

"Conversation," replied Jonas.

"Oh! I see said the blind man," replied Doug.

Jonas chuckled!

Jonas told Doug about the trip they were on, and where they had traveled from.

"Tazewell County, that is where I was born, but it was Russell or maybe Montgomery back then," said Doug.

"This world is getting smaller every day," added Doug.

Crockett was listening, and wondered what that ment? How can the world get small, he thought?

Jonas told Doug about John Bunyon Whitt living up on Right Beaver Creek.

"Is he a big strong feller?" asked Doug.

"Yes he is a big man," replied Jonas.

"I have heard of him, he is well known in these parts," said Doug.

"Good man I hear, and he don't take nothing off nobody," Doug added.

"Sounds like him," said Jonas.

"I know where that is, I figure it is about ten to twelve miles from here, you all should be able to make it there tomorrow," said Doug.

"Sounds good," replied Jonas, as he spit a well aimed ambeer in the fire.

"Now Douglas, how did you wind up here?" asked Jonas.

Doug explained how he got this land.

"I have been here for some time now," Doug said," I came here with my Paw back about 1814."

"I was too young to fight in the war of 1812, but Paw did," Doug said.

Doug explained that his Paw came here on the way to join the militia.

"He got this whole mountain for his service, so we settled here, said Doug.

"When he came here the Indians were still sulking around trying to burn out the settlers.

"I don't remember too much about it, except the for stories my Paw told!," Doug added.

Crockett spoke up, "My Grand Paw Hezekiah Whitt was an Indian fighter in the War of Independence."

"He also helped start Tazewell County as a Justice, and he is a famous man around Tazewell county," Crockett said boastfully.

"I have heard of your Grand Paw. He is a famous man, Is he still living," asked Doug?

"No sir, Grand Paw went to glory last March, I mean 1846,"

explained Crockett.

"Sorry to hear it, he must have lived a long life," answered Doug.

Jonas interrupted, "eighty-six, and a long good life".

After the three talked about this and that, Jonas said, "to bed, to bed, said sleepy head, oh no said slow, put on the pot said greedy gut and we will eat before we go!"

Doug had a good laugh, after hearing this little saying.

"Does that mean you want to eat again, Jonas," he asked?

"Oh no!, just a little Whitt saying, huh Crockett?" said Jonas.

Crockett had a big smile on his face.

Early next morning, Jonas and Crockett were awaken to the aroma of bacon frying, and coffee cooking!

After a good breakfast the two travlers were ready to get going.

Jonas asked the Inn keeper to give him the directions to Right Beaver Creek, and to the home of his brother John Bunyon Whitt.

"Well it is purty simple, go on down the Levisa towards Prestonsburg, about five miles or so from here you will see where Beaver Creek runs into the Levisa," Doug said.

"Old Bill Adkins will be there about with his ferry boat, " Doug continued.

"Just hollar fer him and he will take you across, you got to cross the Levisa some place any how to get to Greenup County," Doug said.

"Tell old Bill where you are headed so he will put you out on the right side of Beaver," Doug instructed.

"There be a road on both sides of Beaver Creek," said Doug.

"Head up Beaver fer about four miles and the creek splits, you take the right one, that be Right Beaver," Doug continued.

"Your brother John Bunyon Whitt lives up the creek a couple of miles at a place called Maytown," Doug continued.

"It is a nice level valley right smack in the hills," Doug said.

"Do you understand Jonas?" asked Doug.

"I think we can find it, thanks for everything," replied Jonas.

Jonas and Crockett were on the move again and it was another nice spring day.

The morning was passing fast.

They rambled around the hillside road and back down into the little valley beside the river. They enjoyed the spring weather and the smell in the air.

"Look up ahead Paw, I think I see the ferry boat," Crockett announced..

"I see it too," replied Jonas.

"It looks like Mister Adkins is waiting for us," said Crockett.

As Jonas and Crockett rode up, the figure of a tall bent man stood up and waved a welcome.

Jonas and Crockett both waved back.

As they got within speaking distance the man spoke to the Whitts.

"Good morning fellers," said Mister Adkins.

"Morning to you," replied Jonas.

"We are the Whitts, you must be Mister Bill Adkins," said Jonas.

"Yelp," said Bill.

"You fellers needing to cross the river?" Bill asked.

"Yes Mister Adkins, we are heading up Beaver and on up Right Beaver,"answered Jonas.

"Well I need to put you off on the right side of the creek, that will take you to Right Beaver, just follow the road up the creek," Bill said.

Jonas carefully drove the team right on the ferry. He had to untie Jake and move him up beside the wagon.

Bill Adkins closed the gate on the back of the barge like boat. Then he took the rope and begin to pull it toward the back. The boat slowly begin to move.

"Do you want us to help you pull on the rope?" Jonas asked.

"Most folks like to help me get them across," replied Bill.

The mules began to protest, they had never left dry land before.

Jonas helped Bill pull the rope, and he had Crockett go to the front and hold the mules. Crockett talked to them in a soothing voice. The mules calmed down and took the ride as if they enjoyed it. Jake acted up a little, but settled down as he saw the mules get quiet.

When they reached the landing, Bill went to the front and dropped the gate. Crockett led the team out on dry land. Their eyes were still wide, and their nostrils flared, but were no worse for the ride. They seemed to know that their feet were on solid footing, and felt relieved.

Jonas laughed with a little nervous excitement after they were safe on the other side.

"I thought we were all going swimming there for a while," Jonas said.

"Critters act up a might sometimes," Bill replied.

"I guess my mules have never rode a boat before," replied Jonas.

"I had a horse jump through the front gate one time," Bill exclaimed.

"What did you do," asked Crockett?

"He swam, and we followed," answered Bill with a chuckle.

They all had a little laugh.

Bill gave Jonas the final directions to Right Beaver Creek, and even to the home of John Bunyon Whitt.

Jonas thanked Bill, and the travelers were on their way.

The road up Beaver Creek was not as wide nor as well maintained as was the Turnpike. Jonas drove the team for now. He told Crockett to rest while he drove for a while. Crockett knew his Paw would be the better driver in this little bumpy trace.

It seemed to be no time at all they were coming up on the the farm of John Bunyon Whitt.

Jonas and Crockett were welcomed with open arms by John, Sarah, and all the family. Douglas was about the age of Crockett so they enjoyed the visit.

Jonas and Crockett stayed two nights, resting and allowing the animals to rest and graze on the new blue grass on John's farm. They talked about the folks back home in Tazewell County. They talked about current events, and about Kentucky.

John explained to Jonas the best way to get to Greenup County. Simply put by John was follow the Levisa. He told him about a place called Louisa not too many miles down river.He told Jonas about the Tug Fork joining the Levisa to form the Big Sandy River.He also told him to follow the Big Sandy all the way to the Ohio River.

There is a little town at the mouth he understood with a funny name like "Catlettsburg" or something like that.

He also directed them to head down the Ohio, through another little burg called "Poages Landing." (now Ashland)

He also predicted with good traveling days, they should make it to the Ohio River, in less than two weeks. He figured three or four days to the town Greenup.

Jonas and Crockett got some needed rest and so did the animals.

They also got to have a good visit with blood family.

The Whitts had a really good visit, but were anxious to get started towards their goal of reaching the "Truitt Farm on Big White Oak Creek," in Greenup County.

John gave direction to get back to the Levisa with out back tracking. He explained that the road was not good and you have to cross a couple of good sized hills.

One Hill was called "Hippo." He explained that the name came from people being afraid to cross it.

Some feller named it that because he said, "that hill has me Hippoed"

Jonas asked if it was that bad and was it safe for them to cross?

"It is not that bad, folks cross it most every day," replied John Bunyon.

Jonas and Crockett got the wagon ready and the team hitched up.

Next Jonas and Crockett went to each one of John's family giving hugs and goodbyes. It had been a good visit and both families enjoyed it.

As Jonas and Crockett got up on the wagon, Sarah came and handed them a basket of food for the journey. They were real pleased and thanked her profusely.

Once again the Whitt pilgrams were on the move. They were headed over the trace toward "Hippo."

Crockett started the trip driving the team.

"Paw when we get ready to pass through Hippo, I want you to drive," he said.

"When we get there I will, but I bet you could do it," Jonas replied.

Jonas wanted to encourage Crockett, but felt it might be better if he took over at certain dangerous places. "Hippo" sounded like such a place.

The two pilgrims traveled up and over around and through "Hippo" with out one problem. Jonas and Crockett were quite relieved with "Hippo" behind them.

They were now watching for the Levisa once again. The route they took would come out down river of Prestonsburg. Jonas and Crockett were both sorry to miss seeing the county seat of Floyd county.

Jonas and Crockett could relax a little now. The road was better, and they would be back on the main road before long. Jonas would stay viligant, because you can never be too careful.

Crockett started talking about their visit with John Bunyon Whitt and his family.

"Uncle John has a big carpentry shop don"t he Paw?" asked Crockett.

"He sure does, and he has a lot of customers too," replied Jonas.

"He even builds fine furniture," Jonas added.

"His stuff looks great don't it Paw?" Crockett asked.

"Yes it sure does, especially that sideboard and china cabinet," Jonas explained.

"I really loved meeting Douglas," Crockett said.

"You fellers really hit it off," Jonas said.

Crockett changed the subject by asking about the stories told on John Bunyon Whitt.

"Uncle John is well known around these parts, some of the fights must have happened," Crockett committed.

"I remember him as a boy, he could lick just about any jasper in school," Jonas commented.

"He is only about three years older than me, but he has always been much bigger and stronger," Jonas said.

"I remember one time, we had a bully at school, the bully was Billy Whay, and he picked on all the younger boys," Jonas said.

"What happened Paw, did Billy jump on you or John?" asked Crockett.

"Billy was two years older, and a little bigger than John Bunyon," Jonas went on.

"Billy made a big mistake and threw a mud ball and hit John in the center of the back," Jonas continued.

"What did Uncle John do?" Crockett interrupted.

"He walked up to Billy and hit him square in the nose, blood squrted out and down his shirt," Jonas said.

"Did the school marm get after Uncle John?" Crockett asked.

"He didn't say a thing, because he was a little afraid of Billy too, and was glad to see him get his up-comings," Jonas answered.

"What did Billy Whay say or do after that, Paw?" Crockett asked.

"Well he didn't bother any of the Whitts after that," Jonas said.

"Did Grand Paw Hezekiah give him a whipping Paw?" Crockett asked.

"No, Paw never found out for several years, then he just laughed about it," Jonas answered.

"Grand Paw never had much sympathy for a bully," Jonas added.

As they crossed another ridge late in the day Jonas saw the Levisa Fork meandering through the little valley below. It was a beautiful site with the late glimmering sunlight dancing on the water.

Jonas stopped the team and the two just sit there for about five minutes taking in the site.

"Only God Almighty could paint a picture like that son," Jonas said.

"It sure is purty, Paw," Crockett answered.

"Well let's get on down close to the river and find us a good camp for the night," Jonas suggested.

It took about another hour to decend the hill and find a suitable camp site.

"Paw, the Levisa is getting bigger down here," Crockett said.

"Yes it is, just wait till we get to Louisa, it will really grow with the Tug Fork pouring in," Jonas answered.

They set up camp just off the road under a grove of trees. The area had some grass for the mules and Jake to dine on.

There was no farms close by, and it seemed they were out in the wilderness, even though they knew people were not too far away. There was no rock house to camp under, so they set up the tent.

Crockett decided to take his pole and try out the fishing. He fliped over some rocks and gathered a few worms, and went down and sat on the bank. The river was a nice color for fishing, not too muddy nor too clear. Crockett put on a little stick for a float and tosed it over by a submerged log. Bam, the float took off and down deep, stretching out his fishing line. Crockett set the hook and yanked out a really large crappy. Crockett yelled at his Paw to come and join him.

Jonas came over to the river bank and looked down at the busy

Crockett.

"Paw this thing hit as soon as the worm dropped to him, what kind of fish is this?" Crockett asked.

"That is a crappy, and a big one at that," Jonas replied.

"We used to catch them in the New River back in Montgomery County," Jonas replied.

Crockett threw in his line and another one hit, just like before.

"I am going to get my pole," Jonas said as he turned toward the wagon.

In a short time they had a string of six to eight nice big crappie's.

"Well son, looks like we will have fish for supper," Jonas announced.

"I bet we could catch a tub full the way they are biting," Crockett said.

"You know the code of fishing and hunting son," replied Jonas.

"What, You catch you clean?" asked Crockett.

"Yes, and also you don't catch more than you need," replied Jonas.

"Yes sir, I do remember that, even though they are fun to catch," replied Crockett.

They started a fire and enjoyed the good treats from the Levisa Fork.

"Paw them crappie sure are tasty, and fun to catch, why ain"t they any in the Clinch?" Crockett asked.

"Well I don't rightly know, except that this water runs into the Ohio, maybe they swim up the river," Jonas explained.

That seemed to satisfy the boy who had so many questions.

CHAPTER 20

HEADING FOR THE OHIO

Morning came and the two Whitts were on the road early. Both got a good nights sleep, and were ready to travel. The weather was taking a turn for the worse. Temperature had dropped during the night and the wind was whipping the trees.

"Must be Dogwood Winter coming on," Jonas said.

"I just hope we don't get blowed away," answered Crockett.

Even the mules laid back their ears, and protested somewhat, but kept to the task of pulling the heavy wagon.

The sky grew dark, and a hard rain hit them for about five minutes.

"This time of year, the weather just don't know what to do, so it does everything," Jonas said.

"Well Paw, it is less than a week until May, I am ready for spring to come and stay, ain't you Paw?" Crockett asked.

"Yes, son I am, it is just about here," answered Jonas.

That day they had winter, spring, and fall, it seemed. The rain showers came and went, and the wind finally laid down by the middle afternoon. Now the sun was shining brightly.

"I see what you mean Paw, about the weather not knowing what to do, it has done just about everything today," Crockett said.

"Yelp, nothing surprises me about April weather," Jonas agreed.

Jonas and Crockett covered several miles this day regardless of the weather.

They came up on a farm that bordered the road. Jonas noticed that they had a nice barn and it may be a good place to spend the night.

"Pull up here to the gate and I will ask if we can spend the night here," Jonas said to Crockett.

Crockett pulled up as instructed, and set the brake on the wagon. Just as Jonas was stepping down, a man with a shotgun stepped out the door of the house.

"Hold it right there, just get back on that wagon and head on down the road," the man commanded.

Jonas was taken aback, with the way he was treated. Jonas stepped back up on the wagon and waved his hand.

"Hello Sir, we are the Whitts traveling to Greenup County, don't mean you any harm," Jonas hollered.

The man shook the shotgun and waved it toward them.

"I don't care who you are, get your asses on down the road, I ain't got nothing fer you," he screamed.

"Let's go son, that feller is plumb crazy," Jonas whispered to Crockett.

It was not late yet so they traveled for two to three more miles and came up on another farm.

"Well son let's see if these people have any sense," Jonas said.

They pulled the wagon up to this gate, and Jonas stepped down. He opened the gate and walked toward the door. A man opened the door and stepped out, and the Whitts saw no gun.

"Can I help you fellers," he asked in a loud voice?

"We are the Whitts heading to Greenup County, I was wondering if you might let us sleep in your barn?" Jonas asked.

"Well I guess you could," answered the man.

"My name is Dan McCoy, open that big gate and pull your wagon on in," he said.

Jonas opened the gate and Crockett drove on in. By now Dan McCoy had walked up to Jonas and shook his hand.

"Jonas is my name, this here is my boy David Crockett," Jonas said.

"David Crockett is one fine name son," Dan said as he shook Crockett's hand.

Dan showed Jonas into the barn, and gave him corn for the animals. He showed them a meadow with a branch running through it, to turn out the team and Jake into.

"Jonas you and young David Crockett tend your animals, then come in the house, Bertha has a big pot of soup, and some corn bread cooked up, yaw are welcome to et with us," Dan announced.

"Thank you most kindly, Dan," Jonas said.

"We will take you up on it," he added.

After a bit, Jonas and Crockett had everything under control with the wagon and animals. They came to the door and knocked. A large fleshy woman opened the door.

"Clean yer feet and com on in, I am Bertha," she said.

As they came in Jonas stuck out his hand as he shuffled his feet on the rug. Crockett did the same.

"Hello Miss Bertha, I am Jonas Whitt, this is my boy David Crockett," Jonas said.

"We ain't too formal round here, jes make yer self to home," she said.

Dan was already seated at the head of the table, and montioned for the Whitts to come on over.

Bertha served up the hot soup and corn bread, and sat down by Dan.

"We don't know much about praying, would you like to offer grace Mister Whitt?" Dan asked.

Jonas nodded his head, and offered up a prayer of Thanksgiving.

"Thanks Jonas," replied Dan.

"Thank you Dan and Miss Bertha for your fine hospitality," replied Jonas.

After supper, the subject of the farm back up the road came up.

"That is old Bill Pruitt, he don't get along with nobody," Dan said.

"He won't even let his woman off the place," replied Bertha.

"The Pruitts and the Browns back of him, have been feuding for about two years, you are lucky he didn't shoot at you," Dan explained.

The Whitts and McCoys had a long conversation about Tazewell County, Floyd County and even Greenup County. They talked about family, current events, and the unrest between the North and South.

"I hope it never comes to war, but something will happen afore long," said Dan.

"We all need to live and let live," Jonas said.

Dan had a newspaper some one had given him. There was an article about Mormons settling way out in the wilderness next to a salt lake. The article called the place Utah.

Dan wanted to show off his reading ability, so he read it to them.

Jonas told him about hearing about the Mormons and some of their beliefs.

"I hear that they have as many wifes as they want," added Jonas.

"More than one wife," Bertha interrupted.

"Ain't no wonder folks run um off," she added.

Dan and Jonas smiled at her reaction!

Next morning Bertha sent Dan out to get the Whitts for breakfast.

Bertha had a pot of oats and a pot of coffee ready. After breakfast the two men talked about the road and direction to Paintsville and Louisa.

Jonas and Crockett hitched up the wagon and got ready for the road.

Jonas and Crockett came to the McCoys and thanked them profusely.

"Yer welcome and glad you stopped," Dan said.

"Would you offer up another prayer afore you all head out?" Dan asked.

Jonas looked a little surprised, but nodded that he would. The four of them joined hands, and Jonas prayed a Prayer of Thanksgiving and a prayer of blessing and protection on the McCoy house.

"Amen," was said by all four.

Jonas took a minute and explained to Dan and Bertha that they could pray also. He explained that God was always around and would listen to all his children.

Jonas and Crockett were on the move once again. In another day they would be getting into the new county of Johnson. It was establish in 1843 and the County Seat was in the berg of Paintsville. The county was named for Richard Johnson, known as the (Father of the American Cavalry." Johnson was in politics after the war of 1812, and served in various roles.

The name of Paintsville derived from the old Paint Creek Station. There was a station set at the mouth of Paint Creek, where it enters the Levisa Frok. It is thought the area was named this, because of Indian drawings painted on the trees.

Tice Harmon from the area of East Mountain (now Bland County Virginia,) had a station in the area in the late eighteenth century. The famous Jenny Wiley was recovered from the Indians at this station.

Jonas made note that the terrain was changing to rolling hills, and larger distance between the hills. Also the Levisa Valley has swelled out to be quite wide in some areas.

As Jonas and Crockett rolled into Paintsville the two were anxious to see this new place on their trek.

Jonas was looking for an Inn and a place to get a good meal. Crockett was the first to see the Inn.

"Paw over there by the Trading Post, see the sign Sayers Tavern and Inn?" Crockett said.

"Yes I do, head the team over there to the nearest hitching post," answered Jonas.

Tom Sayers was the owner of the establishment, and very friendly. He was helpful by taking Jonas to the nearby livery stable. He also provided Jonas and Crockett with a room and a good meal.

After supper Jonas and Crockett had some good conversations with the locals. Jonas had a couple of drinks of store bought whiskey, and smoked a cigar. Crockett just sat back and listened to the men talk.

Things were going pretty good until a man came in and walked up to Jonas.

"Are you the one traveling through, Mister?" he asked.

"I am Jonas Whitt, and yes I am traveling toward Greenup county, what is your business?" Jonas asked.

"Folks call me Whiskey John, but my given name is John Brull," he answered.

"I was wondering if you might need you a belly warmer fer the night?" he asked.

Jonas grew angry at the proposition!

"No sir Mister Brull, I am a Godly man and I do not indulge in such goings on," Jonas said sternly.

Mister Sayers came over and politely invited Whiskey John to vacate the premises.

"John I told you not to be coming in here and bothering my customers," Tom told him in no uncertain terms.

After Whiskey John left, Tom apologized profusely to Jonas and Crockett.

"Crockett popped up, "Paw, my belly ain't cold, but what would be bad about having a belly warmer?" he asked.

The men at the table roared with laughter.

"I guess it is about time for me and young Crockett to go to bed," Jonas said.

The men all bid the Whitts a good nights sleep and a good journey on to Greenup county. Jonas and Crockett thanked the men and Mister Sayers, and headed up stairs to their room.

Morning came quickly, and the Whitts had breakfast, and were ready to travel once again. The animals had a good restful night and plenty of oats and corn.

Jonas settled up with Tom Sayers and the stable man, and they were on the road once again.

"Paw what is the next town we are heading for?" Crockett asked.

"That will be Louisa," Jonas answered.

"I guess about three days, before you ask," Jonas continued.

"Paw you can read my mind," Crockett said.

"Well maybe," Jonas replied.

The weather was getting nice, almost hot in the afternoon. It was almost May 1847, and the two travelers should not get too cold on the rest of their journey.

As they rode along, Crockett talked about Kentucky and the trip thus far.

"Paw did you hear that feller back in Paintsville talking about how it got it's name," Crockett asked?

"Yes, and I thought it was interesting about the Indian paintings, didn't you son?" Jonas asked.

"Sure did Paw, what is a belly warmer Paw?" Crockett blurted out.

Jonas turned a little pink.

"Well son, do you remember back in Pike county, them three women were trying to get us to stay with them?" Jonas asked.

"Yelp, Paw, them women who didn't hardly have clothes on," answered Crockett.

"Well son, Whiskey John sells women like that for a night at a time, do you understand son?" Jonas asked.

"Is it like what married people do Paw?" Crockett asked.

"Sort of son, only it is without the Lords blessing," Jonas explained.

"Remember back in Pike I told you the Bible says in Proverbs to run from harlots?" Jonas asked.

"I understand now, I think ," Crockett said.

"Them fellers at Paintsville laughed at me cause I didn't know what a belly warmer was, didn't they Paw?" Crockett asked.

"They did not know how innocent you are, and that is nothing to be ashamed of son," Jonas explained.

In the evening of the third day from Paintsville, Jonas and Crockett were coming up on Louisa.

"Paw, ain't this Louisa where the Tug and the Levisa run together?" Crockett asked.

"Yes son, and I think I heard that there is a falls in the river, the name of the river from here to the Ohio is called the Big Sandy," Jonas exclaimed.

"Is this a new county too, like Johnson County?" Crockett asked.

"It is not as new as that, I don't think," Jonas replied.

"Maybe we will learn something about it, I think at the far side we hit the edge of Greenup," Jonas added.

"You mean we are just about there?" asked Crockett.

"No son, I think it will take about another week or more to get to Big White Oak Creek," replied Jonas.

Jonas and Crockett were ready to sleep in a bed and eat a good meal by the time they got to Louisa. They found a nice Inn in Louisa. Jonas secured a room and found good care for the mules and Jake.

After a good supper, Jonas and Crockett went over to talk to some of the local men and maybe Jonas would have some spirits. Jonas led the way over and introduced himself and Crockett.

"Hello Jonas and Master Crockett," replied one of the three.

"I am Richard Alley, the gentleman to my left is Tom Pinion, and the gentleman to my right is William Bailey," Richard continued.

Jonas and Crockett both nodded hello to each gentleman.

Jonas spoke to each and called them by name.

"Are you all just passing through Jonas, or are you settling down in our fair county?" ask Richard Alley.

"We are heading to Greenup County," Jonas said.

"Well sit down and join us for some conservation," William Bailey said.

"Please do Jonas and Master Crockett ," added Tom Pinion.

Jonas and Crockett joined the three gentleman, and Jonas had a drink with them.

After talking about work and this and that, the subject came to Lawrence County. The three men loved talking about their home county and told everything they could about it. They explained that the county was established in 1822. It was made up from Floyd and Greenup Counties.

"How did it get the name of Lawrence?" Jonas asked.

"Caption James Lawrence was a captain on a ship in the war of 1812, in a fierce battle Captain Lawrence was wounded, but he demanded that they fight on," William said.

"On June 1, 1813, Captain Lawrence coined a praise (Don't give up the ship)," Tom Pinion added.

"That is real interesting, tell us about the area," Jonas said.

"Well we are a town of three rivers you know," Richard announced.

"Yes we have heard that, two of them rivers start out over in Tazewell County Virginia," Jonas announced.

"They are little creeks over there in Tazewell County," Crockett interjected.

"I hear tell that we are bordered with Virginia, once we got here in Louisa," Jonas said.

"That is absolutely right," William Bailey agreed.

"The Old Dominion is a big old CommonWealth, aint it gentleman?" Jonas asked.

"Yes it is and so is Kentucky, why it goes plumb to the Mississippi River," Richard said.

"How far is it to the Ohio River?" asked Jonas.

"Pulling a wagon like you got, I figure about three or four days," Richard answered.

"In about a day and a half you will be in Greenup county, (Boyd Now) Jonas," said Tom.

"Where you headed to in Greenup?" asked Richard.

"We are headed to Big White Oak Creek to a place called Truittville, not too far from the town of Greenup," Jonas said.

Being tired and the drink of whiskey made Jonas ready for bed.

Crockett was getting a little heavy eyed also.

Jonas stood up slowly, and shook hands with each of the men.

"You must excuse us gentleman, we need to get our rest, it has been great to meet all of you," Jonas said.

Crockett did like wise, shaking each hand and nodding good night.

"Master Crockett, it was nice meeting you, you take care of your Paw, hear," Richard said to him.

"Yes sir, I will," Crockett answered.

Jonas and Crockett were soon in bed and fast asleep.

Next morning before they hit the trail, Jonas and Crockett walked down to see the confluence of the Tug, and Levisa, and the one big river they produced. Jonas explained that from here to the Ohio, the river was called Big Sandy.

"Look over there across the river," Jonas said.

"What is it Paw?" Crockett asked.

"That land over there is good old Virginia," Jonas replied.

"That is amazing Paw, Virginia being way off up here!" Crockett exclaimed.

"I wonder how my sweet heart Virginia is doing?" Crockett added.

Jonas smiled.

"We better get on the road son," Jonas said.

The evening of the fourth day from Louisa, Jonas and Crockett are coming to the mouth of Big Sandy. This place is the confluence of the Big Sandy and the Ohio Rivers. Just across the Ohio River is the State of Ohio. To the east and across the Big Sandy River is Virginia.

The berg is called Big Sandy Landing, and some folks call it Catlettsburg. The south part is sometimes called Hampton city, even though there is no city there. Catlettsburg was named for the two brothers from Virginia that settled there in the late seventeen hundreds. About 1798 Alexander and Horatio Catlett came and settled here. The Post Office was opened in Catlettsburg in 1810.

"Oh my goodness Paw, look how big the Ohio river is!" Crockett exclaimed.

"It is even bigger than I thought it would be," answered Jonas.

"Look Crockett, coming down the river, it's a big steam boat!"

Jonas exclaimed.

"I see it Paw, look how big it is, and look at them smoke stacks putting out the smoke," Crockett said.

"Son look at the bright colors that thing is painted," Jonas continued.

As the two Whitts stood there gazing at the site, they began to hear banjo and fiddle music coming across the water. As the great boat came closer, they could see folks dancing and moving about. Jonas and Crockett had never laid their eyes on such a sight.

"Paw look at the back of the boat, it looks like a great mill wheel pushing it on the water," Crockett exclaimed.

"It is about the same, only a mill wheel is moved by water, and steam moves the wheel on the boat," Jonas explained.

The Whitts stood there until the river boat was well out of sight down the river.

The two travelers found the Catlett Inn, and got a room for the night.

The Big Sandy Landing showed signs of much activity. The people round about were beginning to send and receive goods from, New Orleans and Pittsburgh.

Some of the latest folks coming down the river were the Irish. The potato famine was sending many poor Irishman to the new world. A flat boat loaded with Irish families had stopped off to spend the night, and set up a little camp of tents and lean-to's in a level area just off the landing. They were talking loudly as they gathered fire wood and began to fix their supper.

"Paw what kind of talk is that?" Crockett asked.

"Those folks are the Irish we been reading about in the papers, they are speaking English, but with an Irish accent," Jonas answered.

After supper Jonas and Crockett were sitting around talking to folks in the Tavern. A few of the Irishmen came in for a drink of spirits to sooth their nerves and give them some glee.

Crockett enjoyed listening to the Irish talk. He thought they really talked funny. As the Irish begin to talk to the American born folks, they thought the locals talked really funny.

Jonas was a little worried about his tools and equipment on the wagon even though it was rolled into the stable for the night. He was afraid the poor Irish might help them selves to something during the night.

Jonas talked to Alexander Catlett about his fears.

"Don't worry about it, the Irish are poor, but I have not heard of them taking one single thing since they have been coming down the river," Alexander explained.

"Alright Sir, if you trust them, I guess I will not worry either," Jonas said.

Jonas talked to the locals about Greenup County, and his destination. To his surprise, most of them had heard of the prosperous Doctor Samuel Truitt. They explained that it would take about five days to get to Truittville pulling a heavy wagon. They gave directions to Greenup, and from there to Truittville.

CHAPTER 21

LET'S GO BUILD A MILL!

Jonas and Crockett head down the river toward the fair city of Greenup. The next little burg is not but a few miles down river. It is called Poage's Landing. The Poage family came to the area and settled just down stream from Catlettsburg in the late seventeen hundreds. This location is now present day Ashland, Kentucky.

Something Jonas and Crockett may have seen was the Iron Furnace's and traffic to and from them. One such furnace was the Oakland. It was started by the Kouns Brothers, Jacob and John in 1834. It ran until 1849.

Many furnace's were built on both sides of the Ohio River during this time. Iron ore was in the hills of Greenup County, and across the river in Ohio. The Great furnace's produced "Pig Iron" and was shipped to other areas to fabricate such things as steam engines and rail roads.

Crockett was alive with excitement. This new land along the Ohio river was like something in a story book.

"Paw some day I am going to swim this big old river," Crockett announced.

"Let's hope you don't tempt fate like that son," Jonas replied.

"Swimming a big river like that can be vary dangerous," Jonas added.

"Well Paw, if I ever do I will have somebody in a boat go with me," Crockett said.

Poage's Landing was not as big or busy as Catlettsburg. Yet there was stacks of Pig Iron ingots waiting to go out on the next steam boat. Also some black fellers were working, in a field near by. Jonas heard from someone that they would be on hand to load and unload the boats.

Jonas and Crockett did not tarry in Poage's Landing. Late in the evening they had traveled to the John McConnell school. (Present day Wurtland, Ky.) It was a really big plantation type house and had several out buildings. One of the buildings looked to be slave quarters.

Jonas and Crockett were very tired so they stopped to see if they may spend the night in one of the buildings. They found out that the man who built this fine house had passed away back in 1834. The man came down the Ohio and started a law office here. John McConnell had served the state in both the house and Senate.

After his death the big house was converted into a private school. Some of the care takers greeted Jonas and Crockett. They were allowed to sleep in one of the out buildings, and even given some food for supper.

Jonas and Crockett were amazed at the size of the Ohio Valley and how flat the land was. Jonas surmised that farming would be easy in such a place, as he watched several black men and a few whites plow the fields around the big house.

"I never seen this many black folks before," Crockett exclaimed.

"I never seen such big fields either," confessed Jonas.

That evening after supper Jonas had Hannah on his mind. He missed the little daughter he left with James and Nancy. He was having second thoughts, and felt bad for leaving her in Virginia. He reasoned within his mind that his decision was right, but it still hurt. She was just too young to travel into the hills of Kentucky with a man and a boy. I will never leave her behind again, Jonas decided.

"What's wrong Paw, you are so quiet this evening?" Crockett asked.

"I have just been thinking about Hannah and the folks back in Virginia," he said.

"I miss them too," Crockett said.

"Don't worry son, we will be all together again, we will build the mills and go back to Hannah," Jonas said.

"Let's get some sleep, we got one long day ahead of us tomorrow," Jonas added.

"Alright Paw, do you think we will get there tomorrow?" Crockett asked.

"We have a good shot at it, now get some sleep," Jonas answered.

Next morning as the Whitts started to move out, the slaves were already at work and singing up a storm. They were singing spiritual songs and enjoying their work.

"Listen to that beautiful singing Crockett," Jonas said.

"I never heard anything like that," said Crockett.

The two moved on down the river and in about half an hour they were coming into Greenup. They could hardly believe they were here already, thinking it was much further to the town.

"Paw is this the town of Greenup?" Crockett asked.

"It has to be, I never thought about it being so close to where we stayed last night," Jonas answered.

It is a pretty town right on the Ohio river, Jonas thought.

"Looks like it could get flooded out if the river got up big," Jonas said.

Crockett drove the wagon down the main street looking at all the buildings, and businesses. They saw the court house, and a church. It seemed to be a place of tomorrow. There was a landing at the bank of the river just below the court house, and a flat bottomed boat was tied up there. They saw a general store and decided to stop there.

"Let's go in the store and see if we can get directions over to Truittville," Jonas said.

Crockett drove the team up close to the store and got down to tie the team to a hitching post. Jonas led the way into the store where a few people were milling around. Jonas and Crockett walked up to the counter where a clerk was busy adding the cost of another mans purchases.

"Be with you in just a minute," the man said.

"Take your time sir, we just need some directions," Jonas said.

The clerk looked up over his spectacles at Jonas and nodded his head. The clerk finished with the customer, and turned to the strangers in his story.

"Hello there sir my name is James Womack, welcome to Greenupsburg," he said.

"Howdy James, I am Jonas Whitt, this here is my boy David Crockett Whitt, did you say Greenupsburg?" Jonas asked.

"Some of us older settlers still call it that, most new folks call it Greenup," Womack stated.

"We are traveling here from Tazewell County Virginia, and heading to Truittsville," Jonas continued.

James shook hands with Jonas and then Crockett.

"Good to meet you folks," James said.

"Same here," Jonas said.

"Well Jonas, you said something about directions, where to Truittville?" James asked.

"Yes James, we need to know the best way to get there," Jonas answered.

"Well Jonas it ain't to hard to get to," James said.

James explained the whole trip and directions to Jonas. He told them to go on to the north end of the street, there you will come up on a bridge over the Little Sandy River. Cross the bridge and go on through a little more town. Follow the road about two miles to a little branch. (Coal Branch) Turn up the branch on that road, it takes you over to Tygart Valley.It is slightly up hill for about four miles then the branch runs out at the top of the hill. Another little branch starts at the top and runs to Tygart Creek. It is a decent road after you get over there in the valley. Follow the road south in the valley for about two more miles headed up stream. Next you will come to a big feeder creek. This is Big White Oak Creek. Cross the creek at the ford, and turn up the creek. You will be in Truittville in another three or four miles.

"Sounds good," Jonas said.

"I sure am beholding to you James," Jonas said.

"Do you think we can make it there before dark?" Jonas asked.

"I think you can be there in about two and a half hours on a good riding horse," he said.

"We will be riding in a heavy wagon, and can't go too fast," Jonas explained.

"I think you might make it before dark Jonas, but don't hold me too it," James said.

Jonas bought a plug of tobacco and a stick of candy for Crockett and thanked James Womack for the help.

Jonas told Crockett that they would push on toward Truittsville, and would only stop to water the animals. He told Crockett they could eat trail food, since they had a good breakfast.

"We can chew on beef jerky, parched corn, and some dried apples that we brought with us," Jonas said.

Fine with me, I want to hurry up and get there, don't you Paw?" Crockett asked.

"Yes I do, we have been on the road for about six weeks now," Jonas replied.

"Has it been that long Paw?"Crockett asked.

"Yelp, we left the last day of March, and today is the tenth of May," Jonas explained.

"Tenth of May, ain't this corn and bean planting day?" Crockett said.

"It sure is, if we were planting, but we are going to build a mill this summer," Jonas said.

Before they knew it they had reached the branch and road that James told them to turn on to.

"This has got to be it," Jonas said.

Crockett turned the team up the hollow toward Tygart's Valley.

"Paw, we will have to really get on it to make it today, I think we got a good ten miles to go, and it is getting on towards noon," Crockett said.

"I may have bit off more than we can chew for one day," Jonas answered.

"The way this road looks we will be lucky to get a crossed it today," Jonas added.

"Just take your time, if we do we do, if we don't we don't," Jonas surmised.

"Like you said Paw, we been a traveling for six weeks, one more day won't matter," Crockett said.

"This hollow reminds me of back in Pike County, except the hills ain't as high," Jonas said.

It was uphill for about four miles so Crockett let the team pull at their own pace. The grade was not steep until they got close to the one big hill that divided the Ohio and Tygart Valleys.

Once up on the crest of the hill they could look over into Tygart Valley. Crockett stopped on the top for a minute to observe the beautiful valley below them.

"This is a fine land," Jonas thought out loud.

"Paw, we still got about seven miles to go, what time is it?" Crockett asked.

Jonas reached down and pulled out his watch, and flipped open the cover.

"We ain't going to make it today, it's almost 4:00 O'clock, Jonas said.

"Let's travel on over close to Tygart Creek and make camp, the team needs water and food," Jonas said.

It took them close to an hour to descend the hill and travel across the valley to the creek.

They set up camp, took care of the animals, and explored up and down the bank of Tygart Creek."Some deep holes in this creek, want to try our luck fishing?" Jonas asked.

"We might as well," Crockett answered.

They were camped at a long deep pool, which reminded them of Grand Paw's Honey Hole back on the Clinch.

Jonas got the fishing poles out while Crockett flipped over rocks and logs for bait.

They baited up and sit down to see what they may catch.

Something hit Crockett's hook first, it was a little Bass about ten inches long.

As Crockett allowed it to do a little fighting a great fish rolled up out of the shadows, and took the bass for his dinner. The great fish nearly yanked Crockett's pole from his hand. The fishing line stretched tight and snapped back on the bank. The hook was still there with only a head of a bass still attached.

The big eyed boy turned to Jonas who was also big eyed.

"Paw what on earth was that big thing that stole my fish?" Crockett uttered.

"I have no idea, cept it looked like a pike, I have read about them," Jonas answered excitedly.

"When that thing rolled over it looked to be four feet long," Crockett said.

"I know, I seen it too," replied Jonas.

"Paw, don't fall into this creek, them things might eat you up!" Crockett exclaimed.

"I doubt they would eat a man, but might a boy," Jonas said

grinning.

"I don't want to catch that feller," Crockett said.

"Don't worry, I doubt it will strike again," Jonas answered.

They didn't get another bite, so they went back to the camp to find something else for supper. They talked all evening about the trip, about the destination, and about that great fish that took Crockett's fish.

While they were sitting by their camp fire a man road up on his horse.

"Hello in the camp," said the stranger.

"Hello," answered Jonas as he put his hand on his pistol.

The man on the horse was a young man of about thirty years.

"I am Alfred Thompson, headed to Truittville," he said.

"I am Jonas Whitt and this here is my boy Crockett," Jonas said.

"Jonas Whitt, are you the one coming to build a mill for Doctor Truitt?" Alfred asked.

"Yes I am, how would you know about that?" Jonas asked.

"Shoot! It is the talk of the county Jonas, we been looking for you for a month," Alfred answered.

"Glad to meet you Jonas and you too Crockett," Alfred Added.

"I got some more riding ahead of me so I better get a going," Alfred said.

"Wait just a minute, can you tell me how far it is?" Jonas asked.

"About four or five miles I reckon," answered Alfred.

"How is the road on in to Truittville?" Jonas asked.

"It is a fine road on in to Truittville," he answered.

"Well thank you Alfred, do you need a drink of water or a bite to eat?" Jonas asked.

"No sir, I will be fine till I get to the Truitt Inn," Alfred said.

"Thank you Jonas for the offer, I will tell the Truitt's to expect you all tomorrow afternoon," Alfred said as he headed up the road at a good gait.

"Paw they must be excited about us coming," Crockett said.

"Reckon so, I guess we will be in demand to build them a grist mill," Jonas answered.

"Paw I was going to ask that feller about that fish we saw, but I couldn't get a word in," Crockett said.

"Don't worry about it son you will have plenty of time to ask about the big pike, we better get some sleep, so we can get on in to Truittville, Jonas said.

"Alright Paw," Crockett said as he pulled his big quilt up around his neck.

"Good night son," Jonas answered.

Alfred Thompson made it into Truittville about an hour after dark. He told Louisa Truitt, Samuel's daughter that the mill builder is only a few hours away. She ran to the Family home and aroused them. Samuel wanted to know what is going on. She told them that Alfred Thompson just rode in, and had talked to the Whitts over on Tygart.

"Glory be, we are going to get us a mill yet," Samuel said.

"I will ride out in the morning to meet Jonas and his son, Polly aren't you excited?" Samuel ask his sleepy wife.

"Sure am, now can we go to sleep?" Polly asked.

"Thanks Louisa for bringing the news, now go back and take care of our guests at the Inn," Samuel said.

"Good night Louisa," he added.

"Good night Paw, good night Maw," Louisa said.

Next morning Jonas and Crockett was up early, had a quick breakfast, and was moving toward Truittville. The excitement and anticipation were building for Jonas and Crockett. Even the mules and Jake were feeling the excitement that flowed from Jonas and Crockett. The mules trotted like fine horses as they pulled the wagon up the Tygart Valley.Before long the Whitts reached the mouth of Big White Oak Creek.

"This has to be it," Jonas said.

"Over there is the fording place, see the wagon tracks heading into the creek?" Crockett asked.

"Go ahead and go to it, just go slow through the water," Jonas cautioned.

The creek was clear and had a rock bottom, so it was an ideal spot to ford.

"This is a beautiful creek," Jonas said.

"Reckon there is any of them great fish like we saw yesterday in here?" Crockett asked.

"I doubt that something that big would come up the creek, but you never know," answered Jonas.

The team took them out of the water and up on a rolling hill, which presented the valley to them. The road was heavily used. They could tell this by the numerous wagon tracks and horse tracks.

As they traveled up the valley, they marveled at this picturesque landscape.

They passed two wagons and one man on horse back, also two boys carrying fishing poles toward the creek.

Most of the leaves were on the trees, and folks were here and there planting the fields and gardens. Jonas and Crockett were in awe at what their eyes beheld.

"Paw this is a fine place, this Big White Oak Valley," Crockett said.

"It sure is, it is much more beautiful than I expected," Jonas said.

As they traveled up the valley another couple miles they saw a buggy come over a rise in the road. It was making good time they noticed.

"Paw here comes a buggy and it is coming lickety-split," Crockett announced.

"I see it son, wonder what is the hurry?" Jonas asked.

In about two more minutes the buggy pulled up beside the Whitt wagon. The driver was an older plump man, and the passenger was a handsome woman in her early twenties.

"Hello there," the older man said.

"Are you Jonas Whitt?" he asked before Jonas could speak.

"Yes sir, I am Jonas and this here is my son David Crockett Whitt," Jonas answered.

"Glad to meet you gentlemen, I am Samuel Truitt and this is my daughter Mildred we call her Millie," Samuel said.

"Glad to meet you sir and your daughter," Jonas said as he tipped his hat toward Millie.

Millie gave them a beautiful smile, as did the gentleman Dr. Samuel Truitt.

"We been looking for you for about a month," Samuel said.

"We have been traveling since the last day of March, had to go slow with this heavy wagon," Jonas explained.

"I brought all my tools, and a few farming implements, plus

traveling gear," Jonas added.

"Well you fellers are a sight for sore eyes, I mean that in a good way Mister Whitt," Samuel stated.

"I know what you mean Mister Truitt, I feel the same way about seeing you and Miss Truitt," Jonas said.

"Mister Whitt, how about calling me Sam?" Samuel said.

"Fine sir, please call me Jonas, after all we will be seeing a lot of each other," Jonas answered.

"Well Jonas, the longer we sit here, the longer it will be before you get to your purpose," Samuel said.

"I will turn this buggy around and get back to the Inn, and get ready for you and young Crockett," he said as he circled the Whitt wagon.

"How much further is it Sam?" Jonas asked.

"You will be there in about an hour, just stop at the Inn right beside the road," Samuel instructed.

"Thanks Sam, we will be there dreckly," Jonas said.

The speedy buggy moved out of sight once again. Crockett drove the team up through the valley at a little accelerated speed. Jonas and Crockett talked about this new land in Greenup County Kentucky. They talked about Dr. Samuel Truitt, and even mentioned his lovely daughter Mildred. Before they knew it they had talked themselves the last mile of the way. There ahead was a big two story Inn, also there was a big family house and several other buildings. One little building had a sign reading "Truittville Post Office."

As they pulled up to the Inn, Jonas had a thought of Hannah and those they left behind.

"Tonight or tomorrow, I am going write to Hannah and the rest of our family and let them know we made it here, I will let them know about this place and that they are dearly missed," Jonas said as he looked at the post office.

"That is a good idea, they don't know where we are, what I mean, they don't know if we made it yet," answered Crockett.

"I understand son, they will be glad to get our letter," Jonas said.

"Our letter Paw, does that mean it is from me too?" Crockett asked.

"Of course, the letter will be from you too, you can even write something in it," Jonas answered.

By now Samuel, Louisa, and Mildred were greeting them at their wagon.

Samuel was a nice looking gentleman, but a little chubby. He had a round face with no beard, only a nicely trimmed mustache. He spoke in a calm manner with a friendly disposition. He was a proper person with good breeding and up bringing. He made everyone feel at ease in his presence.

Louisa was the daughter that ran the Truitt Inn. She was just opposite of her father. She talked a lot and said what she thought regardless of where the words landed.

Mildred was a handsome lady, that smiled at Jonas and Crockett. She did not say much but her feelings could be felt by others.

Samuel took the hand of Jonas and gave him a genuine welcome. And then also shook Crockett's hand. The girls did like wise. Jonas did not want to read anything in it but his heart leaped when he took Millie's hand.

"Did you all have a good trip up from Tazewell County?" Samuel asked.

"Yes sir I think so, but I am glad to have finally reached your home," Jonas answered.

"Well I am glad you all made it without a major problem," Samuel continued.

"Are you gentleman hungry?" Louisa asked.

"Yes Miss Louisa, I think we both could eat," Jonas answered.

There was a man working in the stable that Jonas noticed. Samuel noticed Jonas looking toward the stable. Samuel waved for the man to come over. The man dropped his work on the table by the stable and came to meet Jonas.

"This is Tony Montivon, he makes shoes for our little berg, and does other things to help people," Samuel said.

"Hello there Tony, I am Jonas Whitt, this here is my boy Crockett," Jonas said.

"Glad to meet you Jonas, and you Crockett," Tony said in a deep French assent.

"Where are you from Tony?" Jonas asked.

"I am a Frenchman from Canada," he answered.

"Would you like for me to care for your animals while you have your dinner?" Tony asked.

"We can take care of them," Jonas said.

"No, No, Mister Whitt, let me do this for you and young Crockett," Tony said.

"Let him help Jonas, he loves to stay busy," Samuel said.

"Well if you insist," Jonas answered.

Tony went up and took hold of the halter of the lead mule and led them toward the big barn.

Samuel turned to Jonas and Crockett.

"Jonas, let me show you your room and then you and Crockett eat you dinner, take the rest of the day and get settled," Samuel said.

"If you need anything, anything at all don't hesitate to ask," Samuel said as he led Jonas and Crockett into the Inn.

"Now this bottom floor is a tavern and dining area, and here is the steps up to the rooms," Samuel said pointing them out.

Jonas noticed that a couple of families were eating and a few single men also. It was a nice Inn for the time and area.

Samuel led Jonas and Crockett up the stairs and to the last room on the left. It had bunk beds, a wash stand, a small desk, and a little iron stove.

"Thank you Samuel this will do just fine," Jonas said.

"Welcome Jonas, have you ever used a stove for heat?" Samuel Asked.

"No sir, matter of fact I ain't never seen one, I have heard of them though," Jonas answered.

"It does a fine job, I got one in every room, had them shipped down from Pittsburgh last summer," Samuel explained.

"If you want a bath, just tell Louisa and she will see that you have a tub of hot water prepared," Samuel added.

"I will be around bout supper time and we can talk some," Samuel said as he was heading out the door.

Jonas went over and sit down to try out the bed. Crockett followed him and sit down too.

"Well Crockett, we are here, guess we will have to build Samuel a mill." Jonas said.

"Guess so Paw, when will we start?" Crockett asked.

"In the morning son, we will figure it all out in the morning," Jonas answered.

Jonas and Crockett went down by the barn to get some of their things from the wagon. They walked around in the area of the house, barn, and Inn, just taking in the lay of the land. Both of them were getting hungry, so they took their belongings to the Inn. On the way upstairs Jonas told Louisa that they would like something to eat. After dinner Jonas would walk the creek bank and get some ideas where to build the new grist mill.

After eating dinner, and relaxing a spell, Jonas and Crockett got up and headed out to see the Truitt farm.

As they went by the big house, Mary Elizabeth Gibbs (Polly) was sitting on the porch. She waved at Jonas and Crockett to come closer.

"I am Polly, Sam's wife, you must be Mister Whitt," she said.

"Yes ma-am, I am Jonas, this here is Crockett my boy," he said.

"Well Jonas you call me Polly, everybody else does," Polly said.

"I want to welcome you and Crockett to our place, just make yourself to home," she added.

"Thank you Polly, we are out stretching our legs and are going to look at the creek," Jonas answered.

About that time Mildred came out of the house and waved at Jonas and Crockett.

"Hello Miss Mildred," Jonas said.

Crockett tipped his hat, but didn't say any thing!

"Millie, Jonas and Crockett are going on a walk to see the property, would you mind walking with them and showing them around?" Polly asked.

"I will be glad to show them around if Mister Whitt would like," Mildred said.

"Call me Jonas, and we would be glad for you to show us around," Jonas answered.

Mildred joined Jonas and Crockett on their walk about. She pointed out the Post Office, the little shoe factory that Tony ran. She pointed to a few other cabins and told Jonas who lived in them. They walked down by Big White Oak Creek, so that Jonas could get some ideas as to where to build the new mill.

"This is a purty farm, and everything Miss Mildred," Crockett said.

"Well thank you Crockett, we try to be self-sufficient, Paw is the Post Master, Medical Doctor, Engineer, Farmer, and School Teacher, she said.

"The one big thing we lack in Truittville is a Grist Mill," Mildred added.

"Me and Paw will fix you one of them," Crockett said.

"I know you will, and that will help a lot of people," She said.

"I meant the purty hills and this little valley when I said purty farm," Crockett said.

"Yes, we love our hills here in Greenup County," Mildred answered.

Jonas went down close to the creek and inspected every aspect of it as they walked. The farm was laid out on mostly level ground with a rise on the upper end. The level areas by the creek were well kept and mostly treeless.

"Do you ever have floods that get out of the banks?" Jonas asked.

"Never has yet, but it does get up sometimes, and in the hot part of summer it gets down kinda low," she said.

"That is good to know, there may not be any grinding when the creek gets low, most people do their milling in the fall and winter anyway," Jonas stated.

"Looks like the creek bottom is mostly rock," Jonas added.

"What about fish Miss Mildred, are there any fish in this creek?" Crockett asked.

"Sure is, we catch Red Eyes, and some Small Mouth Bass in the bigger holes," she answered.

This brought a wide grin to Crockett's face.

"Go ahead and ask her Crockett," Jonas said.

"Miss Mildred, I was fishing yesterday evening in Tygart, and a giant fish bit my bass right into," Crockett explained.

"Muskie, you had a Muskie after your bass, I have seen some about four foot long," she answered.

"Will they eat people?" Crockett asked.

"Never heard of it," she said laughing.

"My Paw caught one about three feet long one time, it's mouth was full of teeth, folks come from all around to fish for them, you have to use a wire at the end of your line to fasten your hook on it because of the teeth," Mildred explained.

Crockett looked at Jonas and grinned real big.

"I guess you want to go after one?" Jonas asked.

"When we get the mill done, we might have time, huh Paw?" Crockett asked.

"We will see Son, we will get the mill built as soon as possible," Jonas said.

"Miss Mildred, where could I get some letter writing materials?" Jonas asked.

"Paw keeps some around the Post Office," she replied.

"I bet your folks back home are anxious to hear from you, especially your wife," Mildred said.

"Yes my little girl Hannah is staying with my brother James and his wife, my dear wife passed about eight years ago," Jonas said.

"So sorry to hear that Jonas," replied Mildred.

"Thanks Miss Mildred, we better get back and get settled in I guess," Jonas said.

CHAPTER 22

BUILDING A MILL IN TRUITVILLE

Jonas and Crockett headed to the Post Office on the way back to the Inn. By now it was getting close to supper time and Jonas wanted to write that letter to Hannah and the rest of the family.

Just as they got to the post office, Samuel Truitt was just coming out. Samuel was the post master and he worked about an hour a day in the little office. The post rider only come by on Monday and Thursday, to bring mail and take it back to Greenup and South Shore. Greenup was a bigger Post Office and sent mail out by boat, wagon, and riders, as did South Shore. South Shore lay across the Ohio River from Portsmouth Ohio.

"Hello Jonas and you too Crockett, do you have some mailing to do?" asked Samuel.

"Just looking for some letter writing materials, so we can write the folks back home," Jonas said.

"I will get you some stationary and envelopes, then I am heading over to get Polly, we eat most of our meals in the Inn," explained Samuel.

Samuel gave Jonas a few sheets of paper and a couple of envelopes, and locked the door to the Post Office.

"Jonas I will see you all at the Inn, after supper we will talk about building me a mill, if that is all right with you?" Samuel asked.

"That will be fine, a feller thinks better on a full belly," Jonas said.

Samuel headed over to his big house to escort Polly to supper. Jonas and Crockett headed back to their room to put away their papers and get ready for supper.

"We will write that letter soon as we can get back from supper, remember me and Mister Truitt have some business first," Jonas exclaimed.

"Paw I seen a calendar at the post office, this is Tuesday the eleventh, that means the mail goes out day after tomorrow," Crockett said.

"Don't worry son the letter will go with the post carrier on Thursday," Jonas answered.

"Are you going to write something in it?" Jonas asked.

"I reckon I will, I don't want anybody forgetting me," Crockett said.

"They ain't likely to forget you Crockett," Jonas said laughing.

Jonas and Crockett went to their room, laid their paper on the little desk that Sam had provided. Then they washed their hands and headed down for supper.

Louisa ask where they would like to be seated, and took them to a table by a window. She brought them both a plate of steaming beef stew, corn bread, and hot tea to drink. She also told them about deserts.

They had just started to eat when they noticed Samuel and Polly come in the door. Samuel and Polly both gave Jonas and Crockett a wave. Jonas and Crockett waved back and kept eating. Samuel and Polly both sat at a table in the corner which had a little sign on it, reading reserved.

"That must be the Truitt's favorite table Paw," Crockett whispered.

Jonas nodded his head at Crockett.

After a leisurely meal topped off with apple cobbler, Crockett and his Paw were full to the brim.

"What are you going to do while me and Mister Truitt talk business?" Jonas asked.

"If you don't mind I think I will go up and write my letter," Crockett answered.

"That will be fine, but will you bring that case of my mill drawings down to me first?" Jonas asked.

"Sure will, is it with your clothes bag?" Crockett asked.

"I set it right beside the desk, you can't miss it," Jonas said.

Crockett was up the steps and back in quick time.

"This is it, ain't it Paw?" Crockett asked.

"Sure is son now go write your letter, I will be up dreckly," Jonas said.

"If you get bored you can go out and look around, just don't interrupt me and Mister Truitt," Jonas exclaimed.

"Don't worry Paw, I know not to brother you when you do business," Crockett said.

"Good boy," Jonas answered.

Jonas spread out some of his drawings on the table so he could explain mill workings to Samuel Truitt.

Samuel helped Polly up from the table, gave her a little kiss, and told her he would be home after Jonas and he were finished talking business.

Crockett went up stairs to write his letter.

Mister Truitt lit a cigar and offered one to Jonas.

"I will take one for later Sam, I will do better explaining this stuff without smoking," Jonas answered.

Jonas dug out an old drawing of a bottom shot grist mill, and turned it so that Sam could see it.

"Sam this is the mill that we will build, it is the best type for the creek and terrain I have observed here," Jonas said.

Sam just sit and studied the drawing as Jonas explained.

"It looks complicated," Samuel said.

"It can be, but it will all make sense to you later," Jonas answered.

"Miss Mildred showed me the creek and the land this afternoon, and I feel this is the best type to build here," Jonas continued.

"I think up the creek just below the little knoll, will be a good place to build it," Jonas said.

"How do you get the water to it?" Samuel asked.

"That is a good question, it will involve the most work of the whole thing," Jonas said.

"We will build the mill thirty to forty feet off the creek, and dig a trace off the creek to the wheel," Jonas pointed out.

"Now do you have people to help dig the trace?" Jonas asked.

"We can get the labor for that, what else do we need to think about Jonas?" Samuel asked.

"Well Sir, we need lumber for the building that houses the mill, we need red wood for the wheel, and we need timbers to hold up the great weight of the mill works." Jonas said.

"We will need some Iron brackets, and hardware, Oh! yes we will have to acquire two mill wheels," Jonas continued.

"Granite is best material to make grinding wheels from, but hard to get, so limestone will work," Jonas explained.

"My brother Richard, lives down in Carter County, you know the man that told you about me, he said they had plenty of limestone in that area," Jonas said.

"Yes I remember Richard, is he a stone cutter?" Samuel asked.

"That is not a regular trade for him, but he has cut stone before," Jonas answered.

Samuel looked at the drawing again, and scratched his head.

"That Alfred Thompson that you met on the trail is a fine lumber man, he will fill your order for the boards, and timbers" Samuel said.

"What about foundation stone, I think we can get that out of the creek and out of the ground we dig, do you think that will work?" Samuel asked.

"I would think so," Jonas answered.

"Samuel, do you have limestone or Granite about, and do you know a stone cutter?" Jonas asked.

"Well I will have to think about that," Samuel said.

"I can cut them out, but it will expedite things if I can order them and spend my time building the mill," Jonas said.

"Do you think Richard Whitt can provide the mill stones?" Samuel asked.

"I think he could," replied Jonas.

"Just off the top of your head Jonas, how long do you think it will take to get her built?" Samuel asked.

"Too many factors, but I would give a wild guess of about a year to a year and a half," Jonas answered.

"That is about what I guessed," Samuel surmised.

"Here Jonas explain this drawing, I see the big water wheel, do you have to make the gears to turn the stone grinding wheel?" Samuel asked.

"Yes I have to build it all, the water wheel, the big gear, the little gear and the shafts, shoots and make it all adjustable," Jonas said.

Jonas explained the workings but did not share all the secrets of mill building with Samuel. If everyone knew how to build a mill, who would need a mill-right, Jonas thought.

"I will go out and start laying out the earth works and do some planning in the morning, I have a material list," Jonas said.

"That will be great," Samuel said.

"I will come by and see what you need, but don't worry I will let you be fully in charge, that is what I hired you for," Samuel said.

"I am a might tired Samuel, would you excuse me, I want to write that letter before I retire," Jonas said.

"Of course you are tired, I am just anxious to have a mill, you go and take care of things and I will see you sometime in the morning," Samuel answered.

"By the way Jonas, my stable man is taking care of your mules and saddle horse for you," Samuel said.

"Thank you so much Sam, I thought you were, see you on the morrow Sam," Jonas said.

Jonas went up the steps to his room, wondering if Crockett finished his letter.

As Jonas came in the room, Crockett was sitting at the desk still writing on his letter.

"You still writing, Crockett?" Jonas asked.

"Yes sir, I had to decide what to write and then figure out how to spell some of the words," Crockett answered.

"Well son the spelling is not that important to family, long as they can make it out," Jonas said.

"Good thing Paw," Crockett answered.

"Are you about done?" he asked.

"Just got to sign my name Paw," Crockett answered.

"Would you like to read it and check it over for me?" Crockett asked.

"I can if you don't mind me knowing what you wrote," Jonas said.

Crockett gave the letter to Jonas to read. Jonas sit down on the bed and read the letter.

Dear Hannah, Uncle James and the hole family.

Me and Paw got here in Truittsville today may 11, and it is a purty place. The Truitts are good people I think. Sam is a rich man. Mildred his girl likes me and Paw. We have a orn stove in our room. They are big fish in Tygart creek that are so big one bit my bass into. We had a purty good trip I reckon. Seen some necked women, a man got hung, us and the mules rode a boat a cross vicy river. Me and paw had to stand off a outlaw, and some Fleming fellows. We stopped and seen Uncle John in floyd county. We gonna start building the mill tomorrow. I luv you Hannah, Elizabeth, Emma, James Griffy, John , Rachel, Rhoda, and all your families. We miss you so much and you to uncle James and aint Nancy.

Yours truly David Crockett Whitt

Jonas smiles as he hands the letter back to Crockett.

"Is it alright Paw?" Crockett asked.

"It will be fine," Jonas replied.

Jonas thought to himself, what questions the folks back home would have after reading Crockett's letter.

"Paw did you and Mister Truitt have a good meeting about the mill?" Crockett asked.

"I think so, we are going to lay out some of the work in the morning, and make more plans," Jonas explained.

"It is about to get dark, do you need to go out and visit the Johnny before bed?" Jonas asked.

"I might ort to," Crockett answered.

Jonas sit down to collect his thoughts and put them into his letter home.

This is what he wrote:

May 11, 1847
Truitt Inn, Truittville, Greenup County, Kentucky

Dear Hannah, James, Nancy and Family,

It has been a hard trip, but we made it just fine. We arrived this afternoon and have already got plans to build the mill for Doctor Samuel Truitt. We are fine but are a little tired. We had no great problems on the trip, but it was an adventure.

We spent two days with brother John Bunyon over in Floyd County. They were doing fine.

I intend to get the new grist mill built expediently so Crockett and I can return home to you. I now wonder if I did the right thing leaving little Hannah there. I know she is being cared for and is not subject to dangers of travel. I truly miss her as does Crockett. We miss all of you.

This is a pretty land and the people are good from all that I can tell. We have a nice room in the Truitt Inn. As Crockett mentioned in his letter, we have an iron stove for heat. The food is good in the tavern down stairs.

Crockett and I are both well and ready for the challenge of building the mill. We hope to be on our way back home next spring, Lord permitting.

How is everyone doing in Tazewell County? Please write us letters and keep us informed as to happenings, and your lives.

I hope to visit Brother Richard in Carter County about a days ride from here, while we are here.

Hannah and family we love you! Write soon.

Love you. Jonas Whitt

Jonas took Crockett's letter and put it with his, he folded them and put them in the envelope. Jonas wrote the address on the envelope, Hannah Whitt, C/O James Whitt, Kentucky Turnpike, Tazewell County, Virginia. Next he dropped some candle wax on it to seal it.

"Well Crockett it is ready to take to the post office," Jonas said.

Crockett was laying in the top bunk, and looked at his Paw.

"Paw we still have to pay the postage when we give it to Mister Truitt," Crockett answered.

"Some time tomorrow I will take it in the post office and pay the postage, then Thursday it will go out with the rider," Jonas exclaimed.

"I can't believe we finally got here, can you Paw?" Crockett asked.

"It has been a long trip, but we are here and start work tomorrow," Jonas said.

"I am blowing out the lamp, you go to sleep, I will see you in the morning," Jonas said.

"Good night Paw, don't forget to pray your prayers," Crockett said.

"I will pray out loud, right now so you will know I prayed," Jonas said.

Jonas begin his prayer: "Dear Heavenly Father, we give thanks for your loving kindness, and watch care over your servants. Lord we thank you for bringing us to this new land safely. We pray for our loved ones we left at home, Lord watch over them and keep them safe we pray. Lord we pray for your wisdom and strength to build the mill for Mister Truitt. We ask a blessing on this new land and help us to be your true servants. Dear Lord we pray for the forgiveness of our sins and short comings. Lord we pray that when you are done with us that you will take us unto your bosom and into the promised rest of your Heaven. We ask this in the name of Jesus Christ, Amen."

Crockett fell asleep with a smile on his face. They both slept well and woke to a nice Kentucky May day. The weather was warm and no sign of rain was seen.

"Good morning Crockett, you ready to go and start that mill?" Jonas asked.

"Well I guess so, soon as I can get woke up," Crockett answered.

"We can go down and eat some breakfast and wake up on some coffee," Jonas answered.

Jonas and Crockett jumped in their overalls and hooked their galluses, washed their faces and hands and were ready for the day. They headed down stairs into the eatery.

Louisa was carrying a pot of coffee to each table. She looked up to see Jonas and Crockett coming to eat.

"Good morning Jonas, and you too Crockett," Louisa said.

"Good morning to you Miss Louisa," Jonas said.

"Morning Ma-ma," Crockett said as he headed to the table by the window.

"Coffee?" Louisa asked.

"Yes, a cup for both of us please," Jonas answered.

The dining area was full of folks this morning. Men ready for a days work and some ladies also. Some of them were people only spending the night at Truitt's Inn.

Louisa brought the Whitts coffee, and told them that she had a big skillet of gravy, and some Cathead biscuits.

"I can fix you some bust eggs too," she added.

"Two eggs a piece and some of that Kentucky gravy and biscuits will be just fine," Jonas said.

Jonas and Crockett enjoyed their breakfast, and headed to their wagon to get some items needed to lay out the mill. Crockett also went over and seen Jake and the mules. Bill Thompson (William Randolph Thompson) was working in the big barn caring for the live stock.

"I am Bill Thompson, I work for Doctor Truitt, you must be the Whitts," Bill said.

"That's right Bill," Jonas answered.

"I am Jonas and this is my son, Crockett," Jonas continued.

"I been taking care of your mules and that fine saddle horse for you, do you want them turned out in the field?" Bill asked.

"Thank you so much Bill that will be fine, we have to get some twine, a measuring tape, a hatchet out of the wagon, and get to work," Jonas said.

"Doctor Truitt told me to follow along and do what ever you need me to do," Bill said.

"I didn't know Bill, that will be a heap of help," Jonas answered.

Jonas and Crockett got the tools and headed up the creek to the rise in the creek bank. Bill finished up and let the animals loose into the big pasture, next he followed Jonas and Crockett up the creek.

Jonas and Crockett laid down the tools about thirty feet from the creek.

Jonas walked over to the creek with Crockett and Bill following right behind him. Jonas looked up and down the creek. He scratched his head and spit out a shot of amber. He turned to look at Bill and Crockett.

"At the lower end of that little hole is where we will build the dam, want a chew, Bill?" Jonas asked.

"Got some Jonas," Bill answered.

"What are you going to use to build the dam with?" Bill asked.

"Mostly rocks," Jonas said.

"It don't have to hold back all the water, just enough to convert it through the trace," Jonas explained.

"Trace, what trace?" Bill asked.

"The one we are going to dig from the creek to the mill and back to the creek," Jonas answered.

"I need for you to sharpen me some stakes about two foot long," Jonas said to Bill.

"Bout how many you needing Jonas?" Bill asked.

"About two dozen I reckon, Crockett go with Bill up in the edge of the woods and help cut some of them saplings for stakes," Jonas instructed.

Bill and Crockett headed up the rise and Jonas walked up and down the creek bank looking it over.

Jonas got out the drawing of the mill and looked it over again, gathering the thoughts that would someday transverse into a two story mill with water flowing swiftly under the twenty foot wheel and grinding grain. He carried the paper to the edge of the creek again and looked at the creek and back at the drawing.

Next Jonas stepped off about fifteen paces straight from the creek. He dug in his right heel to mark the spot. This will be where the water wheel will set, thought Jonas.

Crockett come down off the hill with an arm load of stakes, and Bill Thompson continued to cut more stakes.

"Paw, did you say stakes or snakes?" Crockett asked.

"Stakes, don't want no snakes," Jonas answered.

"Bill kilt a copperhead right beside a sapling he was cuttun," Crockett said.

"My goodness, did it strike at him?" Jonas asked.

"It bit his hatchet, and then Bill hacked it in two," Crockett said.

"Thank God it didn't bite you all," Jonas said.

"That reminds me of a story," Jonas said.

"About the rattle snake a biting the log Paw?" Crockett asked.

"Yelp, I will tell it to Bill when he gets back here," Jonas said.

Bill Thompson is back with another arm load of stakes.

"Crockett tell you bout that copperhead Jonas?" Bill asked.

"Yes he did, that sounded like a close call for you," Jonas answered.

"Kinda was," Bill said.

"It reminds me of when a feller back home was logging," Jonas said.

"What happened Jonas?" Bill asked.

Well Bill, the fellers name was John, he cut out a nice ten foot log about a foot through it. He went over to put a chain on it to drag it to the saw mill and there was a giant Timber Rattler. That ol snake reared back and struck at John but missed and bit the log.

"What happened next?" Bill asked.

"Well John came down on that rattler with his double bit ax and whacked off his head," Jonas continued.

"What went on next?" Bill asked.

"Well Bill that log began to swell and it got about twenty five foot long and about four foot thick," Jonas answered.

"What on earth did John do with it then?" Bill asked.

"He got four yoke of oxen and drug it to the sawmill, cut it into fine lumber, and built himself a fine barn," Jonas continued.

"My goodness Jonas, is that all of the story?" Bill asked.

"Nope, in about three days the swelling went out and John had himself a nice chicken coop, it was a good thing he didn't have his horses in it," Jonas said with a grin.

Bill laid back and hollered and laughed.

"You really had me going for awhile Jonas, that is a real good story," Bill exclaimed.

"Well we better get to work, this mill ain't gonna build it self," Jonas said.

Jonas showed Crockett where he had marked the ground with his heel.

"Put a stake right here and drive it in straight, leave about a foot of sticking out," Jonas instructed.

Crockett drove in the stake and stood up for more instructions.

Jonas got out his tape measure and handed one end to Bill.

"Here Bill, hold it on the stake, please," Jonas said.

As Bill held the end of the tape Jonas stretched it out parallel with the creek to a length of eight feet.

"Here Crockett drive in another stake," Jonas said.

Crockett drove it in straight and left about a foot above the ground just like the other.

"That is fine son," Jonas said.

"Now Bill would you hold it on this stake?" Jonas asked.

As Bill held it on the second stake Jonas moved in another direction, straight away from the creek to another eight feet. Jonas squatted down and eyeballed the line to the stake.

"Stake right here Crockett," Jonas said.

Crockett moved to the spot and sunk another stake, straight and true.

"Alright Bill, hold it here on this stake please," Jonas instructed.

"Crockett let me have one of them stakes, Jonas said.

Jonas took the stake, stretched the tape to eight feet back in the down stream direction and marked the spot with an arch drawn with the stake.

"Bill move to the first stake again and hold it for me," Jonas instructed.

Bill moved the tape to the first stake and Jonas stretched the tape measure to eight feet away from the creek to the arch he scribed in the ground. Jonas took the stake again and scribed out another arch across the first arch.

"Stake it right here Crockett, right at the cross of the two arches," Jonas instructed.

After Crockett sank the fourth stake, Jonas had Bill hold the tape measure on one stake as he measured straight across from corner to corner. Then he had Bill move eight feet to the next stake. Once again Jonas measured straight across corner to corner. Jonas pulled the last stake and moved it about two inches. Then he moved the next stake about two inches.

"Alright Bill lets measure from corner to corner again," Jonas said.

"Paw, you are squaring it up, ain't you?" Crockett asked.

"Yelp, trying to," Jonas answered.

Bill held the tape again and then on the opposite corner just like before.

"Great that is real close," Jonas said with a smile.

"I wondered what we were doing measuring back and forth corner to corner," Bill said.

"I ain't never seen nobody square up something before," he added.

"This is where the water wheel will sit," Jonas exclaimed.

"Right cher?" Bill asked.

"That's right Bill," Jonas answered.

"We must be forty, fifty foot off the creek," Bill exclaimed.

"I know, we are going to bring the creek to the mill," Jonas said.

"Alright Jonas, you are the mill builder, I will be quiet," Bill said.

"That is alright, you may ask a question any time you want," Jonas answered.

Next Jonas, Bill, and Crockett laid out a trace to come into the creek just above the proposed dam. They staked it all out as they stretched a line to make it straight and true.

As they were laying out the return trace away from the water wheel area back to the creek, Doctor Samuel Truitt and Millie came over to talk to Jonas.

"Hello Sam and you too Miss Mildred," Jonas said.

"Good day to you gentleman," Samuel answered.

"Please call me Millie, Jonas and you too Crockett," Millie said with a smile.

"Well good day Miss Millie," Jonas answered.

"Hello Miss Millie," Crockett said sheepishly.

Samuel told them he was on his way over to the post office to do a little work and thought he would ask how things were going. Jonas showed Samuel the work that was already laid out, and pointed out the spot the water wheel would be.

"Plumb over here," Samuel exclaimed.

"We are going to bring the water to it Mister Truitt," Bill Thompson explained.

Jonas and Crockett looked at Bill and smiled.

"Alright men, you are the mill-rights, not me," Samuel said.

"Jonas have you got a material lists ready yet?" Samuel asked. Yes sir, It is all written out here in my book, as I said before we are going to build this undershot mill in the drawing," Jonas explained.

"I will let you borrow this book for a day and you can scribe you out a copy, or have Miss Millie do it for you," Jonas suggested.

"Alright I can do that, you show Millie what needs written out if you would," Samuel said.

"Just as soon as we get done with our talk I will show Millie what we need scribed out," Jonas answered.

I have been thinking about the grinding stones Sam, Granite is the very best stone to cut them out of," Jonas said.

"We could order them and have them shipped to us at a later date while we do the other work," Jonas said.

"What about the limestone wheels from your brother?" Sam asked.

"We can get them, but limestone is softer than granite and must be dressed much more often," Jonas answered.

"Well Jonas do you have a place in mind to order them from?" Samuel asked.

"The very best, but most costly come from Italy, the Gerardi Family in Pittsburgh deal in importing them," Jonas explained.

"They usually keep a set and can ship as soon as they receive payment," Jonas explained."Do we really need two grinding stones Jonas?" Samuel asked.

"Yes sir, a set stone and a turn stone," Jonas explained.

"How much would it take to get two stones delivered to South Shore or Greenup?" Samuel asked.

"Now Sam this will be the most costly purchase for the mill, I can make everything else except for some hardware," Jonas said.

"How much Jonas?" Samuel asked.

"I would think between one hundred fifty and two hundred dollars, including shipping them down the Ohio," Jonas said.

"That is expensive Jonas, but I want something that will last and require less maintenance, let's get them ordered.

"Best way would be have the bank draft them a check for one hundred dollars and pay the rest when they arrive," Jonas said.

"You may add my name as the mill-right since I have dealt with them before," Jonas added.

"Jonas you get a drawing and description of the stones ready and write out the requirements, sign your name at the bottom and I will get them ordered," Samuel instructed.

"I will have it ready for the postman tomorrow Sam," Jonas said.

"By the way do you have your letters ready to mail?" Samuel asked.

"Now Samuel we are just about ready to dig, and I want to build a storage building here near by the mill," Jonas explained.

"Alright Jonas I will get you some labor to do the digging, my brother over in Lewis County has eight servants he will contract out," Samuel said.

"Also I will get with Alfred Thompson and have him start getting your lumber to you," Samuel continued.

"Sounds good, we will be grinding grain before you know it," Jonas said.

"Do you have someone in mind to be your miller?" Jonas asked.

"William Randolph Thompson, that is why I put him with you from the ground up," Samuel said.

"Now Sam, I will not have Millie copy the hardware list, I intend having Richard Whitt fabricate it in his blacksmith shop, if that is alright with you?" Jonas asked.

"Long as he is fair and does a good job, I will leave that to you," Samuel said.

Millie took the book and asked Jonas to explain and point out what had to be copied. Jonas explained in a real soft voice as he enjoyed being close to Millie.

"Jonas have you got time to sit on the porch with me for a minute, and make sure I know what to copy?" Millie asked.

Samuel headed to the Post Office.

Jonas sent Crockett to their room to get the letters and take them to the post office, and he headed to the porch with Millie Truitt.

CHAPTER 23

JONAS FALLS IN LOVE

Jonas points out all that needs to be copied. Then he dictates another small list that he wants first. The last list of material will be for a shed to store things in and a place to get in out of the weather while the mill is under construction.

"Now Millie, this last list will be what I want first, I am going to build a big shed to store material in," Jonas said.

"I will explain that to Paw when I give it to him," she said.

"That will be good," Jonas answered.

"Millie I was wondering, what is that growing out in that upper field?" Jonas asked.

"You must be talking about the hemp, we have a market for it here in Kentucky, they use it to make ropes," she said.

"I have used rope made from it for a long time, but I never seen it growing before," Jonas replied.

"Well that's it," Millie said with a smile.

Jonas and Millie sat for a little while talking about Greenup County, and Kentucky.

Jonas was curious about some of the things in this new place that he had come to.

"Millie how did the county get it's name?" Jonas asked.

"They named it after Christopher Greenup is about all I know about that, I do know that he was a Governor one time," Millie answered.

"There seems to be several folks living about," Jonas said.

"I heard Paw say we were getting up to about nine thousand in population," Millie said.

"That is a bunch of people," Jonas replied.

"Yes it is and we have several men from Kentucky serving in the war against Mexico," she said.

"Who is your Governor now?" Jonas asked.

"William Owsley is his name," she answered.

"I have heard of Henry Clay, he is a famous man from Kentucky isn't he?" Jonas asked.

"Yes he is, we just heard that his son Henry Clay Jr. was killed in the Mexican War, which saddened our whole state," Millie said.

"Sorry about that, it seems that the soldiers pay the price for the rich men's wars," Jonas added.

"Sad but true," Millie answered.

"Well, Millie I see Crockett and Bill standing out there, guess I better go out and find them something to do," Jonas said.

"Jonas, Sunday is coming up, would you and Crockett like to go to church with us?" Millie asked.

"Do you all go to the little Baptist Church, we passed coming in the other day?" Jonas asked.

"Why yes, that is it," she answered.

"We will be glad to go and give it a try," Jonas said.

"What time do you leave?" Jonas asked.

"About 9:30, and you all can ride in our surrey, we have three seats so there will be room," she added.

"Make sure it is alright with Samuel and let me know by Saturday," Jonas said.

"It will be fine, Paw already said," replied the smiling Millie.

"Alright then we will be ready, got to go, and thanks Millie," Jonas said with a smile.

Jonas got up and stepped off the porch and almost fell down looking back at Millie. Millie let out a little giggle.

Jonas grinned and headed back to the field where Crockett and Bill were waiting.

A few short days passed and it was Sunday morning. Jonas and Crockett cleaned up and put on their best duds. Jonas even shaved his whiskers and give Crockett and himself a haircut.

About 9:25, the Truitt surrey pulled up to the front of the Truitt Inn.

"Paw you want me to go up and fetch Jonas?" Millie asked.

"Wait just a minute, it isn't 9:30 yet," Samuel said.

Millie was anxious to see Jonas and had become quite interested in the mill builder from Virginia.

"What time is it now Paw?" Millie asked again.

"Go ahead Millie, round them up," Samuel said.

About that time Jonas and Crockett appeared in the door way on their way to the awaiting Surrey. Millie had just stepped down and looked up to see them coming. A big smile appeared on Millie's face as it did on Jonas's face. She stood by the surrey and waited for Jonas to take her hand and help her up. Mary Truitt grinned at Samuel, and Samuel gave her a wink. Jonas took a seat by Millie and Crockett had the third seat all to himself.

"Get up Betsy," Samuel commanded the horse and away they went.

Jonas and Crockett enjoyed their first Lords Day in Greenup County. They had a good service and Jonas felt at home with the congregation. The Minister was an elderly man by the name of John Young.

"How old is Elder Young?" Jonas asked Millie.

"I think they said he will be eighty three on his next birthday," Millie answered.

"He looks old, but I would have guessed about seventy two," Jonas said.

"Yes he doesn't show his age," Millie said.

"Paw is all Baptist preachers names Young ?" Crockett asked from the back seat of the surrey.

"No son," Jonas said laughing.

"I doubt this John Young, knows our David Young back in Tazewell County," Jonas added.

"It is just a coincidence that both the Baptist church's have Preachers by the name of Young," Jonas explained.

Samuel struck up a conversation about this and that. After talking about Elder John Young and the church services, the topic went to the mill. Samuel could not help but think of the mill.

"Jonas I don't talk business on Sunday, but I wanted to let you know my brother George from Lewis County will arrive tomorrow sometime with six of his servants," Samuel said.

"After you get them started digging, you can head down to Carter County and see your brother to order your hardware," he added.

"Thank you sir, I will see to it," Jonas answered.

"Jonas, if you would like, come by the house and I will give you your material book back," Millie said.

"I will be by about 6:00 when it is nice and cool, and you can show me around a little more," Jonas said.

"That will be fine," Millie said with a smile.

Jonas and Crockett got out at the Inn and Samuel drove on to the house.

Mary and Millie got out and Samuel took the Surrey to the big barn.

"Millie, you be real careful, Jonas is much older than you, I don't want you to get your heart broken," Mary said with concern.

"Don't worry Maw, I will be careful, Jonas is so smart and handsome," Millie answered.

Crockett and Jonas took off their best clothes and Crockett shed his shoes. They went down for dinner at the eatery.

Louisa was busy with the Sunday meal. A large group always showed up on Sunday after church for dinner. Louisa had a big pile of chicken fried up, mashed potatoes, green beans from last years crop, gravy and biscuits. She was one busy little woman, going from table to table. Jonas and Crockett's favorite table by the window was taken so they found another one back in the corner.

"Paw do you think Millie is after you?" Crockett asked abruptly.

"I doubt that she is serious about me, would it be a bad thing, if she was?" Jonas asked.

"Well I reckon not, Maw has been gone a long time, I think it would be fine," Crockett said smiling.

"I may spend some time with her, will you get jealous?" Jonas asked.

"I won't get jealous, Paw," Crockett answered sternly.

"Well I am glad to have your blessing, if we were to get serious, which I doubt," Jonas said.

After dinner Jonas and Crockett walked up into the woods and rested. They read the Bible, and talked much like they did on the Lords Day back in Virginia. Jonas talked about the folks back home and about their new temporary home here in Kentucky. They had a really good visit with each other, and enjoyed the nice May weather. Jonas told Crockett about the trip he was going to take tomorrow to Carter County.

"What do you think Crockett, do you want to go with me or are you tired of traveling?" Jonas asked.

"Well what would I do if I stayed here?" Crockett asked.

"Fish, play, watch the men dig the trace, explore the surrounding hills and even wade the creek," Jonas said.

"You are almost a man, and I think you are perfectly able to take care of yourself," Jonas added.

"You can go with me but you will have to ride one of the mules, what do you think?" Jonas asked.

"How long will you be gone?" Crockett asked.

"Four or five days I would think, two days or better traveling, and two days there with brother Richard's family," Jonas answered.

"Paw I think I will go, I haven't seen Uncle Richard for a year," Crockett said.

I haven't seen the cousins for ever, and I wonder what James G. Whitt looks like, Crockett added.

"Paw, how come all your brothers name their children the same names, like Richard, Bunyon, and even James?" Crockett asked.

"I guess we just like some good old family names," Jonas answered.

"You know my cousins Richard Price Whitt, and Abijah Whitt live in Carter County too," Jonas said.

"Richard P. has a son David Crockett Whitt born about two years after you," Jonas added.

"Reckon we might see him too Paw?" Crockett asked.

"We will try to if it don't interfere with my business, I would love to see them all," Jonas added.

Jonas looked at his watch and it was almost supper time again.

"Paw it seems like we eat a lot, don't it?" Crockett asked.

"We are just on a schedule," Jonas answered.

Jonas reminded Crockett that he and Millie were going to take a walk after supper.

"You can come with us or you can just play," Jonas informed him. They went to have their supper, and the Truitt's sat at their regular table near them.

After supper and the normal conversations Jonas and Millie strolled out to walk up the creek. Jonas took Millie by the mill works and gave her a basic idea of the on going construction. He explained that her Uncle George was coming tomorrow and bring his servants to start digging the trace. He also told her that Crockett and he were going to Carter County to see Richard the next day or the next.

"How long will you be gone?" Millie asked in a concerned voice.

"About four or five days I reckon," Jonas answered.

"Do you have to go now, Oh! I'm sorry for meddling in your business," She said.

"That is alright, I do have to go and get Richard started working on making the hardware for the mill, he is also my family, and we have not had a visit for some time," Jonas answered.

"Richard has a son named James G. Whitt, and my Crockett wants to meet him," Jonas said smiling.

Millie took Jonas by the hand and said, "Please hurry back then."

There was a fire of love beginning to burn between Jonas and Millie!

What does this lovely young lady see in me? Jonas thought. Well any way, I can't seem to hold back, what will be will be he thought.

"Millie, I will be back in about five days, this will give us time to think where we are going with this relationship," Jonas said.

"I already know what I think, but five days separation will let you know," Millie said as she squeezed his hand.

Jonas felt the electric impulses of love flow from this beautiful creature.

Next morning brought a nice day, and it looked to get quite warm. They had a hot spell hit in the last week of May 1847 on Big White Oak.

Jonas and Crockett packed up a few things that they would need for the trip to Carter County and left it in their room. They had breakfast and walked around the marked of area for the dig.

George Truitt and Samuel came out of the house, and from around back of the big house came six big strong looking black men. They were not guarded, and looked to be healthy and wore rough but good clothes. They came in single file as if marching.

"Good morning Jonas, this is my brother George, he is going to get our digging took care of," Samuel said.

"Good morning George, good to meet you sir, and this is my son

Crockett," Jonas said.

"Good to meet you Jonas and you too, Crockett," George said.

"These are my servants, and they love to work, Basel is the lead man, if you explain what you want done he will see to it," George said.

Jonas went over to Basel and stuck out his hand. Basel looked dumbfounded.

"Jonas you don't shake their hands, that confuses them," George explained.

Jonas looked at George and back at Basel.

"Well Basel walk with me and I will show you the work," Jonas said.

Jonas walked to the squared off part where they had already laid out, followed by Basel, George, and Samuel. The other five Negroes waited back where they had originally stopped.

Jonas showed Basel the eight feet by eight feet square staked out and string stretched around it, and then pointed down the creek at the staked out trace.

"Basel, I want you to dig a hole the size of the marked off area first, dig it down to bed rock, then start digging the marked area all the way to the creek, understand?" Jonas asked.

"Yep sir Mister Jonas, I understand," Basel answered.

George smiled at Jonas!

"See Jonas he is a fine lead man and he will get the others going in short order," George said.

Basel went back to the other five and told them to go and get the picks and shovels and come back up to Jonas.

"Mister Jonas sir, you want the dirt put over toward the creek side sir?" asked Basel.

"That is right and I forgot to tell you, carry all the rocks back over there and pile them up as you dig them out," Jonas instructed as he pointed to a spot away from where the mill would be built.

Jonas looked at Crockett and saw an expression of amazement on the boys face.

Jonas, Samuel, and George, walked back about ten paces to give the Negroes room to work.

"Jonas I will see Alfred Thompson today, and will get him started on the lumber order, Also I will leave Bill here with the workers," Samuel said.

"If you have any more instructions you can tell them to Bill and Basel, before you head out," Samuel added.

"Alright Sir, I should be back about Friday or Saturday, Lord willing," Jonas said.

"Sir would you mind if Crockett rode that little filly with the blaze on her face on our trip?" Jonas asked.

"Not at all, I was going to offer her for the trip, but forgot," answered Samuel.

"Thank you sir, we better get a going," Jonas answered.

"Is Bill down at the barn?" Jonas asked.

"Think so Jonas, and you might ought to go by the house and tell Millie good by," Samuel said with a sneaky little grin on his face.

Jonas blushed a little, and headed toward the barn.

"Crockett will you go by and fetch our stuff we packed up, and also ask Louisa for a poke of vittles for the road," Jonas said.

"Sure will Paw," Crockett answered.

"I am going to the barn and talk with Bill and get our mounts ready for the trip," Jonas said as he walked away.

Crockett hurried to the Inn to get their things and some food to take on the trip.

As he went he was thinking about the big black Negroes, and also about getting to ride Mister Truitt's little filly. When Crockett got back to the barn, Jonas and Bill had the horses Jake, and Betsy saddled up.

Jonas looked in the packed items and dug out his old revolver and strapped it on.

"Expecting trouble Paw?" Crockett asked.

"No son, just want to be ready in case," Jonas answered.

Then they tied on their satchels including the food Louisa gave Crockett. They mounted up, as Jonas was still talking to Bill. Then Bill looked at Crockett.

"Crockett, your mount is called Betsy, she is a sweet little gal to ride," Bill said.

"Thanks Bill, I will take extra good care of her," Crockett

answered.

"Well son I am going to ride by the house and tell Millie good by, you can ride with me and we will be off," Jonas said.

"Be right behind you Paw, get up Betsy," Crockett said.

Millie was waiting on the porch when Jonas and Crockett rode up. Jonas rode up close to the banister where Millie was holding on to.

"We are about to head south, so we come by to bid you farewell," Jonas said in a low voice.

"You all be real careful and hurry back," Millie said while she stuck out her hand.

Jonas reached and took her hand and gave it a gentle squeeze. They looked into each others eyes as they felt the passion.

Jonas wheeled his horse and said in a much louder voice, "Farewell, we will see you in about five days."

"Good by Crockett, take care of your Paw and hurry back," Millie said.

"I will, and good by Miss Millie," Crockett answered.

Jonas led the way back by the mill construction to see if there were any more questions about the work. Bill was there and walked up to Jonas.

"Basel and his workers are getting right after it Jonas, they are down about a foot and a half already," Bill exclaimed.

"If they get the trace dug all the way to the creek on the down creek end before I get back let them dig up the creek, but stop them about ten feet from the creek," Jonas instructed.

"We don't want the creek running though the trace while we build the mill," Jonas added.

"I understand completely," Bill answered.

"Got to go, we are burning day light," Jonas said.

"Be careful, see you all when you get back," Bill said.

Jonas and Crockett were trotting by the Inn by now, Samuel and Louisa came out and gave them a wave.

Jonas and Crockett waved their hands and were soon out of sight heading toward the Tygart Creek.

"We will keep a good pace, but watch not to over work our horses," Jonas said.

"Jake has not been rode on a trip in a long time, and I don't know what shape Betsy is in," Jonas said in a concerned voice.

"Betsy seems to be up for it Paw," Crockett said.

"They are probably up for it more than our hind ends are," Jonas said with a little laugh.

It seemed like no time at all they were on the Tygart valley road heading south.

"Paw where do we cross over to the Little Sandy River?" Crockett asked."Not sure, Sam said we couldn't miss the road across to the Little Sandy Valley," Jonas answered. (The road is now (route 784)

"There is a little village near the other end of that road called Hopewell," Jonas added.

"That is a good name, ain't it Paw?" Crockett asked.

"Ye-al it sounds good, could be named after some one named Hope," Jonas said.

The ride was going good but the heat of early June was starting to heat up the horses.

"The horses are doing fine for now, but we may have to go a little slower this after noon," Jonas said.

"Paw maybe we can give them water and a little rest in Hopewell," Crockett said.

"Yes, but we can't tarry there for long, we have to get to Richard's before dark," Jonas emphasized.

As they rode along, they talked about first one thing then another. Crockett had some comments about the big black servants digging the trace.

"Paw ain't the Negroes "slaves," and don't they belong to Mister George Truitt?" Crockett asked.

"Well I reckon you are right son, servant is a word they use up this far north," Jonas said.

"The North criticizes the South about owning slaves, yet many of them have their own," Jonas said.

"We will have to watch what we say until we see how they talk about such matters," Jonas said.

"Paw I hope we get to stop by your first cousin's (Richard Price Whitt) so I can meet the younger David Crockett Whitt," Crockett said.

"We will certainly try too, Uncle Edmund lives thereabouts too, if he is still living, he is your Grand Paws brother," Jonas explained.

"That would be great if we got to see him Paw," Crockett announced.

"Yes it would, but I am afraid he may have passed on by now," Jonas said.

"Paw, we have a lot of kin folks here in Kentucky, don't we?" Asked Crockett.

"We sure do, and down in Morgan County we have a lot of cousins that I don't even know," Jonas added.

Before they knew it they had crossed over into the Little Sandy valley, and moved south through the little town of Hopewell.

"I think we are making splendid time Crockett, lets stop and rest by the river under the shade of these beautiful trees, and give the horses a rest," Jonas said.

"I think we are all ready, especially my hind end," Crockett answered.

"Mine too," Jonas said with a little laugh.

They got the vittles bag and pulled out some fried chicken and biscuits and had a nice little trail meal. They also watered Jake and Betsy, then let them graze on some nice shade grass. They ate and rested for about a half an hour.

"We better get mounted up and get on up the river son," Jonas said.

"Paw, Betsy is keeping up with Jake just fine, I would love to have her for my own," Crockett said.

"That may be out of the question, Samuel has not mentioned letting her go," Jonas said.

"I know Paw, I was just wishing out loud," Crockett answered.

"Paw the Little Sandy River ain't that big is she?" Crockett asked.

"No not much bigger than Tygart," Jonas answered.

"Well how come Tygart is a creek, and Little Sandy is a River?" Crockett asked.

"A river is a river because of it's length, not by how deep or wide it may be," Jonas explained.

"Does Little Sandy run a long way Paw?" Crockett asked.

"I have heard it runs deep into Kentucky, but don't really know," Jonas explained.

It was getting late in the afternoon, and Jonas began looking for the town of Grayson. They had passed the Carter County line away back, and even Jonas was getting anxious to reach his brother Richard's property.

In a short time they came up on a little burg, and were told there was a Pig Iron Furnace just west of there. There were signs of much traffic, and there was also the smell of wood smoke in the air. They happened up on two men riding a wagon filled with gray looking dirt.

"Hello gentlemen," Jonas spoke as Crockett and he came along side of the wagon.

"Hello to you," said the driver of the wagon.

"What you fellers hauling?" Jonas asked as he looked at the material in the wagon.

"Ore, that be Iron Ore," the driver answered.

"We be a taking it up here to Pactolus Furnace fer Mister McMurty and Mister Ward," he added.

"I never seen it before," Jonas said.

"Wells, just where you fellers come from?" The driver asked.

"We are from Tazewell County Virginia, but are building a grist mill up in Greenup County, I am Jonas Whitt and this is my son Crockett," Jonas answered.

"What is Pactolus?" Jonas asked.

"Jonas I am Peter Johnson, this is Fred Reed, and Pactolus is just a place where there's a furnace," Peter said.

"Whitt, you say Whitt, Jonas?" Peter asked.

"Yes that is right, do you know any Whitt's here abouts?" Jonas asked.

"I know Richard Whitt, he lives just about four or five miles south of Grayson," Peter answered.

"How far to Grayson?" Jonas asked.

"Bout a mile or two," Fred spoke up.

"Would love to talk, but we need to get on up the river," Jonas said.

"We better get going too, Pactolus is awaiting," Peter said.

"Yeal, they need this Ore," Fred said.

"Nice meeting you all," Jonas said.

"You too Jonas, and you too Crockett," Peter said.

"Is Grayson very big Paw?" Crockett asked.

"Well son I have not seen it before, but I think it may be bout like all the other little county seats," Jonas answered.

"Paw we ain't passed many folks today, must not be too many lives round here except at Pactolus," Crockett exclaimed.

"I thought we would see more, myself," Jonas answered.

In about fifteen minutes they could see little spirals of smoke rising into the heavens, and the outline of some buildings.

"Well Crockett, I think that must be Grayson up ahead," Jonas announced.

"Must be, and I see a wagon heading this way Paw," Crockett said.

"Most likely another ore wagon," Jonas surmised.

Jonas put Jake into a little faster gait, as they came closer to Grayson. Crockett lagged behind for about a minute and Betsy caught up with Jake.

Jonas pulled up Jake as he came up on the stopping wagon. This wagon was loaded with fire wood.

The man looked familiar to Jonas, even thought the years makes changes to a mans appearance. Could this be some one that Jonas would know?

Both men looked at each other intently, as they greeted each other.

"Hello, Jonas Whitt is my name," Jonas said.

"My goodness Jonas, I'm your cousin Abijah, Edmunds son," he said.

"I thought I knew you Abijah, how on earth are you?" Jonas answered.

"Me and Nancy are just fine, and all the kids are growing up," Abijah answered.

"What are you doing up here in Kentucky, Jonas?" Abijah asked.

"I have come to build a mill for Sam Truitt up in Greenup County, and I am heading down to visit brother Richard," Jonas answered.

"Who is that feller with you Jonas?" Abijah asked.

"This is my son David Crockett Whitt, he has come to help me with the mill building," Jonas said.

"Well hello cousin David, I guess we are second cousins, glad to meet you," Abijah said.

"Hello to you Cousin Abijah, glad to meet you," Crockett said in a bold manly voice.

"Where do you live?" Jonas asked.

"Bout five miles on through Grayson, right on the Little Sandy, Me and brother Richard bought a farm from Paw a few years back," Abijah answered.

"How is Uncle Edmund?" Jonas asked.

"Jonas, he passed back in 1840'" Abijah answered.

"How about your Paw, is Hezekiah still living?" Abijah asked.

"No, he and Maw both passed last year, and my bride Susannah passed back in thirty nine." Jonas exclaimed.

"Sorry to hear that Jonas, but we all got to go sometime I reckon," Abijah said.

"Yes but that don't make it easy does it?" Jonas asked.

"For sure, you be right on that," Abijah answered.

"Listen, Jonas I got to get this wood delivered and get back home, won't you and Crockett stay with us tonight?" Abijah asked.

"How far is it from your place on to brother Richards place?" Jonas asked.

"He lives on Big Gimlet Creek, about eight miles I reckon'" Abijah said.

"We will stop and see Cousin Richard Price Whitt. Then we will decide whether to go on today or not," Jonas said.

"Richard P. will be surprised to see you and Crockett, You know he has a David Crockett too, don't you?" asked Abijah.

"Yes, my Crockett wants to meet him," Jonas said.

"He ain't big as you Crockett," Abijah said.

"Well cousin go ahead and get your load delivered, and I will see you either tonight or on the way back from my brothers," Jonas exclaimed.

"Good, I look forward to it," Abijah exclaimed.

"Get up Bill," Abijah commanded.

Abijah traveled toward Pactolus, Jonas and Crockett headed on to Grayson.

Jonas and Crockett slowed to have a look see, as they traveled through the town of Grayson. Then they picked up the pace to get on to the Abijah, Richard Price Whitt farm.

"Nice town, ain't it Paw?" Crockett asked.

"Seems to be, I love this wide valley, and they have it on this rise for floods I bet" Jonas answered.

"We may stop in and look around a little on the way back if we have time," Jonas continued.

"Paw it won't make me and Betsy mad if we stay all night with our cousins," Crockett announced.

"I know what you mean, we might just do that," Jonas answered.

The mounts were still in good condition, so Jonas set a good pace of about eight miles per hour. Before they knew it they were almost to the Abijah, Richard Price Whitt Farm.

"I bet that next farm is it," Jonas announced.

"We made good time from Grayson, didn't we Paw?" Crockett asked.

"Sure did, now lets just walk our horses the last quarter-mile so they can cool down," Jonas suggested.

"That will be good for them, won't it Paw?" Crockett asked.

"Never put a horse away wet, they can die from such treatment, and never let them drink too much when they are still hot," Jonas instructed.

"I already knew that Paw, but it don't hurt none to be reminded," Crockett answered.

Jonas and Crockett rode right up to the front porch, and a shotgun barrel come out the door.

"Hold it right there," a woman's voice rang out.

"Don't shoot us Sarah, Jonas said in a loud voice.

"Who are you and what do you want?" Sarah asked.

"I'm your cousin Jonas Whitt, and my son Crockett is with me," Jonas answered.

The door opened and Sarah came out with a boy of about eight following.

Jonas sat back and grinned at Sarah.

"Jonas Whitt, what in thunder are you doing way out here?" Sarah asked.

"We come to see my Cousins," Jonas said with a big smile on his face.

"We passed Abijah bout an hour back, but where is Richard P.?" Jonas asked.

"He and the bigger children are out in the field, it is time for them to come in anyway." Sarah said.

"I will ring the dinner bell, that will get them in here purty quick," She said.

"Who is this young man with you?" Sarah asked.

"This is my son David Crockett Whitt, and who might that be?" Jonas Asked.

"David Crockett, why that's my name," said the boy standing beside his mother.

"David Crockett Whitt meet your cousin David Crockett Whitt." Jonas announced.

Jonas' Crockett smiled and walked up to the smaller Crockett and stuck out his hand. The Younger one took his hand and shook it.

"Call me Crockett," said Jonas' son.

"Call me David," said Richard Price Whitt's son.

Richard P. and the other children were in from the field and greatly surprised to see Jonas and Crockett. Every one hugged and told their names.

"I better get a going on dinner, Ann how bout washing you paws and give me some help getting these Whitts something to eat," Sarah said.

"Paws, that is what Grand Maw Rachel always said, ain't it Paw?" asked Crockett.

"My Maw always says it too," said David C.

Jonas and Richard P. sat down in the shade of a big Poplar in the front yard.

"Jonas how have you been, is your Paw and Maw still living?" asked Richard P.

"Lost them both last year and lost my Bride Susannah, when little Hannah was born back in thirty nine," Jonas said.

"I talked to Abijah on the road just north of Grayson, he told me about the passing of Uncle Edmund," Jonas continued.

"We both had good parents, didn't we Jonas?" asked Richard P.

"Sure did," Jonas said nodding.

"Did you move to the Blue Grass State, or are you just looking it over?" asked Richard P.

"My brother Richard got me hooked up with Samuel Truitt to build a grist mill," Jonas exclaimed.

"How has Richard been, do you see him much?" asked Jonas.

"Devil Dick Richard, is doing just fine, he is still the big trickster he has always been," replied Richard P.

"Do they still call him that here in Kentucky?" Jonas asked.

"He is one of the nicest feller I know, but the name stuck," said Richard P.

"He loves a prank better than any one I know, back fired on him a few times you know," Richard P. continued.

"Yes of course, that is how he got that handle," Jonas replied.

"He is one big man that I never want to cross, cause he don't mind fight-un," Richard P. answered.

"How is his blacksmithing going?" Jonas asked.

"Excellent, ever time I am there he has a pile of work to do," Richard P. answered.

"That is the business end of my trip to Carter County, I have a big list of hardware for brother Richard to fabricate, I owe him for getting me the job, now he will get the hardware job," Jonas said.

"By the way Richard, how far is his shop from here?" Jonas asked.

"He lives on Big Gimlet Creek that feeds into the Little Sandy, (now just south of Grayson Lake) so I would guess seven or eight miles," answered Richard P.

"You and Crockett are staying with us tonight, you are tired and I want to get caught up on the news from Virginia," Richard P. insisted.

"Wash your paws, and come and get it," Sarah said from the door way.

By the time supper was over Abijah arrived at his house which was located about one hundred yards from Richard P. Whitt's house. The two brothers were partners , and joint owners of the big farm. Actually it was two farms made from the one larger one purchased from Edmond Whitt.

The family bowed, and A prayer of Thanksgiving was lifted by Richard Price Whitt.They enjoyed a simple but delicious meal.

"Jonas do you want any thing else to eat?" Ann asked.

This opened the door for the Old Whitt Saying."I have had sufficient," Jonas said.

Richard P. joined in, playing a hard of hearing old man and ask the question, "Been a fish-un?"

"Had a plenty," Jonas continued.

"Caught twenty?" Richard P. asked.

"Had enough!" Jonas answered again.

"And they were tough?" asked Richard P.

Everyone laughed, especially the smaller children since they had not heard the old Whitt Saying.

"Think I heard brother Abijah roll in about the time we did the fishing thing," Richard said.

"Will he and his family come over here you think?" Jonas asked.

"After they eat they will be right here," Richard P. answered.

"Jonas you didn't say any thing about getting married again," Sarah said.

"No I haven't, it just about killed me when I lost my Susannah," Jonas said.

"Well do you have any prospects?" Sarah asked.

"Well maybe," Jonas said with a sparkle in his eye.

"Miss Millie likes me and Paw," Crockett injected.

Jonas gave him a quick look.

"Abijah, Nancy, and their children arrived from next door.

Greetings and hugs commence again.

The Whitts all enjoyed a good visit and talked for hours.

Next morning the June sun was already bringing on the heat. Jonas and Crockett slept longer than usual as did the Richard P. family. Sarah and Ann, had the smell of coffee permeating the house, and the cows were bawling.

"Get up Crockett, and smell the coffee," Jonas said.

"What is wrong with the cows, Paw?" Crockett asked.

"They want to be milked and put out to pasture I reckon," Jonas answered.In a little while everyone was up and had on their everyday work clothes. Jonas and Crockett would travel the seven to eight miles to Big Gimlet Creek, and the rest would go about their work once again.

COLONEL CHARLES DAHNMON WHITT

After a breakfast of gravy and biscuits, the good byes were said. Jonas thanked the cousins for everything, then they headed over to the Abijah House and bid them farewell also. The horsemen were on the move up the Little Sandy toward the Richard Devil Dick Black Smith Shop.

"Paw we kinda slept in didn't we?" Crockett asked.

"Sure did, we were tired I reckon, all the riding yesterday and the good visits we had bout wore us out," Jonas answered.

"Crockett look at the way the land is changing," the Little Sandy seems to be in a canyon, just look at those beautiful cliffs," Jonas exclaimed.

"Paw this would be a dandy place to get ambushed wouldn't it?" Crockett asked.

"Yes it would, but I don't expect anything like that, Kentucky is a little tamer out here I think," Jonas answered.

"Cousin Richard and Abijah didn't give us any warning did they Paw?" Crockett asked.

"No they didn't, just enjoy the beauty of nature, I got my pistol if trouble would come," Jonas said confidently.

"This road is traveled a lot, just look at the horse and wagon tracks," Jonas said as he pointed to the road.

"We have been traveling for about an hour, so we will be coming up on Big Gimlet Creek any time," Jonas said.

"How far up the creek does Uncle Richard live, Paw?" Crockett asked.

"A short distance from the mouth, I was told," Jonas answered.

"Little Sandy is starting to be little now," Crockett pointed out.

"Here comes a wagon now Paw," Crockett said as he looked way ahead.

"Yelp, I see it, looks to be loaded heavy, it has four horses pulling it," Jonas said.

"Probably more iron ore, Paw," Crockett answered.

In a few minutes the riders and the wagon met, and Jonas waved his hand in a friendly jester. The driver was friendly. He told Jonas that he had just come from the Whitt Blacksmith Shop. He had a big load of hardware headed for the Ohio River. Jonas informed him that they were heading for the shop.

"Bout how far is it?" Jonas asked.

"Bout a quarter of a mile to the mouth of Big Gimlet Creek, then up the creek another quarter I reckon," answered the teamster.

"Thanks Sir, better let you go, you have a pretty good trip ahead of you," Jonas said.

"Any kind of trouble up ahead?" the teamster asked.

"We didn't have any or see any, why do you ask?" Jonas asked.

"Every now and then there could be a bad man or two on the road," he answered.

"Be careful, and we will too," Jonas said.

The wagon began to move down river, and the Whitts trotted toward Gimlet.

"Here's the mouth of the creek, and we go up the road beside it, Jonas said.

"There is a farm cabin, reckon that is Richards place?" Crockett asked.

"Nope, too soon, we are not up the creek far enough yet," Jonas said.

In another five or six minutes they could smell the wood smoke coming from the Whitt Black Smith Shop. A big flat area stretched out before them with a house, barn and a big blacksmith shop. Two wagons and a couple of saddle horses were tied out front of the shop.

"Now this is more like I envisioned it to be," Jonas said.

"It is a big shop and farm, ain't it Paw?" Crockett asked.

"Sure is son, hope Richard will be able to fill our order for the mill," Jonas answer.

CHAPTER 24

ORDER IS IN, GET BACK TO MILLIE

Jonas rode Jake right up to the hitching rail. Crockett followed with Betsy, and they dismounted and walked together into the big shop.

Four or five gentleman were standing around talking. Jonas looked over to a big man hammering hot metal on a big anvil. It was Richard Devil Dick Whitt, Jonas' big brother. I mean Big Brother.

Richard looked up and saw Jonas and Crockett but did not recognize them because he was engrossed in his work.

"I will be with you in a minute Sir, you know the old saying, got to strike while the iron is hot," Richard exclaimed.

Jonas gave him a wave and turned to the other gentleman and joined in their conversation. Crockett just stood there taking in the huge blacksmith shop, and marveled at his big uncle hammering out something out of red hot iron.

A big husky boy about the same age of Crockett came in the door carrying a picture of water to Richard. This must be James G. Whitt the younger son of Richard, Jonas thought.

Richard nodded his head at the young man to sit the water down on a nearby work bench.

"Thanks James," Richard said with a strong voice.

Richard took a big long drink, then he took a rag and wiped the sweat from his brow and looked around. He gave Jonas and Crockett an intense look.

"Little brother is that you?" Richard asked.

Jonas waved his hand at his big brother and said, "Yes big brother it is me, Jonas."

Richard ran over to Jonas and picked him up giving him a big bear hug.

"Hey Richard take it easy you are gonna break me in two," Jonas pleaded.

"What are you doing here, did you get that job from the Truitt's to build a mill?" Richard asked.

"That is right and I owe it all to you, I brought you a big job to fabricate the hardware for it," Jonas exclaimed.

Richard looked around at his patrons while saying, "this is my brother Jonas and his son Crockett."

"They are here from Virginia and I am shutting down the shop for the day," Richard added.

"Hey what about my?" the men tried to say.

Richard waved his hand to hush the customers.

"Men, my brother is here, I will make everything you need, just let me have this time with my family," Richard said.

The men meandered out the door while Jonas and Richard talked.

James G. Whitt, Richard's son of about the same age as Crockett saw the men leaving and wonders what was going on.

James G. came in the door and saw his Paw and this man and boy being really friendly.

"James come over here and meet your Uncle Jonas and cousin Crockett," Richard said.

Crockett met him first with his hand out to shake. James the bigger boy took his hand and gave it a good firm shake.

"Good to meet you James," Crockett said in a really friendly manner.

"Glad to meet you too cousin," James answered.

Then James went over to Jonas to greet him.

After all this Richard pointed to the door saying, "Lets get out of this hot shop Jonas and get cooled down."

"Becca will be glad to see you fellers," Richard said.

Richard led them to the house to see Becca and all the children.

Edmund Ned Whitt and John B. Whitt the sons of Richard Devil Dick Whitt were not at home. They were out on the road gathering materials for the black smith shop. The girls and of course Becca were extremely glad to see the relatives from Tazewell County.

"Becca, I shut down the shop for the day, you girls need to be a fixing something special for our dinner," Richard said with a smile.

"Ned and John will be back dreckly," Richard exclaimed.

"I will be glad to see them," exclaimed Jonas.

"Crockett has been talking about meeting John," Jonas said.

"Ned ain't a big man but he is plenty smart Jonas and John is taking after me, he is big and burly," Richard explained.

"I didn't mean John ain't smart just that he is a big man," Richard said.

"I understand," Jonas said smiling.

Jonas and Crockett spent two glorious days with the Richard Whitt family. Jonas and Richard transcribed the list of hardware, and went over every detail. Jonas even had sketches with precise measurements on some of the more important pieces.

Jonas explained that he needed certain pieces first, so there would be two deliveries to Truittville. They went over and established an estimated price including material and shipment.

Crockett spent all of his time with Ned, John, and James. James G. was his favorite because of his age. They were both born in 1836. James G. was the senior of the two because James was a month older, so they could relate to each other better. James G. was stocky built, but Crockett was more slender and a full inch taller then his cousin.

Jonas had Millie on his mind and had become much more enamored with her than he thought. He tried not to show it, but Crockett could see his Paw was different.

They got up extra early on Friday and made an early start on their trip back. They stopped for a brief visit with the cousins, the Richard Price and Abijah Whitt families.

They let Betsy and Jake have a drink and trotted them toward the county seat of Carter County. Grayson was already busy as they passed through. They did not stop, but walked the horses real slow so they could take in the sights of the town.

With good luck and a steady ride they would be back in Truittville before dark.

Becca had made them a poke of eats for the trail so they took advantage of it about 1:00 PM when they stopped to water and rest their mounts.

Jonas told Crockett that they were making good time and would be back in Tygart Valley before long.

"Paw, wonder how Tygart Creek got it's name?" Crockett asked.

Millie told me it was named for the frontiersman Michael Tygart that discovered this great place. His friend Simon Kenton tried to get him to go on down the Ohio to Limestone (now Maysville) with him and settle. But Michael loved his creek.

She said that Michael was a poor swimmer and had drown in his creek as he was trying to cross and fell from his horse.

"That is so sad," Crockett answered.

"Yes it is," Jonas said.

"Who is this Simon Kenton?" Crockett asked.

"He was a worthy woodsman and Indian fighter," Jonas answered.

"Like Grand Paw Hezekiah?" Crockett asked.

"Well I guess so, but Paw was not as famous as this Simon Kenton," Jonas explained.

"When the Indians come to attack Boonesborough, ol Simon saved Daniel Boone twice in one day," Jonas said.

It was told that when they were under siege, Simon would slip out at night passing through the Indians and hunt during the day. The next night he would slip back in with a full deer on his shoulders. He kept the little group of Kentuckians from starving or giving up to the Indians.

"He must have been a strong man and very sneaky to get by the Indians," Crockett said.

"I reckon you are right on both accounts," Jonas replied.

After a long day's ride the Whitts got back to Truittville about 8:00 PM Friday the 18th on June.

They had walked the horses the last half mile or so to let them cool down.

"Crockett will you take the horses to the barn and see to their needs, I need to see Sam for a short meeting," Jonas said.

"I will meet you later at the Inn and have some supper," Jonas continued.

"That will be fine Paw, I will be ready to eat for sure," Crockett said in a tired voice.

Jonas took his book and headed to the Truitt House to see Sam and of course Millie.

Crockett stopped by the Inn to let Louisa know that Jonas and he would need something to eat in about an hour. She told him that she would find something, and asked about their trip to Carter County. Crockett gave her a short version, so he could get the horses taken care of.

Jonas and Samuel talk briefly about the price and delivery of the hardware from Big Gimlet Creek. The hardware and delivery would cost Samuel Truitt one hundred dollars.

Sam said, "Fine," and did not bat an eye.

"I am glad that your brother Richard is doing it, it seems like a fair price in today's market," Samuel said.

"There is a lot of work there!" Jonas exclaimed.

"Alfred Thompson is bringing you the first order of lumber tomorrow," Samuel announced.

"Wonder if he has the storage shed material first?" Jonas asked.

"That is what he said and also some of the extra timbers for the mill," Samuel answered.

"I guess you saw that the men have dug down to rock bottom and almost to the creek on the down stream side?" Samuel asked.

"I didn't get a good look but I saw they have done a lot of work by the size of the piled up dirt," Jonas said.

Jonas saw Millie in the other room waiting to greet him.

"Sounds good Samuel, I will talk with you tomorrow and go over anything you might have questions about," Jonas said.

About that time Millie walked into the room and ask if they wanted anything to drink. Samuel took this as a sign to leave her and Jonas alone.

"I will see you tomorrow Jonas," Samuel said as he left the room.

"Yes sir," Jonas answered.

Millie walked up close to Jonas and took his hand.

Jonas could not help himself, he put his arms around her.

"Sorry if I am smelling a bit gamey, been on the road all day," Jonas said.

"You smell perfect to me," she said as she pulled Jonas up against her full breast.

Jonas stole a little kiss and said he would see her tomorrow.

"I have to get over to the Inn with Crockett and eat a bite," Jonas exclaimed.

"I am just about tired out and very hungry," Jonas added.

"I understand Sweetheart, you go and eat," Millie said in her most sweet voice.

"We will talk tomorrow and spend some time together on Sunday," she said.

"I look forward to it sweet Millie," Jonas said.

Jonas left her and his heart was throbbing. He had not felt this way since Susannah and he experienced young love.

"I think my Susannah would want me to love again," Jonas thought.

Jonas arrives back at the Inn about the same time as Crockett.

"Did you get the horses cared for son?" Jonas asked.

"Sure did, how was your meeting with Mister Truitt?" Crockett asked.

"Went good, and I also saw Millie," Jonas said.

"Paw I really like that little fillie, she was a good horse to ride," Crockett said.

Jonas laughed.

"What is it Paw?" Crockett asked.

"I was talking about Millie and you changed the subject in mid stream about Betsy," Jonas said.

Crockett laughed.

"Miss Millie sure ain't no horse is she Paw?" Crockett asked.

"She sure ain't," Jonas agreed.

Louisa fried up some pork chops and added some left over soup beans and cornbread for Jonas and Crockett.

"We will sleep good tonight," Crockett said after enjoying the good meal.

"I reckon we will son," Jonas said with a grin.

Morning came in a hurry for Jonas and Crockett, because they were really tired. It was Saturday morning and a work day, even though Saturdays were treated a little different in public works. Jonas would probably have to unload a wagon or two of lumber.

Alfred Thompson was suppose to show up with the first shipment of lumber. Jonas didn't expect him before afternoon. Jonas would not work too hard today doing mostly planning and going over directions with Basel about the dig. Jonas would talk to Bill Thompson also about his future plans.

Crockett was a faithful little worker, and he knew most of the tools Jonas used in the mill work. Jonas was always patient with Crockett and showed him many things about building. Crockett enjoyed all aspects of building and that made him a good apprentice.

After a leisurely breakfast, Jonas and Crockett went out to the job site to look everything over. Jonas was impressed with the amount of earth the servants had dug out. Jonas was also impressed with the precise cut right up to the stretched line and stakes. Basel had his men going at it and the dirt was flying. Also they had accumulated a great pile of large and small creek rocks. They had even separated them into two piles, one of larger and one for the small stones.

The stones would be laid up inside the pit where the under shot water wheel would be located so the precise measure of water could flow through. It would be like two walls with just enough space for the wheel to turn between them. There would also be a need for some foundation and chimney work. A few would be needed to be laid up at the mouth of the trace so that water could be blocked with heavy boards when the mill was shut down. The rest of the stones would be put in the creek just below the mouth of the trace to form a dam.

Jonas went up and greeted the Negroes and gave them a well done.

"Thank you Basel and the rest of you fellers for the good work," Jonas said.

"You welcome Mister Jonas, wee's tried our best to get her done, fore you and young Crockett gets back, but had some miseries with some of duh work," Basel explained.

"Don't worry about it, you fellers have done a splendid job so far, just keep up the good work and before long you will have it done," Jonas commended.

The day passed fast. Jonas, Bill and Crockett unloaded two loads of lumber right after dinner. Jonas was pleased overall with the progress. He told Bill Thompson and Crockett that they would lay out the shed first thing Monday morning.

"Jonas, what is the shed for?" Bill asked.

Crockett started to answer, but waited respectfully for Jonas to give an answer.

"We will store materials in it and also have a place to get out of the weather while we are building," Jonas explained.

"When we have the mill up and running the shed can be used for any number of things," Jonas continued.

Supper time came, and Samuel nor Millie had come to talk. Jonas was glad not to be interrupted while he was working.

Finally George Truitt came out and told Basel to knock off for the day.

"Thank you Mister George, we bin getting her all dug out," Basel answered.

"That's fine Basel, you and the boys go out back and get ready for your supper," George told them.

The Negroes came up out of the trace, each carrying a pick or shovel and marched single file to a tent set up out behind the Truitt house.

George had a table for them to have their meals on. He also provided a cut off barrel full of water to wash off in. They slept in the big tent that they brought with them from Lewis county.

Crockett stood gawking at the site of the black men marching toward the back of the house.

"Come on Crockett, lets go and get ready for our supper too," Jonas said when he saw Crockett staring at the blacks.

"Paw, ain't Basel and the others slaves?" Crockett asked.

"Yes son, but they desire to call them servants this far north, so while we are here we will do the same," Jonas said in a quiet voice.

"I know, when in Rome do as the Romans do, uh Paw?" Crockett asked.

"Crockett some folks up north are hypocrites about slavery, I am still feeling out the folks round here to see how they think about such matters," Jonas said.

"So you want me not to say anything about it, uh Paw?" Crockett asked.

"That is right son, we have good work opportunities here in Greenup County and don't need any friction," Jonas explained.

The Truitt's came to the Inn for their supper and sat at their table close to Jonas and Crockett. After supper Jonas walked Millie back to the house and sat on the porch for awhile.

As twilight came to Greenup County the lightning bugs began to decorate the hills with their little lights. Evening sounds of insects, frogs and birds gave a soothing feeling to all that could hear the music of nature.

Crockett and some of the other boys in the area chased after the fireflies and laughed as they played.

Sounds from behind the house began to fill the air as the slaves sang some of their hymns in a low even tempo. Crockett stopped to listen, he had never heard singing like this before. It had a ring of a foreign language, yet it was understandable. These black men had a rhythm and sound that Jonas and Crockett had never seen or heard. They were hymns of faith the listeners could readily discern.

Jonas and Millie could be heard in a whispering sound undistinguishable to others.

Crockett tired of the play and came up to the porch.

"What is it son," Jonas asked.

"I am tired Paw, will it be alright if I head back to the room?" Crockett asked.

"Sure son, I will be along dreckly, be sure to wash up before you get in your bed," Jonas said.

"I will Paw," Crockett answered.

Jonas and Millie talked for a little while longer. Jonas told her that he missed his little daughter Hannah and is going to figure a way to get her to Kentucky.

"She is going to be grown up before I know it," Jonas said.

"Get her here Jonas, she can stay with me in our house, that way we can get to know each other," Millie offered.

"Thank you so much, you are so sweet to offer my baby girl this opportunity, but what would your parents say?" Jonas asked.

"They would be elated to have a young girl come into their lives," she said.

"Trust me in this Jonas," Millie reiterated.

"I will write to my brother James tomorrow and see if he can find a way to get her here," Jonas said.

Jonas was elated with the idea of Hannah being here with him and Crockett.

It was almost dark and Jonas put his arm around Millie and pulled her close to him.

"Millie, I am much older than you, are you sure of your feelings about me?" Jonas asked.

"Can you not feel the love I have for you, Jonas Whitt?" she asked.

"I know what I feel, and hope you are having this same strong attraction I am experiencing for you," Jonas said.

"I am afraid I have fallen for you Mister Whitt," she said.

Jonas gave her an affectionate kiss and got up.

"Better go and get some sleep, a most attractive woman and her parents will be waiting out side for me tomorrow morning," Jonas said.

"Tomorrow is the Lords day isn't it?" Millie answered.

"Alright sweet heart, I will turn you loose for now," Millie said in a sweet voice.

"Good night sweetheart, I will see you in the morning," Jonas said as he turned to leave.

"Good night Mister Whitt," Millie said in a much louder voice.

This was for the benefit of any ears that may be listening.

Crockett had already washed off and was in his bunk.

Jonas and Crockett talked while Jonas got ready for bed. Jonas told Crockett that he is writing a letter tomorrow to James in Virginia.

"I am going to have him work to help Hannah get to Kentucky," Jonas said.

"Millie said Hannah could stay over there with the Truitt's. What do you think son?" Jonas asked.

"It sounds real good to me, Paw," Crockett answered.

"Reckon Uncle James can get her to us some how?" Crockett asked.

"We can sure try, can't we son?" Jonas asked.

After a good night and a restful Lords Day, it is Monday again. Jonas wrote a letter to James, Hannah, and the family explaining his desire to get Hannah to Kentucky. He explained that Hannah would be able to stay in the big Truitt house with his lady friend, Mildred Truitt. Jonas asked his brother James to go to work and find a way for Hannah to get to Kentucky.

Crockett was elated with the idea that somehow, someway Hannah could come to Truittville. Even though Hannah and Crockett did not see eye to eye on some things, they still loved each other.

Crockett had made friends with some boys in Kentucky, but they were not family. The boys were sons of other men that worked for Samuel Truitt. The shoe maker's son was little Tony Montivon. The farmhands sons were also friends with Crockett. Billy Miller, and John Quillen were just a little older than Crockett but that didn't matter.

Jonas always turned Crockett loose from work when the other boys came to play.

They explored the nearby hills, branches, and of course spent time in Big White Oak Creek.

Jonas, Bill Thompson and Crockett laid out the shed, and started digging holes for the timbers. It was a building some what like modern pole buildings. The plan came right from Jonas' mill building book. Jonas had been careful to write down all measurements and even drew sketches while building past mills and buildings.

The servants as Samuel called them were back in the trace still digging downstream. Their work was coming along good. They would start digging the trace back upstream just as soon as they cut into the creek on the downstream end.

Jonas made it a point to give Samuel his letter to James for mailing, and ask if Millie had talked to him about Hannah coming.

Samuel was for the plan.

"Polly will be tickled to death to have a young girl in the house again, Mary Elizabeth was getting to be an adult." he exclaimed.

CHAPTER 25

HANNAH'S COMING
TO KENTUCKY

Jonas and Crockett get an answer to their first letter. After the post rider came by the Truittville Post Office, Samuel brought the letter straight to Jonas. Jonas thanked Samuel for bringing the letter so quickly. Jonas opened the letter slow and deliberately with Crockett looking on.

"It is from brother James," Jonas thought out loud.

Crockett moves in even closer, wanting to hear every word.

Jonas skims over the letter quickly with out saying a word.

"Paw, what does it say?" asked Crockett impatiently.

"Alright son, hold on and I will read it to you," Jonas answered.

Here is what it says, Greetings Jonas and Crockett. We received your letter yesterday and are glad to hear of your safe arrival in Greenup, County. Things are fine here with the exception of Hannah wanting to come to you. I never thought she would miss you all so much.

Are you in any position to receive her there in Kentucky? We have tried everything to take her mind off of you and Crockett. James Griffith has expressed that he would bring her to you, and have a little visit, if practical.

Have you seen brother Richard yet? He will be glad to see you and Crockett.

How is the mill coming along?

We are all doing fine. All your children and grand children are doing fine.

If at all possible, make arrangements to receive your Hannah, and I will send her to you by James Griffith. Your big brother James.

"Wow Paw, Hannah and James Griffith may be on their way here, since this is the answer to the first letter," Crockett said.

"Yes you are right, if they got our second letter," Jonas exclaimed.

I will send another letter tomorrow, just in case they didn't get our letter asking James to find away to get her to us," Jonas said.

"Good idea Paw, but I bet James Griffith and Hannah are on the way," Crockett said excitedly.

The mill work was coming along good. The slaves have completed digging the fifty yard trace with exception of about ten feet on the upstream end. They were instructed to leave it that way until the mill work progressed. Jonas did not want to fight the water in the trace while constructing the mill.

The storage shed was up, and some of the stone work in the trace was finished. Jonas has been cutting out the boards to build the water wheel.

Crockett had been with his Paw most everyday helping get tools and in many other ways. Crockett took off now and then to play with his friends and take an occasional dip in the creek.

Signs of fall was already appearing faintly.

"It is good that we have our shed done, well before winter comes, there will be plenty of work we can do all winter long," Jonas affirmed.

John Bunyon and James G. Whitt arrived Wednesday August 25, 1847, with the first shipment of hardware from Gimlet Creek. Crockett was extremely glad to see his cousin James G. Whitt.

The work done by Richard Whitt was excellent and Samuel was pleased as well as Jonas.

Crockett and James G. had a good time playing and the other boys liked Crockett's cousin from Carter County.

John Bunyon, Jonas' nephew was impressed with the mill project, and the work creditability of his Uncle Jonas.

Jonas instructed John Bunyon to tell Richard that Samuel Truitt was pleased with his work as well as was he.

Samuel was pleased with the progress, and handed John Bunyon payment in gold for the first of two shipments.

Early next morning John Bunyon Whitt and James G. Whitt headed down stream toward their fathers shop in Carter County.Jonas and Crockett bid them farewell. Jonas said for them to bring Richard on the next shipment. They said they would try.

Samuel mentioned to Jonas that school would start in October.

Jonas informed Crockett, that Samuel Truitt would start school sometime in October.

"School!" you will need me to help with the mill, Paw," Crockett exclaimed.

"Mister Truitt is well educated Crockett, and you are fortunate to have such a man to teach you," Jonas said.

"He knows doctoring, engineering, running business, the three R's, and of course teaching," Jonas said.

"Have you seen his penmanship, Crockett?" Jonas asked.

"Yes Paw, Mister Truitt has a great hand writing,"Crockett confessed.

"It will be sometime before school starts, so enjoy the season," Jonas said.

Jonas and Millie had become really close and spent time together most every evening and also on the Lords Day. People began to speculate as to when an announcement may be forthcoming.

Even Crockett's friends began to tease him about his Paw and Millie. This did not set well with Crockett and he felt a little resentment toward Millie Truitt.

Millie has done nothing but give Crockett her best. Millie and Jonas could not help it, they were in love. Jonas walked around all day with a smile on his face, as did Millie.

James Griffith and Hannah left Tazewell County August 20, 1847 on horseback. They would make the trip much faster than did Jonas and Crockett as they were not riding a heavy wagon. If they have a good trip they could be in Truittville by the first week of September.

Friday September the tenth, James Griffith and Hannah rode into Truittville about supper time.

Jonas and Crockett were walking toward the Truitt Inn, and Crockett said, "There is James and Hannah!"

Crockett took off in a run and Jonas followed.

"Well I be!" Jonas said excitedly.

Hannah leaped from her horse and ran to her Paw and brother Crockett. James Griffith Whitt got down from his horse elated to see the reunion. After hugging Hannah, Jonas walked up to James Griffith and gave him a big hug.

"Thank you son for doing this for me and Hannah," Jonas said.

"Welcome Paw, I wanted to see how you and Crockett were fairing' too, I like Greenup County," James exclaimed as he scanned the beautiful little valley.

"I have been anxious to see Kentucky since you and Crockett left," James Griffith continue.

"Did you all have any trouble on the road?" Jonas asked.

"No sir, we talked to some folks that remember you and Crockett traveling through, "James Griffith said.

"Dan McCoy and his wife Bertha both talked highly of you, they made us stay all night with them," James Griffith said.

"They said you showed them how to pray, Paw, you taught me too," Hannah exclaimed.

"You learned quick my little darling," Jonas said with a smile.

"Well Paw, it is easy, Jesus is my friend and I just talk to him," she answered.

"That is a really good answer," Jonas said.

By now Samuel, Polly and Millie were there on their way to supper, and of course to meet Hannah and James Griffith.

"Let me get someone to take care of your ponies and you can visit as you eat supper," Samuel said.

"Thank you Sam, that would be real nice of you," Jonas answered.

Everyone greeted each other and went in the Inn. Samuel was back from the barn in short order.

"Got a boy caring for your horses, did I miss anything?" Samuel asked.

"Don't think so," Jonas answered.

Louisa became excited when she saw that Hannah and James Griffith Whitt had arrived. She took them all to the biggest table so they all could eat together and visit. Millie sat beside Jonas and he had Hannah and Crockett on his other side. Jonas kept hugging Hannah as they talked.

Louisa was a little taken by the handsome James Griffith Whitt. She kept leaning on him while she served up the supper. He turned once and gave her a special smile that she instantly returned. He enjoyed the attention of Louisa, especially when she leaned her full bosom on his shoulder.

Crockett was really glad to see his little sister and big brother. They both were really glad to see Crockett also.

"Crockett, you must have grown a foot since you left Virginia," James said.

"It's this good Kentucky food Louisa is feeding him," Jonas commented.

Alfred Thompson the lumberman came into the dining room to get some supper, and Hannah noticed him.

"Who is that man?" she asked Jonas in a whisper.

"He is a lumberman that is bringing the lumber for the mill, why do you ask? Jonas asked.

"I think he is handsome," Hannah said.

"Honey you are just a baby," Jonas said.

"I will always be your baby, Paw!" she answered.

The Whitts and Truitts sat for hours visiting and getting acquainted. Each one having a time to tell a story or ask a question.

"James Griffith had to inquire about Crockett's letter home, "what was that about seeing naked women on your trip?"

Crockett turned a little pink.

Jonas saw Crockett was embarrassed so he came to his aid.

"We will tell you all about our trip when we have more time," Jonas said.

"It is getting late, we had better get ready for bed," Jonas continued.

"Hannah you come to our house to sleep in my room," Millie said.

"James Griffith, you can have a room here at the Inn, on me, Louisa will take care of you, and find you a good room," Samuel said.

Crockett and James Griffith followed Louisa up stairs to show them his room. Jonas walked arm and arm with Hannah and Millie back to the Truitt house.

Samuel and Polly said, "Good night all," and went into the house.

Jonas gave both of his favorite girls a hug.

He looked into the beautiful hazel eyes of Hannah.

"You look so much like your Maw, long as you live Susannah lives in you," Jonas said.

Then he took Millie into his arms and gave her a little kiss.

"I will see you all tomorrow," Jonas said as he headed off the porch.

"By Paw," Hannah answered.

"Good night Mister Whitt," Millie said sweetly.Millie and Hannah went into the house elated with the days happenings of the two finally meeting.

"I am so glad that you are here Hannah," Millie said."Me too, are you and Paw fixing to get married?" Hannah asked abruptly.

"How would you feel about that?" Millie asked.

"Well if it makes Paw happy I am for it, I don't remember my Maw, cept by the stories I heard," Hannah said.

"Well honey, if you look like her as your Paw says she was very beautiful," Millie said.

"Every one says she was a beautiful and wonderful lady," Hannah said.

"Well to answer your question, your Paw has not come right out and asked me yet, but I hope he will," Millie said.

"Miss Millie, you are a beautiful lady too," Hannah said.

"Well thank you Hannah, I am glad you think so," said a surprised Millie.

"You know I or nobody else could take your Maws place, but I do love your Paw," said Millie.

"I understand Miss Millie," Hannah said.

Back in the Inn, James Griffith and Crockett talked away the hours.

Finally Jonas spoke up, "boys it's time to get some sleep, some folks have to work tomorrow."

"Sounds like old times don't it Crockett?" James asked.

"What's that brother?" Crockett asked.

"Paw telling us to go to sleep," James Griffith said laughing.

"Alright Paw we will hush up, I am going to my room," James said.

"Good night son," Jonas said as James was leaving the room.

"Good night Paw, and good night to you little brother," James said, closing the door.

Morning came quickly to those that had visited late into the night. All of the Whitts were groggy and were ready for that first cup of coffee.

Word spread quickly around the little community of Truittville that James Griffith Whitt and the fine little lady Hannah Whitt had arrived last evening.

Little Tony, Billy Miller, and Johnny Quillen were hanging out to get a glimpse of the new young lady from Virginia. Even the older people were curious to see James Griffith and Hannah.

Jonas would do little work this day, he would get Bill Thompson started on some of the wood sawing and drilling. Also Alfred Thompson had arrived last evening with more lumber and timbers so that would have to be unloaded and stored in the big shed.

James Griffith and Crockett would help with the unloading and what ever Jonas wanted them to do. Jonas told them to help with the lumber and then he would take time to visit some more.

Samuel saw James Griffith, Crockett, Jonas, Bill Thompson, and Alfred Thompson all working like beavers. He went over to Jonas and told him to take the afternoon off so he could spend some time with the family. Jonas told Samuel he had made a deal with his sons, that if they would help get rid of the wagon he would take off some time.

Millie and Hannah slept in a little late this morning, and leisurely walked over to the Inn for their breakfast.

Crockett's friends lined up and gawked at Hannah as she swayed by. She rolled her big hazel eyes at them but said nothing.

Millie smiled at the situation.

James Griffith was friendly and enjoyed the attention of Louisa Truitt, but he did nothing out of the way. He remembered his sweetheart Nancy Webb, back in Baptist Valley Virginia.

The Truitts and Whitts all gathered for supper a little early. An evening of visiting and telling stories would be the theme at the big table.

James Griffith Whitt stayed for two more days, and left for Virginia via Carter County. He decided to go by and visit his cousins and Uncle Richard on Gimlet Creek. Then he wanted to stop off and see his Uncle John Bunyon near Maytown, in Floyd County. He thought he may never have this chance again, since it was quite a trip through the mountains and consumed much time.

Everyone gathered around the morning James prepared to leave. He hugged all the Whitts, Millie, and Louisa Truitt. He shook hands with all the rest of the folks, and personally thanked Samuel Truitt for the great hospitably. James Griffith got on his horse, took the bag of traveling food Louisa had prepared.

James Griffith Whitt reared up his saddle horse, waved, and turned down Big White Oak Creek, and did not look back. Everyone was sad to see him leave, especially Hannah ,Crockett, and Louisa Truitt.

Time seemed to fly by. It was mid October and Crockett and Hannah joined the other Truittville children in the church each day for school. Samuel Truitt was a masterful teacher that truly inspired the students, even though the boys grew tired of writing each letter repeatedly. Samuel wanted each child to express themselves in excellent penmanship. Samuel demanded that each student write each letter perfectly before he allowed them to go to the next. Finally the children began to see the fruits of the redundant writing of each letter.

Samuel also taught the children history and government of this new nation. He instilled the importance of voting and taking part of civic duties. He also taught them arithmetic, and even some general things like business. He read a Bible story each day.

Samuel taught the boys the basics of civil engineering, and farming. He had Millie come and teach the girls about sewing, quilting, and cooking while he worked with the boys.

Crockett liked school for the first time. There was a good looking older girl in his class that he adored. Millie's little sister Mary Elizabeth Truitt was about four years older than Crockett, but that did not hold back the attraction shared by the two.

The mill work progressed a little each day. The great twenty foot water wheel was finished and stood menacing on the foundation and shaft. It stood there in a waterless trace waiting for a job to do.

Some of the other foundation was laid out and waiting for scheduled materials to arrive. Each part of the mill had to be built in the proper sequence, to insure proper operation and future maintenance.

Jonas always told Crockett, "Some things just can't be rushed."

"It's kinda like a big clock, ain't it Paw?" Crockett asked.

"That is a real good analysis," Jonas answered.

"Paw you know a lot of big words, don't you?" Crockett asked.

"I sure do, I know Mississippi and watermelon," Jonas said laughingly.

Crockett laughed too!"

Jonas and Millie were spending even more time together. A wedding date was expected to be announced anytime.

Jonas went to Samuel and Polly Truitt late in the evening on November 21, 1847.

"Sir I need to speak to you and Miss Polly, if this is a convenient time?" Jonas asked.

"We can talk now, is something going amiss with the mill?" Samuel asked.

"Let the man talk Sam, Jonas has something important to ask us," Polly inserted.

"Oh," Samuel answered with a special interest.

"Sir, and Miss Polly, you know that Millie and I have been keeping company purty steady as late," Jonas said.

"Well yes Jonas, go ahead and tell us what's on your mind," Samuel said.

"Shhh! let him talk Sam," Polly countered.

"I have asked Miss Millie to marry me providing you give us permission," Jonas said.

"If that is a question Jonas, we give our blessing, don't we Polly?" Samuel asked.

"I was concerned about our age difference, but Millie said that don't count for nothing sir," Jonas said.

"Polly and I have talked many times of this moment Jonas, and have come up with the same answer," Samuel said.

"Sir I promise to love her and take the best of care of her," Jonas said.

Finally Polly got to speak again.

"Jonas I think you and Millie will make a great couple, but will you wait another two or three months to make sure?" Polly asked, surprising them both.

"I think that is a fair request Ma-um," Jonas answered.

"If Millie agrees we can wait until early spring," Jonas continued.

"Be alright if I talk to her and tell her what we have decided?" Jonas asked.

"I will go and fetch her, she is upstairs teaching Hannah cross-stitch," Polly said.

CHAPTER 26

JONAS TAKES A BRIDE

Jonas is waiting with Samuel as Hannah and Millie descend the stairs. Samuel has a glass of wine in his hand, and held it high when Millie came in the room.

"Well Paw, what are you doing?" Millie asked.

Jonas was standing there awkwardly waiting to talk to his lady friend.

"Plans are being made and Jonas wants to talk to you about it," Samuel said.

"What is it Paw?" Hannah asked in anticipation.

Finally Jonas got to speak. He looked around at everyone and then straight into the eyes of Millie Truitt.

"Millie if you will agree, we can be married in two or three months," Jonas said.

"I agree," Millie said excitedly.

"But why wait two or three months?" she asked, as she looked at Samuel and Polly.

"We all just want you to be really sure," Jonas said.

"Paw and Millie's getting married!" Hannah shouted gleefully.

Crockett is over at the Inn wondering what his Paw is doing this evening. He has felt neglected by Jonas, and even Hannah lately. He has enjoyed school with Samuel Truitt being his school master, and the lovely Mary Elizabeth Truitt being in the class.

The November evening was cold so Crockett put another chunk of wood in the little iron stove. Where is Paw, he thought? He is most likely with that woman, I am afraid he might get married, then what will happen to me, Crockett continued in thought. I may have to just up and leave, he thought. Uncle James and Nancy would be glad to have me, he thought. I could even stay with James Griffith on the

Indian Creek farm, he considered.

His thoughts were interrupted with a knock on the door.

Crockett opened the door, "It's just me Jonas," Jonas said.

Crockett was back from his world of thoughts.

"Come in Paw it's cold out tonight," Crockett answered.

As Jonas comes in out of the cold hallway he has a big smile on his face.

"What you been doing son?" Jonas asked.

"I studied from this book a little bit, and kept the fire," Crockett answered.

"What book is it?" Jonas asked.

"It's about the war here in Kentucky Paw," Crockett said.

"What war?" Jonas asked.

"You know Paw, about the Indians and British fighting the people at Boonesboro," Crockett answered.

"Our forefathers paid a price so we could have this free country didn't they son?" Jonas asked.

"Sure did, I would have loved to met that Simon Kenton and Daniel Boone, wouldn't you Paw?" Crockett asked.

"Fine men, son," Jonas answered.

"I have something to tell you Crockett," Jonas said.

Here it comes, thought Crockett.

"Well what is it Paw?" Crockett asked.

"I have been over to the Truitts and have asked Millie to marry me," Jonas said.

Crockett's countenance fell!

"What's wrong son?" Jonas asked as he seen the visable difference in his son.

"Why do you have to marry her Paw? Why?" Crockett asked in a raised voice.

Jonas was greatly surprised, at his son!

"What will happen to me?" Crockett asked.

"You will be just fine son, you will live with me, Millie and Hannah," Jonas explained.

"Don't you understand, Millie will be a mother to you," Jonas said.

"Millie can't take my Maws place!" Crockett insisted.

"I know son, no one can take your Maws place, but Millie can fill a void in our lives," Jonas answered.

"We will all live together in a cabin or over at the big Truitt house," Jonas said.

"Well Paw when will you and Millie get married?" Crockett asked in a more somber tone.

"We have not set an exact date, but in two to three months," Jonas answered.

Jonas hugged Crockett!

"Don't you know I would never abandon you for any woman? Jonas asked.

"What did Hannah think?" asked Crockett.

"She seemed pleased at the idea," Jonas said.

"This will be a good thing for you, Hannah, and me," Jonas said.

"Don't you know that Millie loves you and Hannah?" Jonas asked.

"Not really," Crockett answered.

"We have two months to get use to the idea, please give her a chance son," Jonas said.

"I will, Paw," Crockett said half way smiling.

A few days passed and the weather had been great for the end of November. Jonas and Bill took advantage of the good weather to get as much done as possible on the mill. The main gear had been fashioned and installed on the opposite end of the great water wheel. A number of the support timbers were set and walls were up to the second story on three sides. The floor joists on the second floor were installed except where access was needed to work on the mill apparatus.

The mill stones had arrived in South Shore and Jonas took Bill Thompson to get them. Crockett was in school and missed this trip. The wagon had to be beefed up with heavy timbers to support the weight of two heavy grinding stones. Also a tandem team of mules was used to pull the wagon.

When Jonas and Bill arrived at South Shore the stones were already unloaded and sitting on the side of the river. They had been handled carefully it appeared. When Bill saw them he was amazed at the black granite and smoothness of the surface. Grinding furrows were cut in the sides deep toward the center and shallow toward the outer edge.

A cross shaped opening was cut in the center of the turn stone and the set stone had a smaller round hole.

"Jonas these things are beautiful, they would make grand tomb stones," Bill said.

Jonas laughed at the idea.

"These stones cost more than some farms, so we must take real good care handling them," Jonas said.

Bill took a step back as if afraid to touch the precious grinding stones.

"Don't be afraid of them Bill, we just can't drop them," Jonas explained.

The grinding stones were round like wheels four feet in diameter and one foot thick. The set stone was marked as weighting 998#, the turn stone was marked as weighting 980#.

"How come that one is heavier?" Bill asked.

"Cause it don't have a cross cut in it, I reckon," Jonas said.

Jonas went in to claim the grinding stones and make provisions to get them loaded.

The owner of the river port had a makeshift crane boom brought out and with help of a couple of hands the stones were loaded into the reinforced wagon on a bed of straw.

Back at school Crockett was beside himself with anticipation of the grinding stones coming. He might as well have went with Jonas and Bill to get them, because his mind sure was not on school today. Samuel tried to get Crockett's attention back on his studies but even he was not as attentive today.

Excitement was in the air because the mill stone wheels were coming. This made the mill a reality, not just a big wheel standing in a trace next to a partialy built building.

It would be late in this December day before Jonas and Bill would get back with the precious cargo. The days were short now and darkness would catch them on the trail.

While Jonas was in the little burg of South Shore, he did a little shopping. He bought a pair of dress gloves each for Millie, and Hannah. He also bought Crockett some store bought britches. He also got Crockett a good skinning knife for his upcoming birthday on the 13th of December.

Jonas and Bill arrived about 8:00 PM back in Truittville with the grinding stones. Most of the little burg were waiting in the Truittville Inn, hoping to finally see the costly stones from Italy.

A loud voice rang out, "Here they are!"

Everyone in the Inn followed Samuel Truitt out in the cold night to see the grinding stones. Jonas held his lantern high and threw back the canvas cover to reveal the shiny black granite wheels.

A hush fell over the entire group.

"They are beautiful," Polly exclaimed.

Everyone there was amazed at the fine grinding stones.

"They are too pretty to grind corn," someone said.

"I have never seen such beautiful stone," Samuel said.

"They will be used for their purpose," Samuel continued.

"We have the best looking grinding stones in Kentucky," Polly announced.

Crockett stood there indignant!

"Ain't nobody ever seen grinding stones before?" asked Crockett.

"Not this purty," Bill Thompson exclaimed.

"They are purty I reckon," Crockett answered.

"Me and Paw have seen a whole pasel of then, ain't we Paw?" Crockett asked.

"You are right son, but these are the finest stones I ever seen," Jonas said.

"The Gerardi family have outdone themselves this time," Jonas said.

By now Millie and Hannah had worked their way over close to the stones.

Millie reached over into the wagon and felt the smooth stones and felt down into one of the carved out grinding grooves.

"Oh!, that is sharp!" she exclaimed.

"Be careful, you may skin your finger," Jonas cautioned.

Crockett snickered quietly.

I never seen folks act so silly about grinding stones, Crockett thought.

"Bill, we better take the wagon out by the mill and unhitch the mules," Jonas said.

"Yes, I bet you fellers are about frozen," exclaimed Samuel Truitt.

Crockett and some of the other boys followed the wagon out by the mill to help with the mules, so Jonas and Bill could hurry out of the cold night air.

After the animals were cared for Jonas went back to the wagon and retrieved three small packages and stuck them under his heavy coat. The packages were the gifts he had purchased in South Shore.

This day was Friday the 10th of December 1847. Monday would be Crockett's birthday, and a little party had been planned by Millie for after church on Sunday. She was planning to bake a cake just for Crockett, and she had also crocheted him a neck scarf from bright blue yarn.

Millie and Hannah waited for Jonas inside the warm inn, while he tended to the mules.Louisa heated up some fine beef soup, knowing the two men would be hungry and cold.

When Jonas and Bill came into the inn, Millie, Hannah, and Louisa were seated at a large table waiting. Louisa had big bowls of soup and cornbread waiting.

Sunday came and Crockett was wondering if anybody was going to remember his birthday. Well it is not until tomorrow he reasoned.

Jonas, Millie and the others have kept the party a grand secret. They had not said a word. They all gathered at the church for worship the same as usual. When church was over everyone headed to the Truitt Inn for dinner as usual.

Maybe they will remember my birthday in the morning, Crockett thought.

When the surrey arrived at the inn, everyone walked in the inn as usual, except Crockett was delayed because Jonas asked him to put out the weight and tie the horse to it.

Everyone gathered around the center table where a large cake was waiting for David Crockett Whitt. When he came in everyone yelled surprise! Crockett was taken completely by surprise, and stood there in amazement.

"Good birthday to you son," Jonas said loudly.

Everyone cheered!

They did not sing "Happy Birthday to you" because, the song had not been composed by the schoolteacher Mildred J. Hill in Louisville, Kentucky until the 27th of June 1859.

Hannah was as excited as Crockett. She gave him a big hug, and ate a huge piece of cake that would fill up a lumberjack.

After dinner was over, Jonas stood and called Crockett over to him. He took out the package that was wrapped in brown paper and tied with twine.

"Crockett you are almost a man, and I am giving you a manly gift," Jonas said.

"Even thought you have used these before you did not have one of your own," Jonas said as he gave the package to Crockett.

"Thanks Paw," he said as he untied the twine, and slowly unwrapped the present.

Crockett's eyes widened as he gazed upon the shiny new skinning knife.

"This is a wonderful birthday Paw, thanks so much," Crockett said.

Hannah was a little disappointed because it was not her birthday. Jonas called her over and told her that she would have her birthday on the 15th of April.

"I do have a little surprise for you though," Jonas said as he handed her the little package bound like Crockett's present.

Her big hazel eyes sparkled with excitement. She hurriedly opened her gift, and revealed the new pair of dress gloves.

"Oh Paw," she said with glee.

Jonas and the other adults laughed at the little darling.

Crockett went around the room showing his prized skinning knife. Everyone congratulated him for his birthday and the grand present.

Jonas walked Millie home and surprised her with the nice dress gloves he got for her when he purchased Hannah's gloves and Crockett's knife.

"Mister Whitt, I am tired of waiting, I want to set a date for our wedding," Millie said.

They looked at the Calendar for February 1848 and decided on Sunday February the thirteenth.

"Now that that is decided, lets not grieve our selves with anticipation," Jonas said.

"Alright darling, now that I know for sure that you will be mine, I can wait," Millie exclaimed.

The work on the mill slowed but continued through December and into the new year of 1848.

Crockett went to school everyday that Samuel conducted it. Crockett was amazed at the improvement of his penmanship, and reading ability.

Samuel Truitt had a way of instilling pride into the children as they could visable see great strides in their education.

Crockett and Samuel both were a bit concerned about Crockett's spelling.

"Don't worry Crockett, it will come around," Samuel said in encouragement.

February came around and Jonas talked to Samuel about a trip into Greenup. They planned their trip to the court house, for February the 8th. 1848.

Samuel and Jonas went together to accquire a marriage license and get a bond placed which was the law. Samuel was needed, to give consent for his daughter Mildred Truitt, to marry Jonas Whitt. A friend of the family, Mister William Corum went the bond for Mildred. Everything went according to plan for the wedding that would be Sunday afternoon the 13th of February 1848.

Elder John Young had been asked to perform the Wedding Ceremony, even though he was almost eighty four years old. Why not as he was still very agile for his age and conducted worship services every Lords Day?

David Crockett Whitt, was over his animosities, and felt alright about his father getting married. He had ample time to get used to the idea.

Jonas had talked to Crockett on several occasions in prepairing him for this change in his life. Jonas also honored Crockett by asking him to be the best man at the wedding.

Jonas and Millie worked out a plan to move in with the Truitt's until a house could be built next summer. Samuel agreed to give Jonas and Millie a few acres to build on near the mill. Crockett and Hannah would share the upstairs rooms with Mary Elizabeth Truitt, and George W. Truitt. Jonas and Millie would have a room of their own. George W. Truitt was grown and stayed in Lewis County much of the time with relatives.

Not much would change as to the meals, all four in this new little family would eat at the Truitt Inn for now. After the mill contract was fulfilled Jonas would be expected to provide for Millie, and of course the Whitt children.

What a difference a year can make in a persons life. A move to a new land, and now love and marriage for Jonas. This was a big change for Hannah and Crockett also.

Sunday morning the 13th of February 1848 was here.Elder John Young has prepared for the wedding following the morning worship service. The wedding was an open church wedding and open to whoever wanted to come. Invitations were not sent out but the date had been announced at church the last two Sundays.

After the closing prayer, the unusually large crowd remained for the wedding. Elder Young went to the the front of the church directly in front of the pulpit. He raised both arms as a sign for Jonas and Millie to come to the front along with the wedding party. Every one stood as the bride and groom made their way.

Jonas took Millie by the arm and went to Elder Young. Crockett went and stood beside his father. Hannah Whitt and Mary Elizabeth Truitt took their place as bridesmaids beside of Miss Mildred Truitt. Samuel stood behind his daughter as father of the bride.

There was no music as was the custom of the old Baptist. The congregation remained standing until Elder Young waved for all to be seated.

"Who gives this woman to be wed?" Asked Elder Young.

"Her mother and I," said Samuel Truitt.

Samuel turned and walked back to be seated by his wife Polly.

Elder Young took them through a short but very religious ceremony. He had them kneel for most of the wedding ritual. He had them stand and pronounced them man and wife.

Jonas took Millie into his arms and gave her a a big, but dignified kiss.

Everyone cheered and the young ladies hurried toward the front in hopes of catching the brides bouquet.

Millie faced the eager group of young ladies. Then she turned her back to them and tossed the bouquet over her shoulder. Hannah and Mary Elizabeth both jumped for the prize. Mary Elizabeth being older and taller out jumped Hannah and retrieved the bouquet. Everyone cheered.

Samuel walked to the front and held up his righr arm, and a hush fell over the church.

"Thank all of you for being here today to see my Millie marry Mister Jonas Whitt," Samuel said.

Cheers went up from the congregation.

"We are having a reception in about an hour at the Truitt Inn, cake and tea will be provided for all, come and help us celebrate this great occasion," Samuel announced.

Crockett was alright with todays happenings, at least for now. He was trying his best not to resent his new stepmother.

He and Jonas would be moving their things over to the big Truitt house after the party.

Some things, Crockett will just have to use to, Millie thought. She has felt some negative vibrations from Jonas' son. Millie decided to do as Crockett, try to make it work for the benefit of Jonas.

The reception was enjoyed by most everyone on Big White Oak Creek. Samuel brought out his finest spirits and a large amount of tea was brewed. Also a grand wedding cake was provided. Banjos, fiddles, and other musical instruments were brought in and a dance began.

Crockett got into the spirit of things and asked Mary Elizabeth Truitt to dance with him. She too was in the spirit of this happy time. She smiled at Crockett and went on the dance floor with him. They had several dances together, before William Randolph Thompson (Bill) cut in on Crockett and occupied Mary Elizabeth's time the rest of the night. Crockett was hurt by Mary and his friend Bill, because he had special feelings for Mary.

Crockett and Jonas moved their things over to the Truitt house after the wedding party. At least Crockett would live under the same roof as Mary Elizabeth. He would have opportunity to win her over to his way of thinking. At least that was his plan.

Crockett stayed busy with school and helping Bill and Jonas with the building of the Mill. Mary was always flirting with him, which kept him committed to his plan to capture her heart.

Also at the dance Hannah had flirted with Alfred Thompson so much that he had a dance or two with her. He still considered her a child but she had other ideas in the back of her young mind.

Mary Elizabeth and Hannah were the best of friends and were always together even though Mary was much older.

Everything went well with the living accommodations and things settled down between Crockett and Bill Thompson. They worked well together and with Jonas leading and teaching, the mill project was coming along splendidly.

Spring was coming to Greenup County. The Robins had been back for some time and even a Buzzard had been seen circling high over Big White Oak Creek. Some of the early plowing had begun so that potatoes and other early crops could be planted. Tobacco and even lettuce beds had been prepaired.

The mill works were in place and almost ready to test. The chimney was being layed up to provide heat on both the first and second floor of the mill. Samuel ordered two potbellied stoves to serve as heat rather than having fire places. He kept telling Jonas that it is time they come out of the dark ages and use modern things. Jonas was not too sure about some modern things.

Alfred Thompson delivered the lumber in a timely manner as Jonas needed it. Hannah always made it a point to bring Alfred a cup of tea and do a little flirting. Alfred enjoyed the attention of this lovely young lady.

Mary Elizabeth was a good friend to Crockett and always treated him well. She was a flirt with all the young men, especially Bill. This drove Crockett crazy, even though he tried not let it show. Crockett decided that she was just friendly with everyone and kept Bill as his friend.

The new grist mill looked naked to those that had not seen a mill being built before. The great water wheel and all the workings were still exposed because the siding had not been put on yet. A frame work for the whole thing was in place and even the roof had been applied to keep out the falling weather.

Jonas was getting anxious to test the workings before every thing was enclosed. He had built a sluice gate in the water trace upstream of the waterwheel. It was built close to the earth still remaining in the trace. When things were right the last ten feet of earth would be removed. Then the excess stones that had been gathered wiuld be put into the creek to form a partial dam. This would force the creek through the sluice gate and under the twenty foot waterwheel. The water rate through the gate would be used to control the mill workings. In the best mills the waterwheel turned ten revolutions per minute.

The mill workings were built with the ability to adjust. The set stone could be raised or lowered to the millers preference. The closer the stones the finner the flour or corn meal.

The rate of feeding the grain into the mill stones is set by raising the shaker shoe under the hopper. Also the slower the feed the finer the flour or corn mill.

The finer the flour the more power is needed to turn the waterwheel, the slower the milling, the greater the wear on the stones. The excellent granite stones imported from Italy would wear much better than most other mill stones.

The coarser the flour and the faster the mill turns, the more grain is ground. If the grain stop flowing for any reason the mill stone will grind against each other, get over heated, worn and probably be damaged. Everything had to be in perfect adjustment and a miller had to stay in attention while the mill was grinding. Also Jonas had warned Bill and Crockett to stay clear of moving parts. A waterwheel had the power to run the gears and turn the stone. It could also grab an unsuspecting person and crush them to death. The mill parts would be covered as much as possible to protect the miller, once everything was ready.

As Jonas, Crockett, and Bill installed each part, the bearing points had been packed with heavy grease. Jonas had Crockett and Bill turn the great waterwheel by hand while he had observed each moving part and made adjustments. He was feeling confident about the operation of the new Truitt Mill.

The day the water would be released to the waterwheel was coming soon for the first test. There was a real rush of excitement the first time a mill come to life, so everyone was anxious for this day to come.

Jonas knew this mill was built strong and true, he had used iron parts as reinforcement throughout the mill. Richard Whitt had done a splendid job of fabricating the pieces needed for this in his blacksmith shop.

Samuel Truitt was excited that a test was coming for his mill. He had relayed to Jonas that he wanted Bill Thompson trained in all aspects of running the mill and maintaining it. William Randolph Thompson would be the miller of Truittville.

Later Jonas would have to show Bill how to lift and turn the turnstone so it could be dressed and also be able to dress the setstone. Even the best of grindstones wore down after extended use. At that point everything would be re-lubricated. Bill would have much to learn about adjustments, and staying safe around so many moving parts. Another thing to learn would be to re-dress the stones which was a skilled chore.

Crockett, Bill, and Jonas worked diligently through the spring and summer on building the mill. Everything was in place for a test run, the earth in the upper section of the mill trace could now be dug out. The last step would be to carry all the rocks to dam up the creek.

Samuel Truitt had every employee muster in to Jonas with picks and shovels. Jonas directed them as to digging out the earth and when it was almost cleared to bed rock the stones were carried out into the creek to build the dam. Crockett and the other boys made a game of it playing in the creek.

Big White Oak Creek began to rise and pour into the trace and build up at the sluice gate. Jonas observed all of this and informed them that more rock was needed in the creek.

The creek was down somewhat because of the dry summer. Jonas would have to come up with something to help the situation because of the low water in the creek.

"Crockett you and the boys go to the barn and fetch all the canvas you can find," Jonas said.

The boys ran to the barn and returned with several pieces of canvas. Jonas instructed them on how to put in a piece at a time over the rock dam and anchor it down with some of the stones. This prevented the water from flowing through the stone dam. This worked splendidly. The water rose to the top of the dam and filled the trace behind the sluice gate.

It was the first week of September 1848, and most everyone on Big

White Oak Creek gathered to see the mill come to life. Jonas took corn into the mill and prepared to do the first grind.

"Alright boys start opening the sluice gate and let her flow," Jonas hollered to Crockett and Bill.

The gate was raised and water poured through the trace toward the big water wheel. It was the moment of truth. The power of Big White Oak Creek was released to the mill and the great wheel began to move. The mill become alive. The wheel turned at the exact speed Jonas wanted and he began to grind corn. Everyone hollered and hooped! Samuel ran into the mill and hugged Jonas with excitement.

During this week most every family brought corn and some even wheat to grind. Jonas did the first and then had Bill Thompson take over to learn the routine of milling. Crockett was there learning and participating.

Millie and Hannah was also excited for the completion and success of the mill.

"Paw we should have a party to celebrate the success of your mill," she told Samuel.

CHAPTER 27

MARRIAGES AND DISCORD

Samuel thought the idea of a celebration was in order. He decided to have a dance the evening of the last Saturday in September 1848. This would be a harvest dance and a celebration of the completion of Truitt Mill. Samuel sent the word out by word of mouth that on Saturday, September the 25th 5:00 PM the people will come together for thanksgiving and festivities.

Samuel had asked the Elder John Young to be in attendance, even if someone would have to bring him. John Young was an Elder in all respects, Elder by his position as minister in the Baptist church, and he was also an elderly man in his eighties.

Elder Young was pleased and replied that, "Lord willing I will be there."

Samuel was feeling very thankful for all that the Lord has done for his family and all of Big White Oak. Samuel was so pleased to be able to look at the mill and see the great waterwheel turning about ten times every minute. To Samuel this was a dream come true. He thought about all of his accomplishments and gave God credit for all of it. The little town held his name, and in Truittville he had a shoe factory, a Tavern and Inn. He ran the Truitt farm, and was postmaster. He also found time to teach the children. He also practiced medicine. Samuel never attended medical school, but he was an apprentice for some time to a medical doctor. Some folks always referred to Samuel as doctor. Yes the Lord has been gracious to Samuel Truitt and his family, and Samuel knew it.

Jonas, Samuel, Millie, Crockett, and Hannah walked out together into the field to pick a suitable place for a house. Samuel figured over close to the mill, thinking if anything went wrong Jonas would be close by. Jonas and Millie looked and decided back against the hill.

The edge of the woods looked better to them.

"What do you all think?" Jonas asked looking at Crockett and Hannah.

"I think back at the hill, cause it will be cool in summer," Hannah said.

"I see a fine house in the edge of the woods," replied Crockett.

He remembered Jonas and big brother John Bunyon picking a place to build a cabin back on the Indian Creek Farm. He remembered Jonas saying, "I see a cabin right there in the middle of a Poplar grove.

"I see a fine house in the edge of the woods," Jonas said laughing.

"I see it too," replied Millie.

"Where Paw, I can't see it," replied Hannah.

Everyone laughed!

"That settles it, I am starting to see it too," said Samuel.

The Mill finished and running on an even keel, Jonas put forth his next effort to building a home. He drew up a plan and had Millie interject her ideas into it. He made up an order for lumber and gave it to Alfred Thompson.

As usual Hannah was front and center anytime Alfred was around. She made sure he knew about the celebration and harvest dance coming up next Saturday.

Crockett also talked about it in front of Mary Elizabeth Truitt. He wanted to dance with her again and maybe get a little commitment from her to be his girl friend.

September the 25th came around quickly, and it was time for the folks to gather for thanksgiving and celebration.

People were already coming in from their homes and farms. One of Elder John Young's neighbors agreed to bring him in his buggy to make sure he could attend. The men were wearing their best clothes and the ladies wore their best southern gowns. Everyone was in a festive mood.

After a short talk and long prayer from the Elder, Samuel stood up and gave a short talk about how gracious God has been to the people on Big White Oak Creek. He pointed out that the mill was a great addition to the area. He commended Jonas and others who contributed to the completion of the mill. He also cited the fact that this was a great growing summer. He mentioned that some farmers grew wheat for the first time by faith that there would be a mill to grind it. He offered up a short prayer of thanksgiving and then said, "Where is the fiddler?"

The party was started with the first chord of music and a dance began. Crockett headed for the fair lady Mary Elizabeth Truitt, and escorted her to the dance floor. They had two or three dances and she said she wanted to sit down. Crockett took her to be seated and stood beside her while she sat. William Randolph Thompson saw Mary and came and stood in front of her.

"Miss Mary may I have this dance?" Bill asked in a formal tone.

Mary rose to her feet and accepted graciously! Bill escorted Mary out to where the dancers were and took her into his arms. Crockett stood there indignant. His anger rose up from the tips of his toes to the top of his head. His face became a glowing red. He would not be able to stand here and watch his dream girl dance away the evening with that Bill Thompson. Crockett knew he better leave or something bad might happen. He headed over to the mill and sat in a secluded place to watch the water flow through the trace. This had become Crockett's space for thinking and daydreaming. Crockett slowly cooled his anger, and tried to rationalize that Bill and Mary were just friends as was he friends to both of them.

Crockett sat there for over an hour listening to the music, and thinking. He let his mind wander even back to Tazewell County, and to all that he had done in his short life. After his anger cooled, he felt some guilt so he decided to pray. He prayed out his thoughts to the Lord and asked for forgiveness. Crockett felt much better, so he decided to go back to the party and maybe eat something and visit some with all the folks. Crockett noticed Hannah had corralled Alfred Thompson and they were dancing gleefully. He also noticed that Mary was dancing with one of the other boys. He felt much better about the situation, so he settled down and halfway enjoyed the rest of the evening.

The fall gave way to winter, and Crockett once again enjoyed the teachings of Samuel Truitt. His penmanship was much improved as was his spelling. He learned arithmetic and could figure wages, volume of containers, square feet and even fractions. He also learned the pleasure of reading a book. Samuel was well pleased with his progress.

Mary Elizabeth Truitt went to school this being her last year. She would be turning seventeen and would finish her education at home learning female things from mother Polly and her big sisters.

With the end of January 1849 came the big news that gold was discovered in California by James Marshall a Mormon. He discovered it at Sutter's Mill just lying in the creek. The Gold rush was on; many folks from all walks of life sold all they had and headed to California. Even a few folks from Greenup County, Kentucky would go and try to become wealthy. Many people would lose everything and some even their lives.

Crockett got enthused about the idea, but Jonas showed him the folly of it all. He showed Crockett some Newspapers with folks being killed and becoming destitute for following crazy ventures like this. He even quoted from Proverbs some passages about people trying to run after wealth. Crockett understood, but still thought the adventure would be fun. He decided to stay and learn some more good things from his friend, Samuel Truitt.

In February 1849 news came that the Mexican war was ended with a treaty and a payment of fifteen million dollars to Mexico. Mexico ceded five hundred thousand square miles of great land to the United States. This would create another land rush.

Crockett thought, I am living in exciting times. He had heard so many stories of the western lands. Coming to Kentucky had been a big adventure, he couldn't imagine what it would be like to travel over two thousand miles and search for gold.

The spring of 1849 was upon Greenup County once again. Folks were busy with farming duties, and Jonas was in the process of finishing the new house. It would be good to move out of the crowded Truitt home. Crockett would still be able to see Mary Elizabeth Truitt every day.

One day Crockett was down the creek about a mile and a half. He saw Mister Quillen trying to get his little flock of sheep to cross the creek. Sheep are afraid of water and will not willingly go into it even if it is shallow. Crockett stood there and watched the man try one thing then another. The sheep were only getting more afraid.

"Mister Quillen, I see you are having trouble getting the sheep to this side of the creek," Crockett said.

"Sheep are the dumbest critters on God's green earth," Mister Quillen uttered.

"I never seen it happen, but I heard of a feller back home in Virginia in the same predicament," Crockett said.

"What did he do?" asked Mister Quillen.

"He picked out the leader of the flock and tried to drag it in the water but the dang thang turned around, so he jest drug it across hind part first," Crockett said.

"What happened next?" asked Mister Quillen.

"Well all them other sheep looked and seen their leader backing across the river, so they turned around and backed across the river too," Crockett exclaimed.

Mister Quillen fell to his knees with laughter.

"That is the funniest story I ever heard," exclaimed Mister Quillen.

Crockett laughed with him.

"You may have an idea there son, at least part of it," laughed Mister Quillen.

Mister Quillen picked out the leader of the flock, put a rope around its neck and led it across the creek, all the others followed.

"Thank you Crockett, I would have loved to have seen all them Virginia sheep backing across that river," laughed Mister Quillen.

Jonas received a letter from his brother James stating that he has sold the Dismal Creek farm to Thomas Brown as part of settling the estate of their late father Hezekiah Whitt. Jonas would receive a seventh which would be Twenty-five Dollars, and also mentioned in the letter was John Bunyon Whitt. James wanted Jonas and John to go to the Greenup County Court House and sign over their part of the farm to Thomas Brown and then their money would be free and clear.

Also about this time Jonas received a letter from John Madden Stephenson and Emma Whitt Stephenson asking for some assistance on buying a farm in Tazewell County. John was his son in law and of course Elizabeth was his daughter.

So Jonas went to the Greenup County Court House on the 17th of August 1849 and signed over his part of the Dismal farm to Thomas Brown. They both were able to cash their drafts now free and clear, after John Bunyon took care to do the same.

Jonas was back in the court house on the 19th of August 1849 before the justices making record, giving substance from his wealth to John Madden Stephenson and Emma his daughter on the purchase of a farm in Tazewell County, Virginia.

David Crockett Whitt and Henrietta (Hannah) Whitt were both growing and maturing into young adults. Hannah Whitt was love struck by Alfred Thompson; she would simply die if she didn't get him for a husband. Crockett felt about the same about Mary Elizabeth Truitt. The only problem was that Mary was a flirt and her strongest feelings were for William Randolph Thompson.

In the spring of 1850 Hannah and Mary E. Truitt cooked up the idea for a double wedding in June. Hannah was more or less a child, but seemed to know her mind, and was in love with Alfred Thompson from the first time she saw him.

Mary Elizabeth Truitt still flirted with Crockett when Bill was not around. This added fuel to Crockett's jealousy against his one time friend William (Bill) Randolph Thompson. Bill Thompson was Fifteen years senior to young Crockett, but was not a big man physically. Crockett was only thirteen but tall and strong for his age.

Jonas had stayed busy with his new house, going to Greenup on business, and working around the mill. Also he had a young wife to keep up with as he was senior to Millie by twenty-six years. Jonas knew something was going on with Crockett but figured it was just growing pains!

Hannah and Alfred were going to get married with William Randolph Thompson and Mary Elizabeth if permission was gained from the girls respective fathers. Mary and Hannah thought a double wedding would be great. They even decided to all live together in one house and share the cost.

When Crockett heard these plans he was in an almost uncontrollable state of mind. He went out into the woods and took out his frustrations by lifting big rocks over his head and working out. He had learned to control anger by doing this. He also had developed a strong physical body for his young age of thirteen.

Jonas gave Hannah permission even though he felt she was too young. Samuel also gave Mary Elizabeth permission and asks Jonas to go the bond for both girls. Jonas agreed and went to the Greenup Courthouse on Wednesday June 12, 1850 and placed bond for both girls to be wed.

David Crockett Whitt could not believe Mary was really going to marry Bill Thompson and Jonas was even going the bond. The wedding was only a week away set for June 15th. 1850 and Crockett had some adjusting to do. Another thing Crockett could not believe was that Jonas was letting Hannah get married the same day. She would be a child bride.

On Friday June 14th 1850 Crockett decided to talk to Mary Elizabeth Truitt about this wedding farce. He intended to tell her he loved her deeply and would ask her to call off the wedding. He figured if he talked her out of it even Hannah would put her wedding off.

He mustered up enough courage to confront Mary. He was not well received. He laid his heart on the line and spoke softly and pleaded for her to put off her wedding to Bill. She became obstinate!

"You silly boy," Mary told him.

"You are just immature and have no idea of what love is," she continued.

"I have loved you from the day I first looked upon your beautiful face," Crockett said.

"You need to grow up and find yourself a little girlfriend," Mary answered.

"I am betrothed to be wed tomorrow and you should not be here talking to me like this, go away and leave me alone," Mary said in a very hurtful way.

Crockett's countenance fell! Crockett turned his head quickly and ran off toward the woods to hide the tears streaming down his face. He ran out to do his therapy of rock lifting to try and calm down. Crockett had never in his life felt so rejected by his father and by the girl he loved. His anger did not subside but grew toward Bill Thompson.

Even though Crockett was tall and very strong for a thirteen year old, he knew the man Bill Thompson could whip him in a fair fight.

Crockett thought if he softened up Bill, he had a chance to give him a good whipping. That is what he wanted to do at this very moment. Crockett knew Bill Thompson was always in the barn about this time every evening taking care of all the horses. Crockett looked around and found himself a club and sneaked into the barn. Bill was not there yet so Crockett found himself a hiding place in the shadows.

In a few minutes Bill Thompson came into the barn right on time. Crockett waited until Bill went into a stall and had his back turned to him. Crockett came out of the shadows in a rage and hit Bill over the head with a vicious blow. To Crockett's surprise Bill Thompson crumpled to the straw covered barn floor.

Reality struck Crockett!

"What have I done?" he thought.

"My God, I have killed an innocent man!" Crockett said out loud.

Crockett ran for Jonas, and just so happened Jonas was on his way toward the barn.

Crockett ran to Jonas and stood before him.

"Paw I have done a terrible thing, I killed Bill Thompson!" Crockett said in a whisper.

"What am I to do?" Crockett asked in desperation.

Jonas stood there for a moment in shock!

"What did you do Crockett?" Jonas asked.

"I was in such agony over Bill and Mary I hit Bill in the head with a club," Crockett confessed.

"He is lying in the end stall in the barn, Paw I am so sorry, I only wanted to give him a good whipping," Crockett continued.

Jonas regained his composure and thought quickly.

"Crockett did Bill know you struck him?" Jonas asked.

"No Paw I don't believe he knew what hit him," Crockett said.

"Crockett you have to leave now or face the noose, you go and saddle Jake and head to your Uncle James' in Virginia," Jonas said.

"Do not write nor visit any of our kin on the way there, get out of Kentucky as quick as you can," Jonas continued.

Jonas gave him a twenty dollar gold piece, and Crockett slipped out on Jake and rode away quietly down the creek toward Tygart Creek. Crockett being only thirteen and a half, with only the clothes on his back was running for his life.

Jonas hurried to the barn to check on Bill Thompson! As Jonas came close to the end stall he saw William Randolph Thompson sprawled out on the barn floor. He went close and felt for a pulse. Great Scott, Bill is still alive.

Jonas rose up and quickly looked about. He saw a loose timber just above the stall. Jonas hurriedly got up and took the timber down and laid it beside Bill. He looked around quickly for the club, and it is nowhere in sight. The cover up was in place so Jonas ran to get Doctor Samuel Truitt and others to give aid to Bill.

Samuel grabbed his little doctor bag, and headed for the barn followed closely by Jonas and everyone that heard the news. It was just getting dark so the ladies followed with a lantern.

"My God, that timber must have fallen on him, I told one of the boys to get that thing down just the other day," Samuel said.

Samuel got down close and turned Bill over on his back and looked him over the best he could in the dim light.

"Jonas we got to get him in the house so we can minister to him," Samuel said.

"I agree, everybody get hold of him and let's carry him quickly to the house," Jonas said.

As they picked him up Bill Thompson let out a big groan.

"Bill, you hold on, we will have you in the house in just a minute," Samuel said.

Bill grunted!

They got Bill laid down on the bed and lit three oil lamps. Samuel poured some water from the pitcher into the bowl on the washstand. He took a washcloth and wet it and began to wash Bill's face. Bill's body began to quicken as though he was coming back to life. Bill opened his eyes slowly, and tried to look around.

"Where am I?" Bill asked in a slurred voice.

"Just lay quietly Bill, you are here in my house, you were in an accident," Samuel reassured him.

Mary Elizabeth Truitt was standing close by still partly in shock.

"Paw is my sweetheart going to be alright?" Mary asked.

"I think he will live, and I think he will come out of it alright," Samuel answered.

"Now everyone clear out and let him get some air," Samuel said as he loosened his shirt and ministered to him.

Samuel got in his bag and opened a little bottle of smelling salts, put a little on the tip of a rag and stuck it close to Bill's nose. Bill shook his head in protest.

"Doc what are you doing to me?" Bill asked in a loud voice.

Samuel chuckled as he held up three fingers to Bill!

"How many fingers do you see?" Samuel asked.

"Three," Bill answered.

"Who are you marrying tomorrow?" Samuel asked.

"My sweet Mary Elizabeth," Bill answered.

"You are going to be just fine!" Samuel said.

"My head is a busting Doc," Bill said.

"I will get you some headache powder, and you will be fine by in the morning," Samuel assured him.

Samuel got Bill something for his headache and to make him rest. After Mary gave him a kiss everyone left and she blew out all the lamps except for one on the bed stand. Samuel told Mary to sit quietly and watch Bill for awhile while he slept.

"Wake him up in about two hours and make him talk to you," Doctor Truitt said.

The cover up that Jonas orchestrated seemed to be working fine. Crockett could have stayed Jonas thought. Then he had second thoughts, I guess it is best for him to go back to Virginia.

By now Crockett is going down the Tygart and almost to the Coal Creek trail to the Ohio River. He pushed Jake pretty hard and now slowed to a steady gait of about six miles per hour.

Crockett's head is clearing and he comes up with a plan for a route back to Tazewell County, Virginia. He has decided to swim Jake across the Ohio River, then rest until morning. Then he will go up river to just above the mouth of Big Sandy and cross back in to Virginia near Kenova.

As Crockett started down the hollow toward the river he let Jake walk to rest him before the Ohio crossing. Think goodness the summer was here and the water level was down. Jake would be able to wade much of the way across. (There were no dams on the river in 1850)

As Crockett came up on the river he dismounted and walked Jake to the edge of the river and surveyed the situation. Jake's ears were standing up and his nostrils flared. Jake could sense that he was going swimming.

Crockett mounted up once again and said to Jake, "No time like the present old friend."

Jake made a little protest whinny! Crockett patted Jake to reassure him.

Crockett guided Jake into the waters of the great Ohio River. Jake waded about one third of the way before the bottom dropped off. When Jake started to swim Crockett took his feet from the stirrups and stretched out on Jakes back to take a little weight off but held on to the saddle horn with both hands.

"You are doing just fine Jake, you are a good boy," Crockett encourages!

Jake is a fine horse, even in the middle of the Ohio River, he stayed calm and kept to his task. Jake kept up a steady swim, slow and easy. About one third way from the northern bank the bottom came back up under his feet, and he began walking the bottom again.

Crockett pulled himself back into the saddle and kept encouraging Jake. Where Jake came out of the water the bank was a little steep, but Jake carried Crockett right up to the top without stopping. Now they were out on good level ground in the State of Ohio.

Crockett petted Jake on his neck and dismounted. Crockett kept praising Jake for doing so good! When Crockett talked to him Jake turned his head toward him and rolled his eyes to see Crockett. It was pretty dark but Jake could see pretty well.

Crockett and Jake were both dripping wet, and the night air seemed extra cool. Crockett decided it would be better if they traveled on for a while. He knew that they would dry quicker traveling. Crockett knew that you don't ride a horse hard, and put him away wet. Jake was not a spring chicken any more, or should I say spring horse?

Crockett guided Jake north for a short time until Jake found the road that traveled basically east and west. Crockett turned Jake up the road to the east. They traveled about an hour toward Hanging Rock and found an isolated barn. Crockett checked it out and found that it had some hay for Jake, and a good place for him to lie down until morning. Crockett unsaddled Jake and hung up the blanket. He made some hay available to Jake and he lay down to get some rest. Crockett figured it to be about midnight. Crockett drifted off to sleep and Jake munched on the hay.

Morning came quickly for Crockett. He jumped to his feet when he came to his senses. The sun was already shining. Crockett took a peek out the barn door but saw no one. Next he put the almost dry blanket and saddle on Jake and led him out.

As he looked east he could see the big hill and cliff protruding almost to the river.

"Jake we are almost to Hanging Rock," Crockett said as he petted the important anima.

Crockett knew that without Jake he would be sunk.

As Crockett looked at the beautiful Hanging Rock the sun seemed to line the south edge with bright gold light. Should change the name to Shining Rock this morning, Crockett thought. Then Crockett thought about the history of this place, Indians have been coming here to Hanging Rock for years. From the summit the river could be viewed several miles both east and west. Even the great Chiefs, Tecumseh, and the white man turned Indian Blue Jacket, were known to visit this place.

Crockett had a hunger in his stomach so he began to look for something he could eat. Off the road about fifty yards to the north was a little grove of Paw Paw bushes. They were not ripe as they should be. There was an abundance of fruit on the higher branches, as the animals had eaten all the low Paw Paws. Crockett rode up to the bushes and picked from the back of Jake. He filled his saddle bag with the fruit and Jake even picked himself a treat or two.

"Kinda sour ain't they boy?' Crockett asked Jake.

Crockett began to pass a few folks on the road and came up on the newly founded town of Ironton. Ironton was a natural shipping port, because of the iron smelted in the surrounding Ohio hills. Crockett rode Jake through the burg nonchalantly not wanting to attract attention to himself. On the far east end of Ironton, Crockett came to a creek. He dismounted and let Jake drink his fill of the clear water. (This creek is now called Ice Creek.)

Crockett kept thinking back to the events of yesterday. If there was some way to take it all back he would do it in a minute. Then the dread of being chased by a posse hung heavy on his mind. Could he ever be forgiven by the Lord and by his Paw, he kept asking himself.

Crockett wondered what folks thought in Truittville? What did Mary Elizabeth Truitt think? What did his sister Hannah think?

Crockett set himself a goal of crossing back across the Ohio River into Virginia before dark. (Now West Virginia.) He wanted to cross into (present day Kenova) just to the east side of Big Sandy River. He was thinking about what Jonas told him, get out of Kentucky as quick as possible, and back to Virginia. He was out of Kentucky, now he had to cross the big river one more time. He did not look forward to it, but doing it in daylight should be better.

Meanwhile back in Truittville, William Randolph Thompson was doing fine except for having a sore head. He and Mary talked and decided to keep their wedding date. Alfred Thompson and Hannah were relieved that everything was still set and there would be double wedding at the Baptist Church for this afternoon. Hannah asked Jonas where Crockett was this morning.

"Not sure, he wanted to take an adventure trip," Jonas said.

"He was a little hurt at Mary Elizabeth and Bill so he thought it would be a good time to see Kentucky and visit some of his kin," Jonas continued.

Jonas kept to that story all day as others asked. Not too many were surprised that Crockett left for a while.

Both Hannah and Mary married their beaus this day and would spend the night in the Truitt Inn. Tomorrow both couples would move into a little cabin together. They thought for now, this would be less costly and besides that both couples were best of friends.

A reception was held at the inn after the wedding, and folks were ready for a dance and celebration. Jonas went along as though nothing had happened, even though he had a heavy heart. Now Jonas and Millie had an empty nest at least for now. Millie had not become pregnant as yet.

Back in Ohio, Crockett and Jake were getting close to the planned river crossing. He sat on the river bank for a spell and let Jake rest and do some grazing on the lush grass. They were right across from the mouth of Big Sandy River. This area of Ohio was called South Point because it was the southern most point in the state of Ohio.

It was getting late in the afternoon of Saturday the 16th of June

1850, and Crockett waded Jake back into the waters of the big river. Crockett was about an eighth of a mile up river from the mouth of Big Sandy River. He could see a few houses on the Kenova, Virginia shore.(Present day West Virginia.)(Kenova established 1857)

David Crockett Whitt did as before and let Jake take his time with the crossing. He continued talking to his good friend. Jake seemed to have them on Virginia soil in no time at all. (Now West Virginia.)

Crockett and Jake rode by a few homes and continued up the east side of Big Sandy for about an hour. They came up on a nice level area in the Big Sandy Valley, and it was almost dark again. (Near Present day Prichard, West Virginia.) The area had lush grass and looked like a good place to spend the night. He unsaddled Jake and hobbled him. Then he hung up the wet blanket and saddle on a lower limb of a tree. Crockett gathered some leaves and straw and made himself a bed. He next gathered some firewood and lit himself a fire by flint and steel which he hastily grabbed when he left Truitteville. It was Paw Paws for supper, and hopefully he could settle down tomorrow and get some real food.

Crockett got warm by his little fire and dried out his clothes. Jake's blanket would be dry by in the morning. Jake grazed peacefully near by.

Crockett had no way of knowing things were fine back in Truittville. William Randolph Thompson was not dead. He was actually enjoying his wedding night, as was Hannah and Alfred Thompson.

Jonas prayed for his beloved son, David Crockett Whitt.

Crockett and his horse Jake were worn out and the good nights sleep was refreshing. Crockett was not so on edge this morning when he awoke. He was in Virginia, even though it was about one hundred fifty miles to Uncle James' in Tazewell County.

Crockett was hungry and needed some supplies, so he felt safe in stopping at the next little burg. He needed a good man sized meal and a night in a good bed, and Jake could use some rest and a fill of oats. Crockett put the blanket on Jake and saddled up.

"Don't worry old friend, no big rivers to swim today," Crockett said.

Jake rolled his big brown eyes at Crockett.

Crockett guided Jake on up the Big Sandy on the Virginia side toward

Fort Gay. (Now Fort Gay, West Virginia.) Crockett remembered that he and Jonas had looked across from Louisa, Kentucky when they came through back in 1847. Fort Gay is directly across the river from Louisa. And this is where the Tug and Levisa forks merge to form the Big Sandy.

Hopefully there will be a store and maybe a place to spend the night. He had the twenty dollar gold piece that Jonas gave him and that would be plenty to get him and Jake back to Baptist Valley in Tazewell County. He just needed to be carefull and not let someone steal it from him. The only weapon he had was the skinning knife he got for his last birthday. He would have to stay alert and not be too trusting of strangers, especially on the trail.

CHAPTER 28

SALVATION AND TROUBLE
ON THE TUG

Back in Truittville, Jonas got off to himself and wrote a letter to his brother James Whitt in Baptist Valley, Virginia. Jonas wanted to be off to himself so that he could use the letter to inform Crockett that Bill Thompson was alive and well. He also told of the cover up, and how it made everything look like an accident. The letter also stated that Crockett had a second chance at a good life and should take it by never raising a hand to another person. The letter also told of Hannah marrying Alfred Thompson, and Bill Thompson marrying Mary Elizabeth Truitt. The letter also had the regular greetings and questions about the kin folks in Tazewell County.

Jonas sealed the letter and took it over to Samuel at the Truittville Post Office about the time the post rider was due through. Jonas paid the postage and the rider came through while Jonas was still there. The letter was on it's way, but it would do Crockett no good until he could see it in a few weeks.

Crockett and Jake traveled on up the Big Sandy until they reached Fort Gay late in the afternoon. Crockett saw a mercantile and also a tavern with rooms on the second floor. He guides Jake to the hitching rail in front of the mercantile, dismounted and tied Jake to the rail.

"You wait right here old boy, I will be out shortly," Crockett said to Jake.

Jake gave him one of those looks, like yeah sure!

"I promise," Crockett said as he turned to go into the store.

Crockett went in and found the bare necessities, and gathered them up. He got a canteen, blanket, piece of canvass about 10 feet by 10 feet. He also got a frying pan, some lard, salt, pepper, an eating fork and a fishing line and hooks. He gathered a few other items of food and two sticks of candy. One for him and one for Jake.

After paying for the goods, Crockett checked on a room for the night and also about livery for Jake. He was told that a room, supper, and bath could be had for a dollar, and Jake could have oats and care in the barn for thirty five cents. Crockett decided to take him up on it because both of them were tired and dirty. Crockett took his stuff up to the room and then took Jake over to the livery stable for the night. He decided to save the candy until later after supper, when he would check on his good friend Jake.

Crockett ate a big supper of cornbread, brown beans and fried potatoes. For dessert he had a fried apple pie. After supper Crockett went over to see how Jake was faring. He had been eating oats and corn. He seemed to be doing just fine. Crockett greeted him and fed him the sweet stick of candy. Crockett petted and talked to him awhile and went back over to get a bath and a good nights sleep.

Crockett was so tired he slept like a log, and awoke early the next morning. He had a big breakfast and carried his supplies to the livery stable. Jake came running up to the gate as soon as he saw Crockett.

"Good morning Jake," Crockett said.

Jake did a little side step in excitement. He was really glad to see someone he knew. Crockett petted him a little and put on the dry blanket, and saddled him up. Jake was anxious to get started on the days adventures Crockett was taking him on.

Crockett had talked to a couple different men at the inn and they both gave him basic directions back to Tazewell County via the Tug Fork. They both explained that the trail was rugged but simple. Both men said that you just follow the river. Both mentioned that it was a winding and crooked river stuck right between the hills. Both men also warned him that road bandits sometimes robbed unsuspecting folks.One of the men wanted to know why he was traveling by himself. Crockett told him he was on an adventure trip and heading back home.

Crockett mounted Jake and headed up the Tug. He would be getting away from the more traveled trails and roads. It was a shorter way back if you could fly a straight course like a crow. But Crockett would find out that the river ran in all directions but mostly southeast.

He rode for about a half a day and stopped to eat a bite and give Jake a rest. This stopping off place was near present day Glenhays, West

Virginia. The road was not a busy route as was the Levisa fork road in Kentucky. This made Crockett feel safer in one respect. Jake grazed for about forty five minutes and Crockett ate a bag lunch prepared for him at the inn. Crockett had Jake moving on down the trail toward Tazewell County once again. The weather was nice, but a little hot.

In late afternoon, after crossing a big hill, Crockett came to a flat river bottom. Grass was good here and the river looked like it could produce some fish for supper. This place was near present day Crum, West Virginia.

Crockett stopped for the day. He unsaddled Jake and hobbled him. He set up his canvas as a lean too and put all of his gear under it. He gathered fire wood and made a fire place with a circle of stones. He gathered the worms he found. He looked around and decided he was camp ready. Next Crockett dug out his fishing line and hooks. Then he looked for a suitable pole to cut. He settled on one and cut it with his skinning knife. Next he flopped over a few more rocks and logs for worms. Having every thing needed he headed down to a hole in the river just below an eddy. The river was pretty clear but gave off an emerald green color because it was lined on both sides by green bushes and trees. Also poison oak and Virginia reaper vines grew everywhere.

Crockett eased up to the edge of the Tug and tossed in his offering for his first fish. Wham!, the pole bent and Crockett set the hook. Out of the river came a flopping small mouth bass. It landed back in the weeds where it came to rest. Crockett pounced on it and put it on a forked stick he had just cut. He baited up again and tossed it back into the depths of the water. He moved it a time or two and tossed it up stream a little. It drifted with the current to just in front of him. Wham!, something knocked it's socks off. Crockett set the hook on the second fish and gave a yank. A fat small mouth about fifteen inches long was in the weeds. Once again Crockett moved swiftly to put it on the branch. Crockett fished for a little while longer and caught one more nice fish.

He would have fish for supper and one for breakfast he thought. Crockett had diverted his thoughts off of why he was traveling. After supper and cleanup the agony returned. Why did I kill my one time friend? Why did I allow myself to fall into such trouble? Why did I have to disappoint Paw and the family? Crockett kept asking himself these questions, then the tears began to flow. He felt so alone and hated.

Then he remembered his religious training and knew he had at least one friend as the Holy Spirit spoke to him. Crockett had been humbled by his great mistake, and he remembered the Lord would always listen and was always ready to forgive. Crockett started praying silently and then out loud to Jesus to please forgive him and give him peace. He asked the Lord to take over his life and do with him as he would. Crockett felt an unusual warmth envelope him and a sense of peace soothed his soul. This was the conversion of David Crockett Whitt on the banks of Tug fork in the summer of 1850.

Crockett slept like a baby and woke up feeling altogether different this morning. He shut his eyes and prayed for the Lord to be with him today and protect him as he traveled.

Crockett got up and put his clothes on and walked out to where Jake was grazing.

"Good morning Jake, did you get a good nights rest old boy?" Crockett asked.

Jake shook his head back and forth as if to say he did.

This made Crockett laugh and put a smile on his face.

"Jake you are some hoss!" Crockett said.

Crockett ate the biggest fish he had saved from last night, and broke camp. He got Jake saddled up and all his gear tied on.

"Alright boy, lets head up the river," Crockett said.

Jake started to trot with his head turned steep to the left side like a proud thoroughbred, which he pretty much was.

"Show off, lets just go," Crockett said.

They had traveled about a half a mile and came up on a little village, by the name of Crum. It was mostly a few scattered cabins and a little church. A few folks were about. Crockett nodded his head to each person he passed. He saw three old fellers sitting on the steps of an old weathered storehouse. They were chewing tobacco and spinning yarns, Crockett guessed. This looked like a friendly place. But today the whole world looked favorable to Crockett.

Traveling today went well, the terrain was not too objectionable and Jake kept a good pace. They stopped for a little rest in the early afternoon and Crockett let Jake drink from a creek that fed the Tug. Crockett chewed on some hardtack and some strips of jerky. They had come by a few scattered cabins near Stone Coal, and stopped near present day Stepp town. (Present day names.)

Today Crockett did not dwell on the grief of his past sins, but still wondered what was going on back in Truittville. He decided if a posse did catch up with him he would go willingly to the punishment due him. He would not hurt any one trying to bring him to justice. Yet he would do as Jonas taught him about self defense if he was confronted by some evil person. Jonas had always instructed him never to bluff, but take what ever action needed to defend himself and his property from evil people.

Crockett camped in a little bottom near the river and did some more fishing for his supper. He was lucky to catch some sunfish, and big red eyes, and gave God thanks for providing for him. Crockett noticed himself talking to God as a friend!

Crockett noticed the valley was getting more narrow as he went deeper into the mountain region. It reminded him of the area where Dismal farm was located in the Levisa Valley. The Tug was different in that it went in all directions. The river meandered to the left, right, and sometimes traveled back toward Fort Gay. It was a crooked river.

The trail went about like the river, up and down and around boulders and other obstructions.

"I see why Paw took us down Levisa with our wagon," Crockett thought out loud.

Next day Crockett and Jake traveled on through the area now called Kermit. The Tug Valley spread out again and a nice level area lay out before Crockett. By late in the day Crockett had traveled to another little spread in the Tug Valley. He would spend the night near present day Naugatuck, West Virginia.

Crockett noticed the further he traveled up the Tug, the less folks were saw. He also was aware that danger could be waiting around the next bend. He slept more lightly and paid more attention to his surroundings. This area was pure wilderness. Crockett even heard a panther scream during the night. He heard the hoots of an owl, and little rumblings in the woods round about. Crockett got up and built up his fire, then he brought Jake over and tied him on a long rope closer to the fire. He was on edge, but knew this was good to be a little afraid. This kept his senses sharp.

Back in Truittville, Jonas' nephew James G. Whitt son of Richard Whitt showed up. James G. told his Uncle Jonas that he and his Paw had a difference. Richard sent him to visit Crockett and help Jonas for a spell. Jonas made him welcome but explained that Crockett was also gone on an adventure trip.

"Did you and Crockett have a difference Uncle Jonas?" James G. asked.

"No not really, Crockett just wanted to go on an adventure trip and do some visiting, I thought he may show up down to your place," Jonas continued.

"We ain't seen him," replied James G. Whitt.

"Well I'm sure he is fine," Jonas answered. "You can stay with us for a spell, but you will have to carry your weight," Jonas said.

"I will sir, I would like to learn a little about the mill and how to grind the grain," James G. said.

"I think that can be arranged, Bill Thompson can always use a young man to help," Jonas said.

The little cabin up the creek was staying busy with the two newly wed couples all living together. Millie told Jonas that trouble in paradise was on it's way.

"Two families just can't live in harmony in such a little cabin," Millie said.

A notice was sent out to every family on Big White Oak Creek that the 1850 Census was going to be taken. Every family in the area was to report to the Truittville Post Office in the near future and give a report of family.

James G. Whitt, Son of Richard, Devil Dick Whitt was counted with Jonas and Mildred (Millie) Whitt. (1850 Census) The four Thompson's living up the creek in the little cabin gave their report, and Hannah Whitt Thompson felt that she should raise her age somewhat. She knew she was too young to be married, but Kentucky had no limit of age. She stated that she was 19, even though she was only about 13. (1850 Census) (1860 Census she stated her age at 23.)

Alfred Thompson, Hannah Thompson, William Randolph

Thompson and Mary Elizabeth Thompson reported that they were all living in the same house. (1850 census)

Jonas was very concerned about Crockett, but the only thing he could do was to pray. He hoped that he would get there safe and get the letter he sent. Then he would be free to send an answer back to Kentucky. But for now Crockett thought he was running away from murder, even though all is well in Truittville.

Back on the Tug Crockett woke up the next morning a little more focused on his surroundings. Jake was looking at him as if to say, "You going to lay there all day?"

Crockett got up, broke camp, and he headed up the little road Things seemed pretty normal until Crockett saw a horseman who appeared to be waiting on the trail ahead. Crockett's heart began to race as he realized this man must be an outlaw. Crockett kept up his same speed and showed no alarm but became very focused on the situation. Jake sensed trouble too.

Crockett whispered a prayer for God to be with him, and rode on toward the man. Crockett could see a rifle across the saddle. When Crockett got within speaking distance, the rough looking man spoke.

"Howdy thar sonny," where you headed?

"Hello sir, just going to visit some family," Crockett answered.

Crockett started to ride past the rider, but stopped when the man hollered, "Wait a minute sonny."

Crockett stopped Jake right in front of the man only a few feet away. Crockett could see the man was dirty with unkept hair and beard. His yellow teeth cast off a breath that smelled of death. Crockett knew this was one of those times that he must have some quick decisive action or maybe end up dead.

The outlaw spoke in a graveled voice, and ask, "Got any money sonny?"

Crockett screamed and ran Jake straight at the outlaws horse. The outlaws horse was shocked and reared up in panic and the outlaw fell to the ground with a thud. The outlaws horse ran up the road about thirty yards and Crockett rode after it. Crockett knew he had to get out of range before the outlaw recovered. He caught up with the horse grabbed the rein and galloped up the road and around the next bend. Crockett kept a good pace for at least a mile before he stopped.

He dismounted and unsaddled the other horse. He threw the saddle into the weeds.

Then he looked into the outlaws saddle bag. He had some jerky and parched corn. He also had a small leather bag filled with gold and silver coins. No weapons were in the Saddlebags. Crockett counted the money and decided this must be blood money taken from the outlaws victims. There was almost Four Hundred Dollars in gold and silver.

Crockett hurriedly took the money and put it in his saddle bags , and threw the outlaws saddle bags in the weeds on the other side of the trail. Then he got back on Jake and hurried on up the trail leading the saddle-less horse. Crockett was thinking as his heart still raced. What am I to do with all of this money?

Then he realized that he was a hunted man by the law and by an outlaw. Crockett led the horse a few more miles until he came to another little settlement. (Present day Williamson, West Virginia established in 1892)

As Crockett slowed down and walked Jake into the little village, a man came out to Crockett.

"Young man, where did you get that horse you are leading?" the man asked excitedly.

"Why do you ask?" Crockett answered.

"A devil riding that horse came here and robbed us and beat up some of the folks just the other day," The man answered.

"How much money did he take?" Crockett asked.

By now five or six men joined the first and recognized the horse that Crockett led. The men talked about the money the bandit took and figured it to be close to Four Hundred Dollars.

Crockett knew in his heart what he must do. He got down and told the people about his encounter with the outlaw and described him to the men. They were shocked that a young fellow like this could have outwitted the devil.

Then Crockett went to the saddle bag and pulled out the little leather sack. Well folks I have recovered your money for you, Crockett said.

The men marveled and cheered when they saw the money as Crockett poured out some gold and silver in his hand. Crockett put the coins back into the little sack and handed it to the man that first came to him.

"Here you go, you fellers will have to decide who gets what," Crockett said.

The men could not believe it. They were so happy. By now the women and children had gathered around. Crockett told them that the outlaw was walking and most likely would be after him.

A Hatfield man spoke up, "Don't worry son we will take care of him if he comes this way."

All the men agreed that they must do away with this devil, when he came back.

"We must reward this fine young man," declared one of the elderly ladies.

"He has restored our wealth and must be rewarded," she sounded the second time. "God has answered our prayers through this young messenger," another lady said.

Each of the men gave Crockett a five dollar gold piece and the women ran home to gather traveling food for Crockett. A feed bag filled with oats was brought out from a barn, as a reward for Crockett's fine horse.

"That is not necessary," Crockett exclaimed.

"Yes it is, son, go in peace, we must get ready for that varmint that is coming this way," the man said.

"Son can I ask the name of our hero?" a McCoy man asked.

"Well sir I ain't no hero, but my name is David Crockett Whitt," Crockett answered.

"For what happened down the river today, I must give God all the credit for being with me, and delivering me from the hands of the evil man," Crockett said.

Crockett gave the outlaws horse to the people to use as they saw fit. It was probably tied there in town to draw the bad man out in the open.

Crockett rode on down the trail with thirty dollars and saddle bags full of food. He turned Jake sideways and waved to the people. They all cheered and waved. As Crockett rode out of sight the families made plans to be ready for the bad man. The village men planned an ambush and the women hid their wealth and children.

Crockett never heard about what happened, but imagined that the outlaw devil paid his due. Crockett rode along thanking God for his protection and love. Crockett petted Jake and told him he was a good boy. Crockett realized how valuable Jake had been to him.

That night Crockett camped near present day Sprigg, West Virginia. He dined on some good old fried chicken and other leftovers that the good ladies down river gave him.

Crockett wished that Jonas could have seen him today, even though Crockett did give God the credit. The encounter could have very well turned out in tragedy for Crockett, had not the Lord intervened. Jake did not even have a scratch from the encounter. Jesus was Crockett's new best friend!

Crockett felt good about helping the folks down river today. He even felt a little sorry for the outlaw. He wished that he would find Jesus and not come looking for trouble. Most likely the evil minded man will pay his due tomorrow, or maybe already has. Crockett remembered the Bible saying, be sure your sins will find you out. Crockett reckoned that was why he was on the run from the law. Even though he was guilty he knew he was forgiven by the Lord. He felt so alive and did not fear the wilderness he was traveling through. This was some of the most primitive lands still in eastern north America. The woods teemed with wildlife and the trees were mostly virgin timber. This area was isolated just because of where it lay. It was protected by the very mountains that surrounded young David Crockett Whitt

Since Crockett had been traveling up the Tug he has heard a panther scream, and wolves howling! He has seen bear, deer, turkey, squirrels, rabbits, foxes, beavers, river otters, and one big bull elk. He reckoned it would not be too big of a surprise to see a band of painted warriors running around one of the hills. He knew that the wild Indians were out to the west by 1850.

Crockett kept a pretty big fire and Jake close to him during the nights. Crockett would hang the feed bag on Jake and let him enjoy it for awhile, then let him graze too many oats is not good for a horse.

Crockett didn't fish or do much other work this evening, other than gathering fire wood. He just sat back and reflected on all that had happened in the last two weeks. He felt real bad about hitting Bill

Thompson, but could not take it back. He knew that he was forgiven by God, and that was most important. He knew that folks in Truittville, may never forgive him.

Crockett vowed to never let a woman influence him so mightily again. He reckoned women were mostly trouble for men, except maybe a few like his Maw Susannah, or Grand Maw Rachel.

Crockett's mind wondered back to the family in Tazewell County. He decided once he got back to Uncle James' he would sit down quietly and tell him the whole blessed story and put himself at his mercy.

It has been a long three years since Jonas and he pulled out for Kentucky. He reckoned he was a new uncle several times by now. He would be glad to see his older brothers and sisters again.

Crockett made one mistake during his travels in the wilderness. He should have been hanging his food up high in a tree. Crockett had his food under his lean to and a hungry bruin got a whiff of it. Crockett awoke with a startle as Jake was raising cane. Crockett jumped up and thinking fast, he grabbed a blazing stick from the fire and waved it and screamed. He scared that poor bear out of two years growth. Crockett understood his situation as for keeping food in camp from then on.

The little valley the Tug ran through begin to close even tighter. There was not many places offering good grazing for Jake, so every time Crockett saw a patch of grass he would let Jake do some munching. One good thing the cliffs offered many rock houses to shelter in at night. One day Crockett stopped at an over hanging cliff for the night and as he cleaned back the leaves he found a pick and shovel. The handles were rotted away and the shovel was mostly rusted away. The pick was in pretty good condition. How in thunder did these things get here, he wondered. He decided to keep the pick.

Crockett always cleared back the leaves before making a bed in one of the many rock houses along the Tug. He drug a black snake out one evening, which gave him and Jake some excitement. Crockett was not too afraid of most snakes long as he knew where they were. He and Jake did have a close call one day on the trail when they happened upon a huge timber rattler. Jake just about threw Crockett off, but managed to get by the deadly viper. Crockett prayed a prayer of thanksgiving and praised the Lord for his protection.

The Tug fork was getting to be a small stream now and Crockett knew it would not be far to his destination. He figured another week or so and he would ride in to Baptist Valley. He would head straight to Uncle James and Aunt Nancy Whitt's house. He knew it well, as it was the old home place of Grand Paw Hezekiah Whitt. He has had a great adventure for the past three weeks. He has tasted hunger and thirst, he has experienced fear and destitution. He also experienced valor and happiness for overcoming many obstacles. The best thing he could think of was the conversion that night on the banks of the Tug. Whatever he had to face, he knew the Lord would be with him. He did not have a Bible, but he craved to study Gods word.

Today Crockett passed through what is known as today as Wyoming City, West Virginia. It would be about two days to area know today as Paynesville, West Virginia. Another two days he would be in the area know today as Pea patch, West Virginia. About two more days and Jake would carry Crockett through Bear Waller then to Harmon, then to what is now called the town of Bandy. A half days ride from Bandy through the area know as Bust Head and another mile he will be home again. Crockett figured about the 15th or 16th of July 1850 he would be there.

After another grueling week in the wilderness of upper Tug Fork, Crockett begins to see more cabins and more people. Crockett guides Jake up a feeder branch and crosses over into the water shed of the Clinch River. Today he starts out near present day Bandy, Virginia. He worked his way down the trail toward Indian Creek and to his destination.

Crockett is anxious to get to the James Whitt house, yet he has some dread also. He is going to do as he planned, and that is to get Uncle James off to himself and tell him the whole story of why he is here. He will do what ever it takes, either to stay with James Whitt, or move on if he is shunned. Crockett knows in his heart that he is forgiven by the Lord, and the Lord will be with him. He is not sure what James will say or do, but feels that James will welcome him.

Finally Jake carried Crockett to Indian Creek, on the 16th day of July 1850. In just a short ride he would be there. Crockett's heart was racing a bit, knowing he would be with family in a short while. He traveled up the Kentucky Turnpike into Baptist Valley. Crockett saw the turn off up Green mountain road and turned Jake. Jake seems to know this place also. There on the little rise on the right is the old Hezekiah Whitt house. Now it is the James Whitt house and there on the porch is a lady sitting there doing something.

Crockett gets closer and recognizes her as Nancy Whitt his aunt. She is stringing new green beans.

Crockett rode Jake right up to the porch and with a wide smile says, "Hello there Aunt Nancy."

"Oh my gracious, is that you David Crockett?" Nancy asked.

"Yes ma-um it is me," Crockett said.

"How in thunder did you get here?" Nancy asked.

"Jake brought me," Crockett said with a laugh.

"Well get up here and let me hug you," Nancy said.

Crockett got off Jake and tied him to a porch support, and walked around to come up on the porch.

"My goodness Crockett you are so tall," Nancy said in amazement.

"Yes ma-um, reckon I have grown up a might," Crockett said.

Nancy gave Crockett a good welcome hug, and Crockett felt a little more at ease.

"Where is Uncle James, is he about today?" Crockett asked.

"He is out in the barn I think, want me to ring the bell?" Nancy asked.

"No Ma-um I would rather surprise him, I will take Jake to the barn and see to his needs and surprise Uncle James," Crockett said.

Uncle James was working on repairing a single tree when Crockett walked in through the barn door. James looked up in astonishment as he recognized Crockett.

"Well I be Crockett, you are so tall," James said.

"Son is everything alright, is Jonas with you?" James asked.

"No sir just me and Jake, I need to talk to you Uncle James," Crockett said.

James pointed to a bench over to one side, and said," Let's go and sit over there and you can tell me all about it."

"Let me get Jake took care of first, can Jake have some oats Uncle James?" Crockett asked.

"Sure can, I will fill a feed bag while you unsaddle him," James said.

"This place sure looks good to me," Crockett said as he took off the saddle and all the gear that was tied on it.

James noticed the rusted pick, but didn't say anything about it. With Jake cared for, James and Crockett sat down together on the bench.

"Uncle James, I don't know hardly where to begin, I am so ashamed of what I done, but I know that God has forgiven me," Crockett affirmed.

James sit there waiting patiently.

"Well Crockett just start at the beginning, and tell me, I am your family and you can confide in me," James said.

"Uncle James it all started right after we got to Kentucky, Paws new wife Millie has a little sister, and I fell for her," Crockett said.

James nodded for Crockett to go on.

"Well sir she flirted with me, but decided to marry Bill Thompson," Crockett said.

"I was filled with rage and wanted to give Bill a good whipping, but I figured I wern't man enough yet," Crockett continued.

"What happened next?" James asked.

"Well sir, a reasoned that if I softened him up a might, I could handle him, so I plotted out a quick plan, I knew that Bill always took care of the Truitt horses every evening about dark, so I got myself a club and hid in the barn," Crockett continued..

James sits with his mouth opened, and listens.

"When Bill came in and walked into a stall, I gave him a good lick, and got ready to fight, but He fell to the floor dead," Crockett said with tears welling up in his gray eyes.

"What happened next?" James asked.

"I panicked and ran for Paw, and Paw was coming toward the barn when I saw him," Crockett said.

"What did Jonas tell you to do?" James asked.

"Paw was hurt and shocked, but he told me to saddle up Jake and get out of Kentucky real quick, he gave me twenty dollars and me and Jake slipped out of Truittville," Crockett stated.

"Paw told me I would get hung if I stayed around and to come to you, never to write or let anybody know where I was," Crockett added.

James was in shock at the story Crockett told him.

"Uncle James I never set out to kill poor old Bill, I just wanted to do some whipping for taking my girl," Crockett said.

"Bill was a good feller cept for marrying Mary Elizabeth, Uncle James I prayed on the trail and have accepted Jesus as my personal Savior, and I know He has forgiven me," Crockett said.

"I hope in time Paw, and You can also forgive me," Crockett pleaded.

James took out his pipe and filled it while he pondered on the situation. He lit the pipe and gave it a puff or two. James looked at Crockett really intently.

"Son do you want to stay here and work for me for room and board?" James asked.

"I was hoping to do just that Sir," Crockett answered.

"Well alright we will try this out, I don't want you to tell another soul of what you just told me not even Nancy, do you understand Crockett?" James asked.

"Yes sir, I understand completely," Crockett answered.

"Alright son you are welcome here, and I will protect you the very best I can," James said.

"If for some reason you don't hold up your bargain, or cause us any trouble I will send you packing, understand?" James asked.

"Yes Sir, I understand, you will not have any trouble out of me Uncle James," Crockett answered.

"Alright Son we will not talk of it again, just consider yourself as my adopted son and me as your adopted Paw," James said.

Crockett reached out to shake his hand, but James grabbed him and gave him a big hug. Crockett felt a big burden lift from his shoulders, as he realized James has forgiven him.

"I have one question Crockett, where did you get that old rusted pick?" James asked.

"I cleared out under a rock house to spend the night and found it and a rusted away shovel," Crockett said.

"Handles rotted away?" James asked.

"The handles, and most of the shovel," replied Crockett.

"Reckon who might have left them there in the wilderness?" Asked Crockett.

"Only one name comes to mind, and that would be just a big guess," replied James.

"Who was that Uncle James?" Crockett asked.

"There is a story been floating round these parts since I was a young-un, and that feller's name was Jonathan Swift, he supposedly had a silver mine here in the mountains someplace," James exclaimed.

"That might be his pick," Crockett responded.

"Could very well be, that is the only answer for how a pick and shovel ended up out there in the wilderness," James said.

"What happened to that Swift feller Uncle James?" Crockett asked.

"The story was that he dug out a fine cache of silver, smelted it into English Coins and went back east, then he went blind and never could get back to the silver he hid so well," answered James.

"I reckon that stuff might be Jonathan Swift's old pick and shovel I found," Crockett said.

"Was there any thing else that might make you think a silver mine might be around?" James asked.

"Not a thing Uncle James, but I wasn't looking for none neither," Crockett responded.

CHAPTER 29

HOME IN TAZEWELL COUNTY

While Crockett was in Kentucky his brothers John Bunyon, and James Griffith Whitt had handled the sale of the old Indian Creek Farm for Jonas. John and his family had moved to the extreme western section of Tazewell County. (Now McDowell County WV.) John and Catherine Beavers Whitt have four children. Polly the youngest was just born in 1850.

James Griffith has played the field, but now is caught by Nancy Webb. He lives in a little cabin, near the Webb's. The wedding date is set for September 4, 1850. Crockett got back to Virginia just in time to be the Best Man at the wedding. Rhoda and her husband John Bunyon Lowe now have four children also live in the western area of Tazewell County. Rachel Whitt Beavers has three children and she and Adam live on a nearby farm close to the Beavers family. Emma Whitt Stephenson has four children, and lives on their new farm with John Madden Stephenson. They were able to buy this place with the help of her father Jonas Whitt. Elizabeth Whitt Baldwin lives up the valley with her husband "Bige". She has no children yet, but they have a whole household of his children by a prior marriage. She seems to be really happy with her situation.

Somehow the word traveled around the county to all the Whitts that Crockett was living with James and Nancy Whitt. Nancy planned a get-together for the next Saturday. All of the Jonas Whitt family would be there except Hannah and of course Jonas who lived way over in Greenup County, Kentucky. Crockett wished that everybody in Tazewell County didn't know he was back.

While the family had their reunion, William Thompson the High Sheriff of Tazewell County stopped by to welcome Crockett home. Crockett handled it all just fine, after all Sheriff Thompson was a friend of the family.

The gathering went well and Crockett rejoiced at seeing all of his brothers and sisters. Crockett told all of them he could see that they all had been busy while he was gone.

Sister Rachel asked, "What do you mean by that little brother?"

"You all have little Whitts everywhere," Crockett said with a laugh.

"Guess you are right about that," Rachel answered.

"Little brother it won't be that long before you get bit by the love bug," John Bunyon said.

James gave Crockett a little grin.

"No plans right now," Crockett said laughing.

"Tell about your trip and why you couldn't stay away from good old Tazewell County?" James Griffith asked.

"I just felt a hankering to come back and see all of you, and I might just stay here and aggravate my big brothers and sisters," Crockett said.

Everyone laughed.

What happened on the trail, any thing worth mentioning?" asked James Griffith.

"Well I did have one encounter that you all might like to hear about, besides the bear and panther," Crockett said.

Crockett told them how wild the Tug Fork Valley was, and his encounters with the wildlife. Then he sat back and begin telling them about the worst animal of them all.

"What animal is that?" Rachel asked.

"An outlaw bent on mischief and malice," Crockett continued.

"We had an experience with three of them coming here from Montgomery, didn't we John?" Rachel asked.

"We all know about that, I want to hear about Crockett's bad man," Rhoda said.

"Well it was like this," Crockett said.

"Me and Jake was riding along up the Tug Valley when all of a sudden I spy a feller waiting for something up ahead," Crockett said.

"What was he doing, waiting for you?" Emma asked.

"That is exactly what that old devil was doing," Crockett continued.

"What happened next?" Emma asked.

"Well I will tell you," Crockett said.

"I knew it in my gut that feller was up to no good, so I begin to pray to the Lord to be with me," Crockett said.

"He was an awful looking feller with dirty clothes, and un-kept hair and beard, his big yeller teeth shined through all his whiskers," Crockett continued.

"He was just sitting there on his horse with a rifle laid a cross his saddle, and when I spoke to him and started to ride by he hollered for me to stop," Crockett said.

"What did he say?" asked James Griffith.

"He said, "Hay sonny you got any money?"

"His eyes told me I might die," Crockett continued.

"What did you do?" asked James Griffith.

"I reckon it was the Lord told me what to do, when he saw this evil man planning on killing and robbing me," Crockett said.

"He told me to run Jake straight into this feller," Crockett continued.

"I screamed and ran Jake straight at him, and his horse reared up and dumped him on the ground with a thud," Crockett said.

Everyone sit quietly waiting for more of the adventure.

"His horse tore loose and headed up river with me and Jake right after him, we had to get around the bend before that evil devil could get a shot off at us," Crockett said.

"Did you get the mans horse Crockett?" James asked.

"Sure did, I grabbed his rein and we galloped for a good mile before we stopped," Crockett continued.

Even Uncle James and John Bunyon were sitting on the edge of their seats by now.

"I stopped and took off the saddle bags and found a little leather pouch and a little jerky, then I threwed the saddle bags over in the tall weeds," Crockett said.

"What was in the pouch?" asked James.

"Gold and silver coins," Crockett answered with out batting an eye.

"I gave it a quick count and there was bout Four Hundred Dollars in that little pouch," Crockett said.

Every ones eyes were big, and their ears were waiting to hear more.

"I knew it was blood money so I put it in my saddle bag, then I took of the saddle and throwed it in the weeds on the other side of the road," Crockett continued.

"What happened next?" James asked.

"Well I got Jake up to a good trot and traveled up the road for another mile or so leading the other horse," Crockett said.

"Then I come up on a little village of about six cabins, and a feller wanted to know where I got that horse," Crockett said.

"What did you tell him?" John Bunyon asked.

"I told him the truth about that feller trying to rob me and maybe even kill me so I took action," Crockett said.

"Why did he want to know about the horse?" James asked.

"Turns out that old devil had robbed all of them and beat up a couple of them a day or two back," Crockett said.

"I asked them how much money he took off of them and they told me bout four hundred in gold and silver," Crockett continued.

"What happened next?" James asked.

"By then all the wives and children were out in the street, so I got off Jake and got the money and handed it to that first feller that I met," Crockett said.

"You handed him all that money?" James asked.

"The Lord gave it to me to give it back, the way I figured," Crockett said.

"What did they do?" John asked.

"They danced in the street, and were so amazed that a young feller like me could outsmart that old devil, and that I was so honest to give them their money back," Crockett said.

"Did they reward you in some way?" Emma asked.

"Sure did, they gave me Thirty Dollars in Gold and filled my bags with food, they even gave Jake a feed bag full of oats," Crockett said.

"What happened next?" Emma asked.

"I told them I had to get going cause that feller would be out to kill me, they told me not to worry, they would take care of that varmint," Crockett answered.

"I gave them the fellers horse to do with what ever they would, and they tied him up in the open and I left," Crockett said.

"I figured they was going to use the horse to draw that bandit out so they could shoot him, but never heard any more bout it," Crockett told them.

"I prayed that, the evil person would repent before he got to that place," Crockett said.

"Where was that place, Crockett?" James asked.

"It was a wide place in the Tug Valley where the river made almost a circle, one of the fellers there went by Williamson, another was a Hatfield, and I also remember a McCoy," Crockett answered.

"I am so proud of you Crockett," said Aunt Nancy.

"We all are," said Uncle James.

"I wish Jonas knew about this," Uncle James said.

"I am sure he will when you write," said Nancy.

The Whitts had a good day of visiting and Crockett felt much better to be home and feel so welcome. Crockett fits right in at the James Whitt house. He was exactly what James needed to spruce up the farm and catch up on needed repairs. Crockett worked hard on fencing, cutting hay and pitching it on great hay piles. He started the winter woodcutting, and hoed out the garden. He gathered the produce that Aunt Nancy wanted to pickle or can.

Crockett stayed busy and attended Church the last two Lords days! Aunt Nancy got a little Bible and gave it to Crockett. Crockett was so pleased and felt the peace of the Lord as he read each night!.

After about three weeks, a letter came addressed to James Whitt from Truittville, Kentucky. Two letters were in the envelope, one to James and one to Crockett. James opened the envelope and handed the one addressed Crockett, to him and James read his.

It's from brother Jonas, James announced.

Crockett took his letter aside and read it slowly, taking in every word and thought. Crockett eyes filled with tears of joy as he discerned the meaning of the joyful letter.

The letter read: "Dear Son, I have great news for you that should take away your worries. William Randolph Thompson is alive and well. It appears that a timber fell from the barn loft and hit him in the head. He was able to wed Mary Elizabeth Truitt the very next day. Your little sister also wed Alfred Thompson the same day. All is fine in Truittville. I hope and pray that you had a good safe trip back to Tazewell County. You may keep Jake, and take good care of him.

Start yourself a new life in Virginia, hopefully we will meet again."

"Your loving Father," Jonas.

Crockett's eyes were filled with tears of joy. He handed his letter to James. Nancy looked at Crockett and saw his eyes filled with tears.

"What is it Crockett, did you get bad news from your father?" Nancy asked.

"No Ma-um, I got great news, didn't I Uncle James?" Crockett asked.

James nodded his head and smiled.

"The Lord is so good to me," Crockett exclaimed.

"He is good to all of his children, but why are you so happy?" Nancy answered.

"I did a bad thing, but God turned it all into good," Crockett answered.

Crockett felt so relieved and had no ill will against Bill Thompson nor Mary Elizabeth. Crockett was even happy for his little sister, as long as she was happy. He had been so against her marrying Alfred because of her young age. She was only thirteen and Alfred was thirty one when they wed back in June. Now at this point and time Crockett had no enemies, and it felt wonderful.

"I have to sit down today and write brother Jonas. He will sleep better once he hears that Crockett is here safe and sound. I will tell him how good thing are going and that Crockett has really helped on our farm. I will also tell him about the good deed Crockett did on the trail coming here," James stated.

Crockett felt so good and enjoyed a little praise from Uncle James.

James got his papers, ink, and a pen and went to the kitchen table and wrote a long letter to Jonas. He assured his brother that Crockett was here in Baptist Valley safe and sound. He told Jonas that Crockett found the Lord one evening on the trail and is now a born again Christian. He told of the ordeal Crockett had with the bad man and how he restored the Four Hundred Dollars to the people on the Tug.

James congratulated Hannah on her marriage to Alfred, and wished the best for all of them in Truittville, Kentucky.

James encouraged Jonas to bring his wife Millie, daughter Hannah, and her new husband Alfred for a visit before everyone got too old. James was the oldest of the Hezekiah Whitt children and would be sixty eight years old on the 28th of October 1850.

Crockett also wrote a letter to Jonas and reassured his Paw that everything was fine and praised God for all his good fortune. He put it in the same envelope, with Uncle James' letter. James could not help but notice the great penmanship Crockett displayed.

"Where did you learn to write like that?" James asked Crockett.

"Samuel Truitt taught me, he made me write every letter about a million times!" Crockett answered.

"Well son you have a great skill in penmanship, you could probably get work as a scribe some time," James said.

Crockett just smiled and handed the letter back to James for mailing. James sat on the porch and watched for the post rider to come by. James and Crockett both felt better once the letters were on the way.

Crockett noticed in an old news paper that the 1850 census was taken in Virginia.

"Aunt Nancy, wonder when they will count the people in Tazewell County?" Crockett asked.

"Oh Honey, they did that just before you arrived here, we went into Jeffersonville and your Uncle James gave them our information," Nancy answered.

"Well, looks like I might not get counted for another ten years," Crockett said disappointedly.

"Don't worry about trivial matters, you are counted highly by me and your Uncle James," Nancy said lovingly.

James had another news paper given to him just lately. There was an article in it about the railroads, and some comments from Philip Horn the mayor of New York City. It stated that between 1830 when there was twenty three miles of track, and now in 1850 there was some nine thousand miles laid. The article stated that Philip Horn was now sixty nine years old and longed for the good old days when things were not so fast. He longed for a time when horse drawn buggies sped along at six miles per hour.

"Reckon we will ever get a railroad here in Tazewell County?" Crockett asked.

"I doubt that I will ever see it, but I venture that you will live to see a train and even ride one," James told Crockett.

Crockett told James all about the great steam boats he saw on the mighty Ohio River. He also told James about the numerous pig iron furnaces on both sides of the big river. Crockett also told him about the slaves working in the fields and how they all sang as they worked.

"You have seen many wonderful sights, these old eyes will never see," James told him.

"Well sir the world sure is changing, yet you can travel over on the Tug and think you are alone in the world," Crockett said.

"That pretty well describes how Tazewell County was when I come along," James told Crockett.

"Everything is changing and not for the good," He said.

"I expect trouble between the South and the North before it's all over," James continued.

"The South believes in a state having rights, and of course the Yankees are fussing about slaves," James told Crockett.

"Paw talked about such matters pretty regular," Crockett answered.

"Your Paw is one of the smartest men I know," James said.

"Not only does he know mill building but he understands a host of things," James continued.

"Yes sir, Paw is very wise," Crockett agreed.

James Griffith Whitt asked Crockett to be the best man at his wedding. Crockett agreed but reluctantly! Another wedding this close after just getting back from Kentucky, only brought back the memories of Mary Elizabeth Truitt. Crockett had to talk to God and get this taken care of. It is an amazing thing how a good prayer changes things, Crockett thought.

The wedding would be at the Joseph Webb home. Joe and Susannah Web had a great wedding planed out for their daughter Nancy and James Griffith Whitt. The wedding would be on the 4th of September 1850.

James Griffith was twenty five and Nancy was about eighteen, so both of them had time to think it all over. James had loved Nancy for several years, and had patiently waited for her to mature and fall in love with him. James was a good looking young man and well known in Tazewell County, so he could have had a pick of the county. One thing that made him known was the shooting match a few years back that he won hands down against the best shooters in the county.

On September the 4th. 1850 James Griffith and Nancy stood before a large group of friends and relatives and took their vows of Holy Matrimony. Crockett stood with his big brother as best man.

Crockett was still thinking that he would never marry. He was still thinking that women were just too much trouble.

No one knew that the American civil war was looming on the horizon in just a short decade. Everyone knew that things were not right between the North and South, but did not predict an all out shooting war. So everyone went on with their lives as normal as possible.

The word hit Tazewell County with a wave of shock, President Zachary Taylor is dead. He became ill after a hot July 4th celebration and died on the 9th. Vice President Millard Fillmore is now the new president. He would come to be know as the President of Compromise. The North and the South were at odds over the new territory in the south west. The North wanted it to be free states and the South wanted it to have a choice as each new state was formed. Some of the Southern states threatened secession. Zachary Taylor being a military man had been prepared to take force against any state that would pull out of the Union. Now that he has passed away, President Fillmore would try to make both sides satisfied.

Zachary Taylor was a Southern man, but forty years in the U.S. Army appealed to the North. He was known as "Rough and Ready", and his Union ideas made him popular in the north. He also owned over one hundred slaves, which made him a good southern vote getter. Now that he was gone, President Fillmore would do what he could to soothe the feelings of both the South and North.

We can look back at this time in history and see that a great split in our country was avoided, or at least postponed. It is ironic that Richard Taylor, son of Zachary Taylor would serve the Confederate Nation eleven years later as a General.

On September 18th 1850 the U.S. Congress passed the Fugitive Slave Law to help curb the running away of slaves. The police of the north were turning their heads as slaves made it into the northern states. This action taken by congress would pay police twice as much to help capture and return slaves to the Southern owners. Also by September 20th President Millard Fillmore signed into law to admit

California into the Union as a free state. A settlement to pay Texas for the land of New Mexico, and give New Mexico a U.S. Territory status. Also a law that would place Federal Officers at the disposal of slave holders seeking run away slaves. The new law abolished slave trade in the District of Columbia. With the actions of Congress and President Millard Fillmore the country could settle down even though the North and South were not completely satisfied.

All of this was hashed about in Tazewell County as well as in the rest of the country. David Crockett Whitt was like most young men, he could not really understand what all the fuss was about. He did know one thing for sure, what ever his country the State of Virginia did, he would be there to support it. To Crockett and most Southern people their state was their country, and the Union came second.

Crockett stayed and helped Uncle James for a couple of years and then he wanted to have his own place.

The little cabin that John Bunyon and Catherine Beavers Whitt started house keeping in was empty and the back fields around it were available for sharecropping. Crockett saw a chance to earn a living for himself, so he rented the cabin from the new owners.

He kept Jake and cared for him for his faithful service over the years. Crockett got himself a team of mules to do the hard work, and only rode Jake as a saddle horse. Crockett lived by himself about a year, but visited James and his other kin pretty regular. James was getting old and was basically retired, he only put out a little garden and raised livestock for the table. Any time James and Nancy had a chore requiring a strong back Crockett would be there.

James Whitt departed this life on September 19, 1855, from an apparent stroke. Nancy his beloved wife was devastated. Crockett could not believe his uncle was gone so fast.

The whole Whitt clan (in riding distance) came to the funeral. Letters were sent out to all of those that had migrated to other areas, too far to come in for the funeral.

Crockett was 18 at the time of his Uncle James' death, and it had an impact on his life. It dawned on him that life is short and uncertain. The Whitt Cemetery across the road and upon the hill was becoming filled with loved ones!

Jonas, the son of Griffy, felt a calling to move in with Nancy after

James passed. Jonas was about one year younger than Crockett. Jonas (son of Griffy Whitt) and Crockett would spend a lot of time together in the next few years. They would work together, and enjoy some great hunting and fishing. It was an answer to a prayer for Jonas to move in with Aunt Nancy.

Crockett wrote an occasional letter to the Whitt's in Truittville, Kentucky. Crockett learned that sister Hannah now had two babies. baby Mathew was born 1852, and baby Alfred was born in 1854.

Jonas (father of Crockett) and Mildred (Millie) also had two children, William Randolph Whitt born 1851, and Jesse Monroe Whitt just born in 1855. Crockett found it interesting that he had two little brothers over in Kentucky.

Crockett's milling experience come in handy, as he took on part time work at the McGuire Grist Mill just a ways up the Clinch from the mouth of Indian Creek. Crockett put out large fields of corn and tobacco, and supplemented his income with the mill work when he had time. He liked working at the mill because he had the skill, and also he met so many people. One family that came to have their corn ground was the Robinett's that just moved to the area.

The Robinett's had one little girl that caught Crockett's eye. Arminda Robinett was way too young for courting, but held the interest of David Crockett Whitt. It has been about five years since his heart was broken by Mary Elizabeth back in Kentucky. He swore off girls then, but time has a way of changing things.

Franklin Pierce was elected President in 1852 in an apparent time of tranquility between the North and South. Pierce tried to continue to keep the calm, but a war would come to this land that would pit brother against brother, and friend against friend.

The North and the South found many things to bicker about, from the choice of slavery to the right of each state. They even became at odds of where the cross country rail road should be built. The north wanted a northern route, which would better serve them and give them more control. The South thought it would be better if it was built through the new southwest to funnel people into the area of New Mexico, Texas, and California.

The Kansas-Nebraska Act, which repealed the Missouri Compromise opened up the question of slavery in the west. Northern and Southern folks rushed into Kansas to settle it and establish it to be free choice or non slave. This many people with different view points could not coexist in the new land of Kansas, with out a few shots being fired. The ugly name of a new land emerged as "Bleeding Kansas", and became a household name.

The people of Tazewell County and around the young United States began to take sides. Why wouldn't the Yankees mind their own business was the question that rambled through the South? Why are those unlearned Dixie folks so obstinate? Why do they bring the sin of slavery on our new nation, many Northern folks asked?

The North thought that God was with them and their thinking. The South thought that God was with them, they even said that the Yankee people can't even read and understand the Bible. The Bible plainly speaks of folks having slaves, and they are better off being slaves here as to being wild men in the jungles of Africa. The term of "Dammed Yankee", derived from this thinking. If the Northern folks can't even understand the Bible they will be dammed to hell, was the thinking of many Southern folks.

Crockett did not say much either way, but he knew that if Virginia was to ever be invaded, he would stand to defend her.

Crockett could understand from the letters from Kentucky they were divided in their thinking also. Even the children of Samuel Truitt were not getting along when it came to the issue of North verses South. Millie and her sister Louisa had a spat and quit speaking to each other.

By 1858 Crockett became enamored by the lovely Arminda Robinett which was at the courting age of fourteen. She thought Crockett was the greatest and best looking man she had ever known.

Crockett began a formal courtship with Arminda with the blessing of her mother Christina. They would go to church together and spend Sunday afternoons together. Any time there was a community outing such as a "corn-shucking" they would attend. Crockett did not pay too much attention to current events, during this time of lovely distraction. Friends and relatives of Crockett and Arminda anticipated an upcoming announcement.

David Crockett Whitt got down on one knee one evening in the sitting room of the Arminda Robinett home. He asked in the most graceful and formal way he could muster, for her to become his wife. She pulled him close and gave him a long passionate kiss, took a breath and agreed. Crockett was twenty two and Arminda would barely be fifteen by the time they would wed on May 12, 1859.

Crockett came out of his cabin one morning around the first of May, to be shocked at seeing Jake his beloved horse laying dead in the corral. He ran to him to check on him, but he was gone. Crockett's eyes filled with tears as he patted his good friend. Crockett cried out loud as he dug a grave next to where Jake lay. Jake had been one of the best horses he ever knew. He had been Jonas' horse for years before he gave him to Crockett. It was a long sad day. Crockett thought of all the times Jake had been there as a friend. He thought about how Jake carried him across the waters of the great Ohio. Not once but twice. Jake had helped save his life the day the bandit tried to rob him back on the Tug. Jake had more sense than some folks, Crockett thought.

Crockett tried to figure out how old Jake was but did not know. He had known Jake all of the twenty-two years of his life. Jake had been a friend and faithful horse to Jonas and the Whitt family. Jake must have been pretty young when Jonas brought the family from Montgomery County to Baptist Valley. He would write a letter soon to Jonas and the family in Truittville, and tell of Jake's passing. No doubt Jonas will be saddened by the news.

Crockett rode one of his mules over to see Arminda that evening. She was so hurt to hear about Crockett's friend passing. She tried her best to console him and get his mind off of Jake.

"Jake was a great horse and good friend to you, time will heal," Arminda said with great passion.

"I know, it just hurts so much to give up a friend like that," Crockett said sadly.

"There are several new foals around the valley this spring, you need to get your self a new baby," Arminda said.

"I will check into it, but no horse could ever replace Jake," Crockett answered.

"I know sweetheart, but you will learn to love a new little horse, and you can always remember Jake as your old friend," Arminda said.

Her words were soothing to Crockett and each day got a little better. He took her advise and went about looking at the new colts that would be for sale. John Hankins a long time neighbor to the Whitts had a nice little red horse that caught Crockett's eye. When Crockett went to look at him the colt came to him. Crockett noticed that he had that special look in his eye that Jake always had. Crockett had to have this colt, so he worked out a deal with John and paid him. John noticed the comradeship between Crockett and the colt.

"This little horse picked you, Crockett," John said.

"Yes he did, I think I am suppose to have him," Crockett answered.

"I sold him cheap, but I know he will be loved by you," John said.

Crockett stuck out his hand and thanked John. John took it and gave Crockett a good hand shake.

"What are you going to call him?" John asked.

"Billy, he looks like a Billy," Crockett said.

Crockett petted his new horse and called him "Billy". Billy responded by shaking his head up and down.

"He likes his name," said John.

"I think you are right," Crockett said laughingly.

Crockett took Billy home and began to train and care for his new horse. Billy responded but showed he had a lot of spirit. Billy was still too young to ride, but Crockett taught him to wear the saddle and spent a lot of time with him. Billy was really smart and came running every time he saw Crockett coming. Losing Jake didn't hurt quite as bad. Billy had the same qualities that Jake had. Arminda was well pleased that Crockett found Billy and now he could push away the melancholy state he had been in. After all a wedding date had been set and was almost here.

Rhoda Whitt Lowe, Crockett's sister and her family lived near Crockett. She was concerned that Crockett had no father nor mother to help with the wedding. Susannah had passed away years ago when Crockett was still a baby, and Jonas was way off over in Greenup County, Kentucky. Rhoda talked it over with John Bunyon Lowe her husband about having a wedding party on their farm, and he thought it would be a good idea.

"With just our eleven children, Crockett and Arminda will have a crowd," John B. Lowe said laughingly.

The Wedding was set and the Robinett family from Grandfather

Sampson Robinett on down came for the ceremony. The Whitts were well covered also with John Bunyon Whitt and James Griffith, and the John Madden and Rachel Whitt Stephenson family being there. Christina Robinett, Arminda's mother would give her unto the marriage.

The now elderly Elder David Young would officiate the marriage. Crockett had been going to church most every Lords day since he got back to Virginia. Elder Young was glad to see this marriage come about. He felt that Crockett needed a wife to fill in some emptiness in his life.

Even though the wedding would be on Thursday, everyone seemed glad to take a day off from the farm work for this special occasion. Spring planting and farm work was done Monday through Saturday, and folks usually rested on the Lords day.

Everyone gathered that Thursday in the front yard of John Bunyon Lowe to join the twenty two year old Crockett and the barely fifteen year old Arminda in Holy Wedlock. Crockett and Arminda took their vows and formed a union that would last until one would pass on. In those days a marriage and vows meant something, when you said I do, you did.

Crockett and sister Rhoda had reminisced the week earlier about Grand Paw Hezekiah marrying so many of them. Crockett wished that Grand Paw was still around to do the marrying, but knew he was much better off up in Heaven with Grand Maw Rachel. Somehow he felt that Grand Paw was looking down on them this fine May day.

After a party and celebration, folks began to head back home and Crockett took his bride to the little cabin at the back of the old Indian Creek Farm. Crockett and Arminda had no idea that a chivalree was planned. All the younger folks led by Rhoda, Rachel, John and James Griffith surprised their young brother and his bride just about dark with a great noise of pan beating, cow bells and yelling.

Crockett cracked open the door and waved. John Bunyon Whitt and Catherine realized this very thing happened to them at this same little cabin seventeen years ago. "Where have the years gone?" Catherine asked. "I don't know but we have nine babies to prove the years," John answered.

CHAPTER 30

CROCKETT IS COUNTED,
BABY FLOYD IS ON THE WAY

The reminder of 1859 flew by like a flash. Crockett and Arminda were so in love they barely noticed the time and happenings. Crockett and his new help mate kept the crops in order. Sometimes Arminda would go to the McGuire Mill with Crockett and help with the milling.

Crockett also made time to train Billy his wonderful horse. Billy was growing and learning from his new master. It looked like Billy would be a tall slim horse, just what the southern boy desired for a mount.

The conversations around the mill and on each farm in Tazewell County was full of the current events. The Southern states were upset with the Northern states imposing their ideas on them. President James Buchanan was more or less playing referee between the North and the South. He was President from 1857 to 1861. He tried to keep a balance in his appointments, and tried to follow the Constitution of the United States.

The southern states were threatening to secede from the Union. He said that they did not have that right, but held that the Federal Government legally could not stop them. He hoped for compromise, and basically gave up.

Crockett was glad to hear that the census would be taken down Indian Creek at Cedar Bluff. He and Arminda went to the Post Office on the 10th of August 1860 and gave their information. He was glad to be counted, because he felt an injustice in the last Census. The 1850 Census in Greenup County Kentucky was taken after he left, and was taken in Tazewell County Virginia before he got there.

"Well honey we are counted this time, by George," Crockett told Arminda.

"Who is George?" Arminda asked innocently.

"George Washington, I reckon," replied Crockett laughingly.

"Crockett, sometimes you just don't make any sense," Arminda said.

"Well do you love me anyway?" Crockett asked.

"Yes I do, but sometimes wonder why," she said with a laugh.

Arminda started having morning sickness in late September of 1860. What on earth could be wrong, she was a good strong girl that could eat most anything and never get sick. She went over and had a talk with Rhoda, (Crockett's sister) about her problem.

"Have you missed your monthly season?" Rhoda asked.

"I did come to think of it, Oh My, do you reckon I am in a family way?" Arminda asked.

"I reckon you might just be," Rhoda said.

Rhoda decided to have a little more fun with the situation and asked Arminda, "You been exposed?

Arminda turned pink but kept her composure.

"Most every night since last May a year ago," Arminda said almost bragging.

"Reckon you know how them Whitts are bout such things, don't you?" Arminda asked.

"I reckon so," Rhoda said with a laugh.

"You will have to start watching what you do and what you eat," Rhoda cautioned.

"What do you think Crockett will say?" Rhoda asked.

"I think he will be just fine with it, We just didn't know why I was sick every morning," Arminda said.

"I am a purty good midwife, if you want my help," Rhoda informed Arminda.

"Yes I know, and I would be pleased if you help me bring little Floyd into the world," Arminda answered.

"Floyd, you already got a name, and don't even know if it is a girl or boy," Rhoda said.

"We talked about naming our first born John Floyd after Archibald's son, and I got a feeling it is a little Floyd," Arminda said.

"Could be, but remember the old saying, don't name your chicken till it hatches," Rhoda said.

"That ain't exactly how it goes," said Arminda.

"It is in your case," Rhoda said laughingly.

"Well thanks Rhoda, I am going over and fix Crockett a good supper, and then I will tell him the news when he is full and comfortable," Arminda said.

Crockett worked in his fields today doing some harvesting, and as he brought the mules in to the corral, Billy began running up and down by the fence trying to get Crockett's attention. By now Billy was about a year and half old and had not been ridden. Crockett had spent a lot of time with Billy and had him use to the saddle and even had the bit in his mouth on a regular bases.

"I see you Billy, are you ready to take me for a ride?" Crockett asked.

Billy responded to Crockett's voice with by shaking his head up and down and a snort.

"Let me tend the mules and I will get on your back, will that be alright?" Crockett asked.

Billy ran up and down the fence again, as if he knew what Crockett said. After Crockett cared for the mules he got the saddle, and other tact and brought it out to the corral. He put the blanket on, and Billy stood for him just like usual. Crockett put the bridle and saddle on next and secured it. Crockett walked the tall 17 hands high saddle horse around the corral talking to him as he had before. Then Crockett did something new. He walked to Billy's left side, took hold of the saddle horn, stuck his foot into the stirrup and pulled himself up in the saddle.

Billy froze and then turned his head around sharply to look at Crockett. The big red horse had a puzzled look in his eye.

Crockett talked to Billy and continued to pet him and console him, while being ready for anything. Billy just stood there not knowing what to do next. He seemed confused with this new experience. Billy wanted to buck Crockett off, but at the same time he had great trust for his master. Billy stood there for a long minute and then begin doing a twisting walk looking left, then right to see what Crockett was doing there on his back.

Crockett dug in his heels and leaned over the saddle horn and Billy took off running around the corral. Billy just couldn't help himself, he begin bucking and Crockett held on. Crockett continued to talk to Billy in a calm voice and Billy quit bucking but continued to run the fence row all around the corral. After what seemed to be a long time, Billy began to trot and Crockett noticed the beautiful gait Billy was doing.

Crockett stayed on Billy for a short time while continuing to praise him. Billy responded, and wanted to please Crockett, yet he was a little uncomfortable with Crockett straddled across his back. Crockett rode Billy back to the starting point, pulled back on the bridle, and Billy stopped.

"Good boy," Crockett said as he dismounted.

Crockett led Billy around the corral a lap or two talking and praising his big red horse. Billy trotted about proudly as if he really did something.

"Well that is enough for today Big Boy," Crockett said as he unsaddled Billy.

Crockett was going to go slow breaking Billy to riding, as he didn't want to break him down with too much riding. Crockett knew about horses and knew that horses ridden too early had health problems and some become swaybacked. He would work with Billy over the winter and by spring Billy should be mature enough physically to be ridden regularly.

After he finished taking the saddle back into the barn, Crockett brought Billy back a bucket of treats.

"Here Billy, you did good," Crockett said as he poured the sweet oats, corn and other delectable feeds into the feed box.

Crockett headed to the house feeling really good about Billy's first ride. He looked back at Billy one more time before he stepped inside the cabin.

Arminda met Crockett at the door and gave him a kiss.

"I saw you riding that big red horse, don't know who you love the most him or me," she said with a laugh.

"You know I love you the most, but Billy gave his first ride today," Crockett said.

"Do you think he will be a good saddle horse?" Arminda asked.

"Sure do," Crockett said excitedly.

"He has a beautiful gait, and I think he will be able to cover a lot of ground in a short time," Crockett added.

"Well go wash your paws, and get ready for supper," Arminda said smiling.

Crockett went to wash up, and Arminda served up a specially prepared supper. Today is a day of good news for my Crockett she thought. Riding Billy and getting the news that little John Floyd is on the way, should make his day, Arminda thought. After Crockett enjoyed his supper he went into the little sitting room and stretched out on the davenport. Arminda lit his pipe and sat down beside him.

"Do you think you can stand some more good news?" Arminda asked while taking his hand.

"Sure do, I always like good news," Crockett answered.

"Well I guess the best way to say it is that you are going to be a Paw!" Arminda said.

"Paw!, what do you mean?" Crockett asked as he turned sharply to look at his young wife.

"I reckon little John Floyd is a coming," Arminda said.

"Well how do you know?" Crockett asked with a puzzled look on his face.

"I been having the morning sickness and I missed the monthly season," she said.

"No, I mean how do you know it will be little Floyd?" Crockett asked.

"Well I ain't certain on that point, but I really believe the baby will be a manchild," she answered.

"Thank God, He is so good to us," Crockett said.

"Yes, He is and you are a good husband," Arminda said with a smile.

Crockett and Arminda savored the good news. They enjoyed the evening and talked about the baby coming and Crockett couldn't help but talk about his big red horse. They went to bed extra early, and lay there talking about their life and how God has blessed them. Billy, Crockett's horse kept coming up again and again.

"I wonder sometimes just who you love the most, me or that big red horse?" Arminda asked.

"You know I love you, Billy is just my horse," Crockett said in defense.

Arminda took Crockett into her arms and they had a blissful time until they fell into slumber.

Crockett and Jonas wrote each other on a regular basis, and kept each other informed about family. By now Jonas and Millie had three sons, which made Crockett have three new brothers. The three half brothers names were William Randolph Whitt 1851, Jesse Monroe 1855, and Alfred Jackson born 1858. All were born on Big White Oak, Greenup County, Kentucky.

Also Crockett had learned over time that he was an uncle to sister Hannah's three children. Alfred and Hannah Whitt Thompson's children were, Mathew 1852, Alfred 1854, Mildred 1857. Hannah was expecting another baby to arrive in the spring of 1861.

The Whitt's shared good family news, but the current news was also shared. The talk of secession of the Southern states, was hashed over in every state and locale. Jonas gave the slant of the news from Greenup County Kentucky, and Crockett shared what was being said in Tazewell County, Virginia. Mixed feeling were prevalent in the border states between North and South.

The political parties were split in four ways, and four men would run for president. The south declared that they would leave the Union if the Republican Abraham Lincoln were to win the race. The deep South favored Stephen Douglas the Democrat. John C Breckinridge would get some votes, and John Bell would carry the border states of Virginia, Kentucky and Tennessee.

The Election was held November 6, 1860 and Lincoln had thirty nine percent of the vote. He would be declared winner on February 13, 1861 by the Electoral Collage. The South would go nuts! Lincoln had declared he would force each state to stay in the Union by military strength.

The southern states had joined the Union on their own accord, and by George they could leave it if they so wished. Lincoln said he would invade the South and whip each state back into submission to preserve the Union.

It was a sad time and yet exciting time. Many friends and even kin were divided as they lined up on the sides of North or South.

The fall had been a blur, and it was almost Christmas time in Tazewell County. Crockett and Arminda tried not to become engrossed with the troubles that were so prevalent around them. Christmas time was suppose to be a universal time of peace the way Crockett and Arminda saw it. Crockett had cut a nice ceiling high cedar and set it up in the little cabin for their Christmas Tree. Arminda had made popcorn strings and cut out little paper angels to decorate it. Crockett had been spending a little extra time out in the barn. Arminda figured he was out there playing with Billy his big red horse.

Christmas Eve Crockett carried in a beautiful cradle for Arminda's present. Arminda had saved for months and got material to make Crockett some shirts. They would have a good Christmas Eve, and go over to John and Rhoda's for Christmas day.

Newspapers began publishing results of the election and Lincoln had the highest amount of popular vote. It looked like he would have enough Electoral votes to win. This brought quick response from the southern states. South Carolina was the hot head of the south and decided on secession December 20th 1860.

"Lord have mercy," Crockett said as he read about the secession of South Carolina.

"What has happened?" Arminda asked.

"South Carolina has went and done it," Crockett said.

"What did they do?" Arminda asked.

"They have pulled out of the Union, and this will have great ramifications, for all the southern states," Crockett answered.

"Maybe war, and maybe even invading Yankee armies, I think we will be safe back here in the mountains of Tazewell County," he added to console Arminda.

Crockett and Arminda tried to go on as usual, but as January came more talk about a war went on. Everyone you met was having something to say about Lincoln or secession. The deep southern states fell to secession like dominos during January 1861. A list of these were Mississippi January 9th, Florida January 10th, Alabama January 11th, Georgia January 19th, Louisiana January 26th. Texas followed in secession on February 1st 1861, which made seven states no longer part of the United States.

There was excitement in the air, and also a dread in many hearts. Crockett was one of those with dread, because he knew how it felt to see a man die, and he knew how it felt to strike another human being.

Crockett never killed William Randolph Thompson, but he thought he did, which brings the same effect. Crockett had been so relieved to find out Bill Thompson was alive and well. Crockett had made a promise to God not to strike another man, ever. Crockett did not want to have a war.

A book published back in 1852 by Harriet Beacher Stowe, had fueled the Abolitionist with animosity toward the south. The book was "Uncle Tom's Cabin" portrayed the slave owners as cruel and slaves as abused animals. Harriet was from Connecticut and had little idea about the matter. As in all things, some slaves were abused and some well taken care of. At any rate the South rejected this unjust judgment of all slave owners, and The North took the book to be gospel.

All the slaves Crockett had ever seen appeared to be happy and well cared for. They seemed to fit the role that they were given. The slaves Crockett saw seemed to take pride in their work and wanted to please their master, yet Crockett was not sure this was pleasing to God. Crockett had read many passages in the Bible and he could not see anywhere where God forbid slavery.

There was a lot of talk about Virginia taking a vote on secession, but most folks were not wanting a war. As for slavery in Virginia, it was not practiced as much as in the deep south. Virginia was considering doing away with it. It was a subject in a lot of talks in the state house. Yet Virginia did not like a strong Federal Government telling them they had to do this or that. Virginia believed that a state was a country, and it should be able to govern itself with out interference from a bunch of Yankees in Washington.

Crockett tried to keep some of this talk away from Arminda, hoping not to upset her in her condition. Little John Floyd was expected around the end of May, and Rhoda had been over several times helping make preparations, and getting Arminda ready physically and mentally.

The news of war shot through out the South. The newly formed Confederate States Of America asked the Federal Army in Fort Sumpter, located out in the bay of Charleston, South Carolina, to surrender. When they refused, the Confederate Army under General Beauregard fired their cannons at 4:30 AM on April 12 1861. Thirty four hours of shelling brought the surrender. No one was hurt until they had a hundred gun salute as the flag was lowered. A powder keg went off and killed two Union Soldiers.

This first battle pressured the other southern states to choose sides, because there was going to be a war. Virginia had a state wide vote on May 23rd 1861 and would succeed. The vote in Taxewell County was 1406 for and 0 against. Crockett did not vote because he did not want war, but he would defend his homeland if Northern Armies invaded.

All of this war talk was not doing Arminda any good, but things went alright for her first born. Crockett had gone to fetch Rhoda around 4:00AM, and the baby came at 12:20PM, May 30th 1861. Sure enough it was a boy and they named him John Floyd Whitt. Arminda was tired but generally in good physical shape for just delivering her first born. Rhoda said that they both did real well, mother and child. Just the same she would be bedfast for a week, as was the custom. Midwives thought that it took a week for everything to get back in place, and provide enough rest.

Rhoda would spend the days with Arminda and Floyd. Crockett would work during the day and be home with Arminda and Floyd during the night hours. Rhoda had young children, but it didn't seem to be much added work to care for all of them. After all, she had eleven children.

Crockett strutted around in celebration of his new little son. Arminda thought He was funny, but didn't say anything to ruin his celebration.

One evening as he sat with Arminda and Floyd, Crockett wrote a letter to Jonas and all the family over in Kentucky. He told them about the arrival of Jonas' Grandson, John Floyd Whitt. He told them all about the little boy baby and that Arminda was doing well. He also bragged on Sister Rhoda for her midwife abilities.

All and all the letter was a good news letter. Crockett never one time mentioned the state of the country or politics. Crockett finished off his letter with praise to God for his never ending loving kindness.

Now that Virginia and North Carolina has joined the Confederacy the capital would be moved from Montgomery Alabama, to Richmond. Virginia would be a border state and be a target for the North. After all Washington and Richmond are only short distance apart.

The North and the South were racing to raise armies. Many good

Southern Officers were in the Union Army and quickly resigned their commission and returned south to defend their homeland. One of the most famous was Robert E. Lee. President Lincoln offered the Command of the Union Army to Robert E. Lee, but he declined saying that he could not fight against his home of Virginia.

The western part of Virginia was slower to react, but most able bodied men would be called up and placed in the Virginia Militia. David Crockett Whitt was placed in the 72nd Virginia Militia but it was not active at this time. The 72nd would not become active until March 1862, and it would be used mostly to form active Infantry Units.

Crockett received a letter from Jonas not long after he sent his letter about the arrival of little Floyd. This letter from Jonas was shocking and sad. It was primarily regarding Crockett's little sister Hannah. Not long after Her 24th birthday Hannah gave birth to little William Thompson. Hannah departed this world on May 30th 1861 the same day John Floyd was born. Alfred Thompson was left to raise the four children alone. After Crockett read the letter he could hardly speak. Hannah was so young, why did God call her home so soon, was the thoughts of all of her family.

When Arminda saw His face she asked ,"What is it sweetheart?"

Crockett said nothing, but turned and handed her the letter.

"Lord have mercy, Hannah is gone," He said finally as he became able to speak.

Arminda quickly embraced Crockett and held Him tightly for a long minute.

"She is in the arms of the Lord Jesus Christ," Arminda said sweetly.

Thoughts of young Hannah marrying at the young age of thirteen return to Crockett. Now eleven years later she dies in childbirth of her fourth baby. Could this have been prevented, He asks himself? It must be Gods will, but why would a loving God take her, Crockett tried to reason it out.

Arminda knew what Crockett was thinking.

"You can not know why God does what he does, He is all wise and He can not be questioned," Arminda stated.

"Remember in the Bible, Job went through this with all of his family being killed. Job wanted a confrontation with God. God told him that he was not there when He laid the foundation of the universe, so you are not worthy to question Me," she explained.

"I wish that I could have met her and all of them babies," Arminda said.

"You would have loved her, she was so full of life," Crockett said.

"How did your Father sound in the letter?" Arminda asked.

"He tried to hide his feelings, but I can tell he is broken hearted, Paw ain't no spring chicken, I hope he can cope with all of this," Crockett answered.

"Bless his heart, I guess it is really hard to give up your young-un, we just have to accept death as part of life," Arminda said.

This was a mind set that Crockett would need to have in the years to come, because he would see more death in three years than most folks ever would in ten life times. Yes Crockett would march off to war in less than a year.

But for now the war was in the east, and also in the northwest part of old Virginia. The extreme western part of Virginia is under the heavy influence of the Federal Government. After several small battles the Old Dominion is split North to South. The newly formed McDowell County taken from part of Tazewell County is now part of a Union State. Pressure of politics and a stronger force in western Virginia caused the formation of an illegal state. According to the Constitution of the United States, no state is permitted to be divided to form new states. The Union was glad to grab up part of Virginia and make the state of West Virginia.

John Bunyon Whitt and other kinsmen of Crockett reside in McDowell County. Folks in these border counties begin to take sides. Some favor the North, while others favor the cause of the South.

Crockett is not too happy lately with losing sister Hannah and Virginia having to defend herself against Northern aggression. He looked for any newspapers or even reports by word of mouth about the war. He wonders what will happen if he has to go and be in the Army of Virginia, and have to leave his young wife and baby Floyd. Down deep he knows that if it keeps going on, he will have to go and fight the Yankees.

Arminda and Crockett are both a source of strength to each other. There is nothing like young love and having babies to shore up each other.

"Sweetheart don't worry bout me and the baby, if duty calls we will be just fine, you are the one to be concerned about, if you have to be in a battle," Arminda said.

"Well let's not cross no rivers till we come on-um," Crockett answered.

News spread like wildfire about a great battle in northern Virginia. It happened near a creek called Bull Run, just south of Washington City. The date was July 21st, 1861.

The North was so sure that they could whip a bunch of Rebels that even ladies rode their buggies to the hills above the battle ground. They wore their best outfits and even brought picnic lunches to eat while they watched the Grand Union Army whip up on the Rebels. Guess what? It didn't happen that way. It ended up being a big victory for the Confederate States of America. At the onslaught of the battle the Northerners pushed back some of the Confederates. General Thomas Jackson had his men take a stand on a hill. The retreating Confederates fell back behind Jackson's Virginians.

Their Commander said, "Look at Jackson standing their like a stone wall."

The name stuck, and from then on Jackson and his men were known as "Stone Wall." General Jackson was called "Stone Wall Jackson." and The Brigade was known as the "Stone Wall."

Jackson told his men to give them the bayonet and yell loudly when they charged the intruding army. The Yankees came within range of the South's smooth bore cannons, and after a barrage of fire power the Yankee's began to back down. The Confederate's charged with unnerving yelling and the Yankee's panicked. This was the birth of the "Rebel Yell"! They threw down their guns, left their cannons and ran full speed toward Washington City.

The ladies and their picnic lunches headed for home also. The road into Washington City was clogged with running soldiers and wagons. The Confederate's gave chase until a great thunder storm hit. General Johnston gave orders to quit the chase, and the Confederate's began to gather up the war materials left behind by the scared Yankee's.

Many cannons, supplies and muskets were collected to help stock the Southern Army.

A lot of the Confederate officers and soldiers wanted to go on in and take Washington. General Beauregard wanted to, and said that General Johnston would consider it tomorrow, but his orders were to defend Virginia and they did that. The South was in a mind set for defense, not offense. As we look back on this day, what if the Southern Army had gone in and demanded their independence from a position of power?

Crockett and all that loved the southland were happy to hear about the victory. Maybe the war is over, maybe the Yankee's wouldn't come again.

President Lincoln knew the North had a close call. He knew that the war was not going to be won easily. He had it in his heart and mind to preserve the Union no matter how long it took. He knew he had to build an army and get some good leaders, before he would attack again.

For now Crockett and Arminda went about their daily chores as usual and hoped for the best. Crockett had crops to get in, and part time mill work to take his time. He began to ride Billy more and more. Today he rode him all the way to the mill and back home. Billy thrived on the road. He was a high stepping ground covering horse just like Jake. Only difference Billy was much taller and much stronger, but Crockett didn't know if he had the "heart" that Jake had.

Many of the young men around rushed to join the Confederate Army. They were after glory and adventure. They had no idea what war was about.

The winter came and went quickly, and the early spring of 1862 was here. Crockett and Arminda didn't talk much about it, but they both knew that Crockett's Militia would likely be called up. They had not heard of any enormous battles since last summer, yet little skirmishes happened all around the edges of the Confederate Nation.

One cold day in February Confederate soldiers marched through the area. They were coming back to Virginia from Kentucky. These men had spent the winter in Kentucky keeping the back door to Virginia closed. These men were lean, dirty, and in general a poor looking lot. Yet they had a spirit about them that gave them a proud look. The soldiers were coming home to go on furlough to rest up and restock.

They were the 29th Virginia Infantry, mostly from Tazewell and Russell Counties.

They were back from an engagement with Garfield, the Kentucky 22nd Regiment, from Camp Swigert in Greenup County Kentucky and his Ohio Yankees. The battle took place on middle creek near Paintsville and Prestonsburg Kentucky. The 29th did not win but they fulfilled their mission of keeping the Yankees out of Virginia. After a short rest the 29th will regroup and add more companies to their number.

There were several small battles around the South and even out in Missouri. The South had been doing pretty good at holding their ground, but the North was very aggressive.

News about the War seemed to come everyday. Even on the west side of the Blue Ridge people were affected by the war. There had been no news from Greenup County since last fall some time. Kentucky was suppose to be a Southern State, but the Union kept control of her. The last letter Crockett got from his father told of the division in the families round about. Even the Truitt Family were at odds. Louisa, Millie's sister would not even speak to her. Louisa married a man and moved from Big White Oak over to Lawrence County Kentucky. Jonas was starting to get old, his unsteady hand writing showed in that last letter.

One day in the early part of March, a rider came through telling the militia to meet on Saturday and be ready to march. Bring a blanket and haversack. Also bring your musket if you have one and powder. This may be your call so come prepared to be gone for some time. Several of the folks stopped by to tell Crockett, about the call up, this was the most effective way of communication in Baptist Valley.

Arminda got Crockett a good blanket, and helped him gather some items to put in his sack. He did not have a suitable musket, just an old hunting shotgun. He was going to leave about day light so he would be there by the appointed time of 8 AM. The men in the area were to meet in Indian. (Now Cedar Bluff)

Crockett and Arminda did not talk too much about the call up, but held each other tight most of the night before he was to leave. Crockett knew that Arminda and little Floyd would be fine living next to Rhoda and her family. John B. Lowe was not going to go because of his age and large family. He also had a lot of ground, and was expected to harvest foods for the war effort.

Crockett was up early and Arminda rustled up a big country breakfast for him. Crockett ate and hugged his young wife and baby. Arminda tried to hold back the tears, but some showed up anyway. Crockett wiped away her tears and told her not to worry, he was just going to practice with the militia.

"This might be your call into the war, that is what the men have been saying," she said.

"Well I doubt it," Crockett said trying to ease her pain.

"You take care of Floyd, and yourself, and Oh!, Billy too," Crockett said as he headed toward the road.

"I will sweetheart, hurry back to us," Arminda said with a big smile.

As Crockett reached the road he met several other fellers heading to the muster at the mouth of Indian. There was Burdell Brewster, J.W. Birchem, D.C. Lewis, and Isaac Puckett. Crockett knew these men, but not very well. They all had something in common now and would become friends in the next few days.

CHAPTER 31

CROCKETT IS IN THE ARMY NOW

The men all talked as they hurried toward the mouth of Indian Creek. None of them really knew what to expect and were a bit concerned. They did not think they were coming home tonight, but did not think they would be gone long either.

"Well it won't be too long now, 'for we find out, let me tell you fellers this, you better be ready cause "Lee" is going to need every able bodied man this summer," said Isaac Puckett.

The other men did not want to hear this, as they hoped to be back home in a few short days.

As Crockett and his comrades got to Indian (Cedar Bluff, VA.) a group of nearly one hundred men were already there. They were all standing around in little groups talking, and some were telling funny stories to amuse the others. Other groups were more serious, they were talking about the war.

About ten minutes past 8:00 AM a man wearing a gray jacket and butternut britches walked up on the porch of the little Indian Post office. The man was wearing stripes on his shoulders and had a pistol belt around his waist. He also wore a slouch hat with a brass bugle badge on the front.

"Listen up men, I am Sergeant Rufus Brittain, and I am here to march you to Lebanon. The militia is now officially called up for duty. I don't know how long you will be called up for, so don't ask that question," The sergeant said.

"Do you men know how to march?" Rufus asked.

"We did a little bit awhile back," one of the men answered.

"Well I want you to fall in formation four abreast, Now!" the sergeant shouted.

The men scrambled around and before long a long column of four was assembled and ready to march. No one really cared if the lines

Fifty-Dollar Confederate Bill

were straight or even if the men talked long as they did not hold up the march. Sergeant Brittain spoke in a loud voice telling the men always start a march with their left foot.

After a few instructions he hollowed out, "Forward March!" The militia was on the move, and at each little berg down the Clinch they met up with other little groups of militia heading for Lebanon, Russell County. Some of the men had a little more information than others.

There was a camp set up on a nice level field just outside Lebanon, called "Camp Cumbo!" Crockett heard this is where they were headed for now, but there was a bigger camp in Abington. It would take two days of marching to get to Camp Cumbo. Finally on the evening of March 20th, Crockett's group got to Camp Cumbo.

An officer of some sort came out and addressed the men, welcoming them to the camp. He explained that shelter and supper would be provided for them. He had the sergeant dismiss them so that they could go and eat. Campfires were burning round about with big iron kettles bubbling with stew.

Crockett was pretty tired and would be glad to eat and get off his feet. He looked around the camp trying to surmise how many men were in the camp, and figured about 600 or better. He followed the other men to the eating area and got himself a bowl of stew and some cornbread. It was not the best tasting, but it was filling.

Crockett and his buddies he met while leaving Baptist Valley stuck together. They ended up in the same tent that was crowded with eight men to a tent. March nights are really cold in the highlands of Russell County, so it might be an advantage to be crowded in the tents.

When things got quiet Crockett let his mind wonder back to Arminda and little Floyd. For some reason he also thought about his trip up the Tug, coming home from Kentucky.

The next thing Crockett knew a bugle was blowing and sergeants were shouting to get up and fall into formation. A lot of confusion went on that first morning of March 21st.

Crockett and most of the other men were not happy about the way the military gets a feller up. Soon the men were in formation, Crockett followed his new friends into the same group that had marched there together, Sergeant Brittain was a familiar face greeting them with loud commands.

The sergeants had been ordered to march the men about an hour and bring them back for breakfast. These men were not used to such rude awakenings and some were protesting in the ranks. Sergeants were scolding them not to talk in ranks.

Some of the men said that they volunteered for the militia and were willing to fight, but they didn't volunteer for all of this marching stuff.

Sergeant Brittain halted the formation, and gave the men words that wouldn't light on a flower. He told them they volunteered for the militia and that meant they follow orders without question.

"I better not hear another word, or you will be marching all day long," yelled Sergeant Brittain.

The men got quiet and after about an hour, they marched back to breakfast. The men began to learn the discipline of being in the army.

After about two weeks of marching and learning military terms, some high ranking Confederate officers rode into Camp Cumbo. It was General Humphrey Marshall and his officers. The General was well groomed and wore a new gray uniform and knee high polished riding boots. Crockett noticed that the general was a little on the fat side but didn't say anything.

The men were assembled into their groups and stood before General Marshall. He gave them a long speech about love of Virginia and the southland. He explained that the North was invading the Confederate States of America and must be driven back. He also told them that each and every Southern Man was expected to do his part. He talked for some time then he told them he was there to form new companies into the regular infantry. He was recruiting for the 29th Virginia Regiment. He also had good news that each man that enlisted for three years would be given a Fifty Dollar bounty.

He came across in a way that if anyone did not volunteer he would be counted as a coward. So on April 2nd 1862 Crockett and all of the 695 men in the 72nd Virginia Militia enlisted for three years in the 29th Virginia Infantry.

All of the men were read the 20th, & 87th Articles of war and it was explained to them, that once they joined they could not just up and quit. They would be considered deserters and could face a firing squad.

Next the men held their hands on Bibles in groups of five or six and took the oath. Crockett and his five buddies were one of these groups. The officer read a line at a time and the men repeated it word for word.

Crockett said:

"I David Crockett Whitt, do solemnly swear or affirm that I will bear true allegiance to the Confederate States of America, and that I will serve them honestly and faithfully against all their enemies or opposes whatsoever, and observe and obey the orders of the President of the Confederate States, and orders of the officers appointed over me, according to the rules and articles for the government of the armies of the Confederate States.

Crockett and his buddies from Baptist Valley were all placed in Company H, and on the 26th of April they all received their Bounty Money from the Quartermaster V. C. Huff.

The North was once again trying to invade the Confederacy. This time in southwest Tennessee. It was about the middle of April 1862, word came that a Union Army had defeated Beauregard in the battle of Shiloh. General Johnston was killed the first day of the battle April 6th, 1862 and many other men died. Grant and his Yankees were surprised the first day and almost folded.

The Union General Wallace and General Grant had miss-communicated, and the Wallace Army was late. The second day the Wallace reinforcements arrived and the Southern Army had to retreat. This was a real bloody battle that opened up Tennessee to the Yankees. The men in the 29th knew beyond a shadow of doubt that they would see action, they just didn't know when.

The 29th drilled and drilled, the men were so tired of marching, and now they would get a break. The men that had no weapons were issued muskets and instructed in cleaning and shooting them. The muskets were old converted flintlock smoothbore of .69 caliber. Of course most of the men were crack shots already and knew about cleaning guns. The men all tried to out do each other at the target range.

The sergeants told them it was much different to shoot at Yankees while they were shooting back. They told them to learn to reload fast and still take good aim. The sergeants also explained that they should be able to load and fire three times a minute while under fire. Shooting at a deer or other game was one thing, but shooting people and them shooting back was a new concept to be learned.

One of the new recruits got cocky about his shooting, so Sergeant Brittain drew his revolver and walked up to the man. The sergeant held his watch in one hand and the pistol in the other.

"That target is a Yankee shooting at you, now load and fire as fast as you can," he ordered.

Then the Sergeant began to fire his pistol into the ground and hurried the recruit.

"Fire that musket, reload, that Yankee is going to kill you, shoot Damn it!" Sergeant Brittain ordered.

After a timed minute the recruit was so rattled he only fired twice and never came close to the target. He wasn't so cocky now. The sergeant now informed the men not to worry, speed in loading would come, but the main thing was to hit what they were shooting at.

Crockett was so glad he had not been put on the spot like the other recruit.

By now Crockett had received a couple of letters from Arminda, and he almost cried at reading them. He had no idea of how much he would miss them. He had written her a letter a week and also wrote one to Jonas in Kentucky, but could not reveal any information about being in the Confederate Army. Crockett did not write too much to his father Jonas, knowing that the letter may not even get there. He only wrote sentiments of family love and the like. But Jonas would know that something was up with a Lebanon post mark, if he did receive the letter.

Crockett was on firewood detail and on the 14th of May 1862, he had a mishap. Crockett was chopping wood with an ax when it deflected off a log and crashed into his right foot. It was a nasty cut with a lot of bleeding. He was taken to camp and put in his tent. A medical person, not even a real doctor attended the wound and stopped the bleeding. It started getting red around the cut so they knew infection was setting in.

Crockett was sent home to heal up and ordered back to camp as soon as he could march. His new friend Isaac Puckett was allowed to escort Crockett home and bring the horses back as soon as possible. Isaac was thrilled at getting away for a few days, but felt bad for Crockett. They made two days of the trip back to Baptist Valley because of Crockett's lame foot. The foot stayed swolen because of hanging down for two days. Riding a horse is not good for such an injury. Red streaks ran in all directions from the wound. Crockett will need some good medical attention or he may lose his foot or even his life.

Arminda was hanging clothes out to dry on the evening of May 16th when they rode up. She saw the two confederate soldiers and recognized one to be Crockett. He was barely able to sit erect on his horse. She grabbed baby Floyd off the spread he was sitting on and ran to meet them.

"Lord have mercy, what is wrong with my man?" Arminda asked in concern.

"I cut my foot, I will be alright after a day or so," Crockett said in a weak voice.

"I am Isaac Puckett and I was sent to bring him home, he needs some good care," Isaac said.

"Well, Isaac, lets get him in the house and on the bed," Arminda ordered.

They helped Crockett to the bed and Arminda took off his outer garments, and he stretched out on the bed. Next she got a fat feather pillow and placed it under the foot and leg to elevate it. She removed the bandages with the greatest of care. When the wound was exposed she looked at Isaac with shock.

"Isaac, I need for you to go back down on the road and go to the very next farm house on the right, fetch his sister Rhoda," Arminda said.

"Tell her what has happened and for her to bring her doctoring stuff," Arminda explained.

Isaac stood there waiting for more instructions.

"Go Mister Puckett, time is a-wasting," Arminda said in a concerned voice.

Isaac ran out and mounted his horse, wheeled him around and was galloping toward the road.

Arminda put some new kindling on the fire and got water on to boil. The whole time she was working she was praying for Crockett. She went back into the bedroom and tried to make him more comfortable.

Arminda took a wash cloth and wet it with cool water, next she washed his hot red face, and even his chest. She gave him a some cool water to drink. He was burning up with fever.

Little Floyd lay on the bed with his Paw, and sensed something was wrong. He just lay there holding on to Crockett's arm.

Isaac rode his horse hard, right up to the house that Arminda had directed him to. John B. Lowe came out on the porch carrying a shotgun.

"What do you want here soldier?" John asked with the scatter gun trained on Isaac.

"I am Isaac Puckett, I come to fetch Rhoda and her doctoring stuff to Crockett's house, he needs her now," Isaac responded with much anxiety.

Rhoda was behind the door listening, so she came out immediately.

"What's wrong with Crockett?" She asked.

"Well ma-am, Crockett cut his foot with an ax and it got festered up," Isaac answered.

"He got a fever and swelling?" Rhoda asked.

"Yes ma-ma, he does and he is weak from traveling," Isaac answered.

"I will get you a horse while you gather your things," John said.

Isaac dismounted and tied his horse to the hitching post. In a minute Rhoda came out with a satchel and John came out of the barn leading her horse. Isaac stood there not knowing what to do next. Rhoda mounted up and headed to Crockett's cabin.

John looked at Isaac and asked, "You had any supper son?"

"No sir I ain't et yet," Isaac responded.

"Well come on in and get you some of Rhoda's beans and cornbread," John told him.

"Thank you sir, don't mind if I do," Isaac said.

By now Rhoda is tying up her horse at the Crockett Whitt house, and Arminda is greeting her. They rush back to the bedroom to see Crockett.

"Well what have you done to yourself, Crockett?" Rhoda asked.

"Hello big sister, I had a little misfortune and cut my right foot, reckon it is a little festered," Crockett answered in a weak voice.

"Arminda we will need more light in here, look at that young-un laying there with his Paw," Rhoda exclaimed.

Arminda lit another lamp and carried it to the bed. She held it up to light the foot that Rhoda was examining. Rhoda took her first look at the infected injury and did not say a word for a long minute.

"I got to open up that thing and get out the poison," Rhoda said with as much grace as she could muster.

"Set that lamp down and bring me a bowl of hot water and some rags, Oh! And some corn liquor too," she added.

Arminda brought a little brown jug in first, then hurried to get the hot water and clean rags.

"Crockett take you a big swig on this corn and just relax," Rhoda instructed.

Little Floyd reached up to get a sample of whatever Crockett was tasting, and Rhoda laughed.

"This is just for your Paw, Honey," Rhoda said to the youngster.

After Crockett had taken a couple drinks from the little brown jug, Rhoda lay a hot compress on the injured foot to soften it up. While the compress was working Rhoda went into the kitchen and mixed up some herbal tea for Crockett to drink. She brought the bitter drink to Crockett and made him drink the entire cup.

"Shoo-we, if I hadn't drunk the corn first I never could have drunk that awful stuff," Crockett protested.

"You know the old saying, If it don't taste bad it wouldn't do no good," Rhoda said.

"According to taste of this concoction, I ought to be dancing by tomorrow morning," Crockett commented.

Rhoda sharpened up a straight razor, then waved it through a candle flame several times, to sanitize it. Next she raised up the compress and took a look. Then she pressed lightly all around the wound.

"Well it's ready, You ready little brother?" Rhoda asked.

"I reckon I'm as ready as I am ever going to be, Be easy Sis, that thing is as sore as a boil," Crockett said a little concerned.

"Take another big drink of the corn, and lay back," Rhoda said.

"Shut your eyes and relax sweetheart, Rhoda knows what she's doing," Arminda said.

Rhoda gently cut right on top of the original cut, and as she did pressure was relieved and infectious liquid purged from the cut.

"That feel better?" Rhoda asked.

"Yes the pressure is gone," replied Crockett.

"Hold on to the bed, I got to squeeze it to get out the rest of that nasty stuff," Rhoda said.

Crockett braced himself and Rhoda quickly squeezed starting low and working toward the fresh cut. More of the nasty stuff exited the sore foot. Crockett almost passed out while Rhoda did the big squeeze, but now limbered up. She cleaned the wound and was especially careful not to get any of the poisonous infection on her or anyone else.

She wiped the wound with corn liquor, then she made up a paste of herbs and some mold off the top of some working wine. She put a large amount right on the injury and bound it up with clean rags.

"Well now we just have to wait and pray, keep giving him plenty of cool water and continue washing him down with cool water," Rhoda explained.

"See if you can get him to eat some after his fever subsides, and give him all the corn-squeezins he wants, I will take little Floyd back to my house so you can wait on your sweetheart tonight," Rhoda said.

"Thank you so much Rhoda, you are so kind, and thanks for doctoring up my Crockett," Arminda responded.

"Welcome dear, he is my brother you know, I will be back first light to check on him," Rhoda said as she gathered up little Floyd.

After Rhoda got back home everyone wanted a report on Crockett. She told them all about what she done and requested prayer for God to heal Crockett's foot.

John B. Lowe responded , "Let's all gather around and hold hands for a prayer right now."

Rhoda smiled and took Johns hand, all the children and Isaac Puckett followed suite. They formed a circle and John led them in prayer, for God to meet every need for David Crockett Whitt, and even for Arminda as a caregiver. He prayed for the young man Isaac Puckett that brought Crockett home. He gave thanks for God's loving kindness and grace. After the prayer John got blankets and took Isaac to the barn to make him a bed for the night. Isaac's folks had moved deeper into western Virginia and too far for him to visit.

Before daylight, Rhoda was up and fixing breakfast. She had her oldest son Amos who is seventeen, to go to the barn and do the milking. She instructed Amos to wake up Isaac and have him come on down to the house for breakfast.

Amos was burning to get to the war. He talked to Isaac about the army, and Isaac told him all the negative aspects of soldiering like marching, and taking orders. Amos was like so many young men of the time, he wanted the glory of being in the Confederate Army and giving them Yankee's a good whipping!

After a quick breakfast, John saddled a horse for Rhoda. Rhoda and the young Confederate left together to check on Crockett. Isaac would leave for Camp Cumbo as soon as he saw Crockett. Rhoda thanked Isaac for bringing Crockett home. And also trying to talk Amos out of wanting to go to the war.

The report was not too good, Crockett had suffered the long night with pain and fever, even though the redness around the wound had subsided somewhat.

Private Isaac Puckett went into see Crockett and bid him farewell. Crockett managed a little smile and gripped Isaac's hand.

"Thank you so much friend," Crockett said.

"You hurry up and get better, but don't hurry back to camp, I will give them a report and lay it on a little thick," Isaac said.

"It will take several months afore you can march anyhow," Isaac continued.

"Thanks again, you are a good comrade, tell them I will come back when I'm able," Crockett said.

"With that Private Isaac Puckett left Crockett and headed for his horse.

"Isaac do you have anything to eat on the trail?" Arminda asked.

"No Ma-am but, I will be fine, I just et a big breakfast over at the Lowe's," Isaac said.

"You wait right there and I will throw a few things together for you," replied Arminda.

Arminda gathered some biscuits and thick bacon, two big potatoes, a day old fried pie, and a couple of green onions just barely big enough to pick. Isaac took the items and graciously thanked Arminda. Private Isaac Puckett mounted up, and leading the rider-less horse, he headed back down Indian Creek towards the Clinch River.

Folks up and down Indian Creek saw the two Confederates come, and the one leaving. This caused a lot of questions in the area as any unusual happenings did. Who were the two men and why did one go back alone?

It wasn't long before friends and family knew about Crockett hurting his foot while serving in the army. Most everyone in Tazewell County had loyalties for Virginia and the South, so they were concerned for all of their fighting men.

Crockett was a little embarrassed that he injured himself in a stupid accident, rather than in combat. But the folks praised him just the same. He was one of the young men standing up against Northern Aggression.

A lot of the neighbors came by to see Crockett and Arminda, and even though they were people of modest means, all brought a gift of food to the little family.

John Floyd was now about a year old and crawling all about. He was able to pull up and about ready to turn loose and walk. He spent a lot of time with his Paw, sitting on the bed or on the porch where Arminda fixed up a place for Crockett so he could keep his foot elevated. He had crutches to get about with, after he got out of danger.

Crockett had two long weeks in bed before his fever finally went down and the foot started to mend. The old Elder Young had come by several times and prayed with Crockett and Arminda, as did other folks. The foot was awfully slow to start healing and at first Rhoda feared he might not make it, or that he may loose the foot. Crockett was already a slim person, and now he looked like skin and bones because of his lack of eating. His appetite came around and he enjoyed his favorite dishes that the family prepared especially for him. Crockett helped Arminda around the house doing whatever he could while seated. He cleaned and prepared vegetables for preserving and kept little Floyd so that Arminda could do her work.

It was way up in the fall of 1862 before Crockett could put his foot down and put a little pressure on it. He hobbled about the cabin and even out to see his big red horse by the end of October. Crockett was concerned about getting back to his army duties but knew he could not do any serious marching. He, Arminda and the others in the family talked about the situation and concluded that winter was coming and very little fighting would occur. Crockett decided to wait until Spring 1863 before heading back to the 29th Virginia Infantry. Crockett knew his good friend Isaac Puckett gave them a report of the severity of his condition.

In January of 1863 Crockett's Uncle James W. Lowe (by Marriage to Rebecca Whitt) came up Indian Creek. He was on furlough from the 8th Virginia, and back from the great victory at Fredericksburg. The Army of Northern Virginia really gave the Yankees a blow. The Northern Army had to march across an open field to be greeted by the Confederates protected by a stone wall on high ground. Those people marched out very bravely while being cut down by artillery and musket fire. One Artillery officer reported to General Lee, "a chicken couldn't live on that field."

Once again the folks in the South could breathe easy, It would be warm weather before the Yank's came back. Maybe they would give up and leave the South to their independence. James W. Lowe came to see Crockett and filled him in about the big battle and thought Crockett made the right decision to stay home this winter.

"Crockett, you know as well as I do, you got to be able to march and be ready for anything when you are on duty," Uncle James Lowe told him. (uncle by marriage)

Aunt Rebecca was with James and very proud of her man. She held on to him and did not let him get far from her side. Crockett and all of the southern folks were very proud of sending the invaders back home totally beaten.

"I hope that long lanky President Lincoln has learned his lesson about trying to invade our country," Rebecca said.

"Me too, but I think we will have to black their eye a few more times before they quit," Crockett said.

"Well Crockett we will get back in the spring and be ready for-um," stated James W. Lowe.

"Yes sir, we got the best Generals in the world, with the likes of Lee, Jackson, Longstreet and of course Jeb Stewart," Crockett said.

"I think this summer will tell the tale, and they will know we mean business, after all God is with us," said James W. Lowe.

Crockett found out that he had a new General also, Humphrey resigned his commission because he felt slighted by the war department and did not get the assignments he felt worthy of. Humphrey should have done better in the battle of Middle Creek was the consensus of his superiors. General Montgomery Dent Corse was promoted and given the 29th to command, He was a proven warrior and Crockett was glad to hear he had a new leader.

Arminda did not like to think about the war and hear all of this war talk. She wanted Crockett not to ever leave her, but knew a day in the spring was coming and he should be able to march again.

Crockett spent the winter at home healing up, and getting his foot ready for the spring marches. The 29th stayed near the southern border of Virginia through the winter, and had several successful small engagements keeping those people out.

Crockett walked about as much as possible around the farm and strengthened his foot and legs. He had become soft and weak during his convalescence period. He was able to go on short hunts which provided wild game for the table during this winter of 1862-63. When February started arriving Crockett felt that he would be ready to join the 29th once again. His foot still gave him annoying pain, but he knew he must walk it back to good health.

Crockett started trying to find out where the 29th was deployed so that he could rejoin them. He heard that they were in Abington, Washington County Virginia around the middle of February 1863. He sat down and talked to Arminda and little Floyd, explaining that he had a duty to serve and was leaving in the morning. They shared tight hugs and held on to each other for a long time.

Arminda gathered up his uniform, and the things he would need for the service of Virginia. Crockett had a friend to make him a good strong pair of brogans with thick soles. The shoes he wore home were thin and worn, plus one had a great big cut in it.

Arminda got the best blanket they had, and rolled it up and tied it in such a way that he could carry it across his shoulder. She got his haversack and filled it with all sorts of needed items. He got his old converted cap and ball musket out and cleaned it up, got the bag containing powder and mini-balls. Crockett put everything by the door for his trip in the morning.

"I am going to saddle up Billy and ride him over to see James and Rhoda," Crockett said.

"Do you think Billy will let me and Floyd ride on behind you?" Arminda asked.

"He has never carried double before, but he is able," Crockett said.

"Billy is a good smart horse and he trusts me," Crockett continued.

They rode Billy over to the Lowe's and he carried them proudly.

Daylight came the next morning and Arminda was up, and had a big breakfast prepared for Crockett. He got up and put on his gray jacket, and butternut britches. He had on the heavy duty brogans and wool socks. He got his slouch hat and put it by the other things beside the door.

Arminda sat down holding Floyd, and Crockett joined them. Crockett took their hands and bowed his head. He offered up a prayer of thanksgiving, and also asked for protection of his wife and baby. He prayed a long prayer of supplication asking God to be with his country and General Lee. He prayed that those people would stay up North and no more blood would be shed. He also prayed that he would be brave and stand against aggression if it was God's will. He prayed that a truce would come and the war would end. He also prayed for each Confederate Soldier and that God would be their shield, and that if they had to fight those people again, please help our men shoot straight and fast. Crockett closed his prayer by asking a blessing on his Paw Jonas and his family over in Kentucky.

As soon as the breakfast was over, Crockett got up, put his haversack and blanket over his shoulder. He took Arminda into his arms once again and held her tight. He turned her loose grabbed the musket and hat and headed down the Kentucky Turnpike toward Indian. As he got to the road he turned and waved back at Arminda and little Floyd. She waved and little Floyd waved his little arm high over his head.

Crockett got up with the 29th in about a week and a half. He found them near Abington Virginia. He reported to Sergeant Brittain, which abruptly took him to Lieutenant Ebenezer Brewster. Crockett stood straight and tall at attention.

"Whitt, where the hell have you been?" Lieutenant Brewster asked.

Before Crockett could answer the Lieutenant started again.

"Son you are listed as a deserter on the last muster report, did you know that?" the Lieutenant asked.

"Hell some body even said you cut your foot off," Continued the Lieutenant.

"What do you have to say for yourself Private Whitt?" The Lieutenant asked.

"Well Sir, I cut my foot last May and Private Isaac Puckett took me home, I didn't know if I was going to live or not, but with Gods help and my sister doctoring me I finally recovered to walking late in the fall. Sir I was so weak that I would have been of no benefit to the Army. I decided to stay home and build myself up so I could be in marching condition this spring. Here I am ready to serve, Sir," stated Crockett.

"You alright now?" asked Lieutenant Brewster.

"Yes Sir, I think I am ready," replied Crockett.

"Sergeant, take the private and get him settled in, we have orders to move tomorrow," the Lieutenant said.

"Yes Sir" answered Sergeant Brittain.

Before Crockett and the sergeant could leave the Lieutenant spoke again.

"Welcome back Crockett, glad to have you back," said Lieutenant Brewster.

"Thank you Sir," replied Crockett.

As the sergeant and Crockett walked to where he would be quartered, Crockett asked, "Where we headed for Sergeant?"

"We are going in with General Pickett's Division, and General Longstreet's First Corps, Army of Northern Virginia. We are going to serve with General Lee himself," answered the sergeant.

CHAPTER 32

BAPTISM BY FIRE

Your friend Puckett is in the tent over this way, the sergeant said while leading the way.

Puckett and his other friends were all sitting around a campfire enjoying talking and joking. Isaac Puckett looked up and saw Crockett.

"Well look here, you are still among the living!" Isaac said.

"Thanks to you and the good Lord," Crockett answered.

"Well all I done is get you home," Isaac Puckett said.

"Are you able to march on that sore hoof?" Isaac asked.

"Reckon so, I walked down here and it ain't gave me much trouble," Crockett answered.

As Crockett looked around he recognized his friends that joined up when he did. There was Burdell Brewster, J.W. Birchem, D.C. Lewis, Isaac Puckett, and a new man to Crockett, Ias Colston. All of these men were from Tazewell County.

Each of the men stood and greeted Crockett warmly. He felt at ease with these men. Crockett knew that they were all in the same circumstance and would be defending Old Virginia together. As a matter of fact these men were already veterans of several small skirmishes. Crockett knew he would be able to stand against the blue jacketed invaders when the time come, because of these brave friends. Every man in the army knew that he may be called to give up his live for his country and many already have.

Crockett got himself some of the camp stew and corn bread, then settled down around the fire with his friends.

"Better enjoy that beef, might be a long time afore we have fresh meat again," said Isaac Puckett.

Crockett nodded his head understanding the lack of food the army encountered. Crockett mostly listened to the others talk and learned more about the planned departure in the morning. Crockett learned that the 29th has now been attached to Pickett's Division and would meet up some where near Richmond City. The whole 1st Corps would be sent to Suffolk to head off the Yankee's causing mischief in that area.

The 29th was going to march over to the tracks near Abington. They would board the Virginia & Tennessee Line Train. They would ride the rails through Lynchburg and meet up with General Longstreet's 1st Corps and General Pickett's Division near Richmond city. That is about all the information they would receive.

This spring Longstreet will be holding off the Federals in Suffolk. General Lee would win a huge battle against overwhelming odds at Chancellorsville against Union General Hooker. General Jackson would lose his left arm and life after being shot by friendly fire. General Lee would say he lost his own Right Arm when General Jackson passed on to Glory.

General Lee decided to go on the offense this summer up in the North. General Robert E. Lee would gather his forces for this assault and maybe put an end to the war. He wanted to draw out the Yankee Army and destroy it so the South could win.

Crockett asked the others about mailing a letter, and was told that the mail was slow as snails and he could write a letter but didn't know when he could get it mailed.

They warned him about what he could write in it.

"You can't write about any of our marching orders, where we are or where we are a heading," Isaac said.

"In case your letter got into the wrong hands those people might figure out our strength and where to attack next," Ias Colston said.

"Well thanks for the advice, I just wanted to let Arminda and the family know I am alright," Crockett answered.

"You can give it to the soldier that brings the mail when he comes or mail it in one of the towns we go through," Ias said.

As the men sat around talking, they all admired Crockett's brogans, as most of them had worn out shoes, or no shoes at all.

"I had a good friend make these for me, cause my old ones were ruined by the accident," Crockett explained.

"Just the same you are lucky to have them, be careful that somebody don't steal them from you," Isaac Puckett warned.

Next morning the 29th Virginia formed up and each company was addressed by their commanders. They were told that they would be marching over to Abington, and tomorrow they would board a train heading to Petersburg.

Then the men marched toward where they would meet their train in Abington close to the Tennessee line. The men all knew this was the year they must win the war and put an end to the invading Yankees. After a day of marching the 29th reached the Virginia & Tennessee Railroad. The men cooked, ate, and set up camp. Some needed supplies were waiting for them, but no shoes. The train of cattle cars would arrive in the morning.

Crockett had never laid eyes on a train. He walked over and looked at the iron rails nailed to the ties. He had seen pictures and read about the great locomotives pulling many cars at speeds up to near forty miles per hour. In the morning he will see his first, and even ride it. Crockett remembered Uncle James telling him years before that he would see and even ride a train.

"Wonder where this railroad goes?" Crockett asked.

Crockett was over heard by a local man that had a chance to say something funny.

"Hay private, I been living round here fer some time and that railroad ain't went no where's," said the soldier.

All the men that heard, laughed out loud, and Crockett turned a little pink.

Someone spoke up and said, "Knoxville to Richmond."

Next morning the soldiers were awakened early and broke camp. After everyone ate their "coosh" and had their "coffee" the supplies were readied for loading. The officers were all involved in a meeting and the men sat around waiting for the train. ("Coosh" is a concoction invented in the Confederate camps, where the small ration of bacon fat is fried, rendering out the grease, next the meager amount of rationed flour is mixed with water to a creamy state, then blended into the bacon fat until it become a dirty brown. It was now ready to serve.) (the men preferred Yankee coffee, but often had coffee made from wheat and other ingratiates, which had no lift because of the lack of caffeine.)(Tobacco was plentiful in the south and often traded even to

Yankee soldier's for real coffee.)

Crockett took this time to write a nice composed letter to Arminda, but a short one. He told her he was going to see his first train and even ride it, but could not tell her where he was or where he was going. He signed it with, "I Love you, Crockett." He put it away for safe keeping and would mail it at the first opportunity.

Crockett heard a new noise as the distant train blew it's whistle. He stood up and looked to the South to get his first glimpse of a train. He saw the smoke bellowing from it's stack and heard the noisy choo-choo as it approached. Many of the men like Crockett were unfamiliar with trains and railroads, so they stood there gandering at the site. The Engine had two big National Flags (Confederate) waving in the wind. It was a site to behold.

The train was made up of a few flat cars for supplies and guards to sit on. The last car looked like a nice passenger car, and all the cars between were cattle cars. Crockett reasoned that he and his buddies would be riding in the cattle cars.

The officers called for the sergeants to form up the men by companies. There was supplies, horses and men to get loaded. With all the manpower, the supplies were loaded quickly. Horses and mules were loaded next. Then the men were loaded into the cattle cars, they had room to sit, but not much more. A detail of men rode the flat cars with the supplies to stand watch. There were two men that sat on top of each car on guard duty also. The officers were in the passenger car at the back of the train.

The train lunged forward with a jerk. The engine could be heard spinning the steel wheels on the iron track. The train began to pick up speed and a new noisy of clickety-click could be heard. The 29th Virginia Infantry was on their way, and so many thoughts went through Crockett's head. The sights, sounds and smells, were all new to him. He also thought about Arminda, Floyd, and even Billy his big red horse. He also thought ahead to the dread of war. Will I be brave when the time comes he considered?

Something about riding a train makes folks sleepy and before long many of the men were sound asleep. Crockett took some of this time to talk to Jesus in a long silent prayer. He fell asleep also and woke up when the train stopped to take on water and wood.

Crockett had a dream. He dreamed that he was at a great battlefield, and the Southern Army filled the land for miles. As they marched toward the awaiting Yankees, a large white flag appeared, being carried by a Union Soldier. He was waving the flag with all his might. Following behind him was a General and his aid-decamp. The North was offering to surrender. Crockett and the great army of General Lee was happy as could be.

Crockett woke up when the sergeant hollered out, "Everybody get out and stretch."

All the men got down out of the cars and headed for the bushes growing by the tracks. Everywhere you looked men were relieving themselves.

"Smells like the whole Confederate Army pissed here," one man said.

Some of the men laughed out loud.

"Well the whole 29th did," another man said.

All the men took a drink from their canteens as they got back aboard. One of the men complained about riding the train, four men scolded him.

One feller said, "some folks would complain if they hung him with a new rope."

"Would you rather march the whole long way?" one of them asked.

"Reckon not," he answered after a second thought.

The train stopped in Wytheville, and the men were allowed to get off for a few minutes. Crockett took advantage, and mailed his letter to Arminda.

Old men, boys, a few crippled solders, and ladies of all ages were out cheering for the men heading out to fight the Yankee's. The Confederate National Flag was carried back and fourth by a lad of about twelve. The women brought out fresh baked rolls, and they were well received by the men. Most every man got one. The train will not stop again except to take on water and wood since the men had their bread, until they reach Lynchburg.

Orders were given for all aboard, and the men got back on the train. The train traveled through Marion, Wytheville, Dublin, Christiansburg,

Salem, and next big town would be Lynchburg. From there the train will travel more Easterly toward Petersburg. The train would stop and spend the night in Lynchburg and allow the men to have food and a chance to warm up. The weather had been fair but the speed of the train caused the men to have a chill. Most of the men were in good condition after the winter. There were a few sickly men, and they were all together in one car under medical care.

Crockett told some of the fellows about his dream, and some were not too surprised.

"You might get to see that very thing," replied his friend Isaac Puckett.

"I sure hope to see the time when the Yankee's get out of Virginia and stay out," Crockett said.

In Lynchburg the men were provided large tents to sleep in and a good supper of captured Yankee Beef. Colonel Mosby's men were good providers of food and materials they captured from those people. (John S. Mosby had become the leader of Partisan Rangers, that regularly raided the Yankee Army from the rear. They stuck swiftly on their thoroughbred steeds, and he was given the name of "The Gray Ghost.")

Next day the little train took the 29th on in to Petersburg. Everything was unloaded and the men were assigned an area to set up camp.

Crockett was overwhelmed by the site of so many solders, and officers. This was a grand army, even though the men looked tattered with their worn gray and butternut uniforms. Many had their feet wrapped in rags or uncured beef hide. Crockett also saw several flags from several other southern states. This grand army looked powerful and should be able to rid Virginia from the pestilence of those people.

As Crockett looked around he heard the men cheering from a distance and saw men rising and waving their hats. What ever it was, was coming toward the 29th. Oh my, General Robert E. Lee himself is passing through on his gray horse Traveler. He was a grand looking man sitting straight and tall on Traveler. He waved to all the men as he rode through. Many of the men ran close just to touch him or even Traveler.

Crockett felt so privileged to have seen this great man. This bolstered the confidence of all the men that saw their grand leader ride through. Crockett would have something to write home about, telling everyone back home about seeing the grand leader of the Confederate Army in person.

On March the 25th 1863 the 29th marched from Peatersburg to Tuckers Swamp Church, in Southampton County. They were under the command of Brig. General Montgomery D. Corse. Their Division Commander was Maj. General George E. Pickett.

General Pickett's division was apart of the First Corps commanded by Lt. General James Longstreet.

The 9th of April 1863 the 29th Virginia Infantry marched with General Corse from Tuckers Swamp Church in easy marches, to the south side of Suffolk.

On April 13th Crockett saw action as they drove in on the Federal pickets. This was the first time that David Crockett Whitt faced the guns of the enemy. He was quite proud of himself as he marched into battle for this first time.

On April the 14th the 29th Infantry was sent to the very front, and as they marched out in front Crockett's heart pumped like it was going to jump out of his chest. Crockett began to pray that God would be with him, and if He desired to take him home today that would be alright. The Lord sent his peace upon Crockett and he marched out bravely, as he looked across the field seeing the Federals wanting to shoot him. Isaac Puckett reached out and touched Crockett on the shoulder, and Crockett turned and patted Isaac on his shoulder. Crockett and his friends would really be tested this day. In the words of Private Ben Huddle "stood to the Yankees from the dawn of day until the shades of night came on when she released from her labors of the day and marched back to the breastworks!"

General John J. Peck commanded the Union Army of 25,000 men, against General Longstreet commanding 20,000 Confederates. The Union was behind formidable breastworks. The Confederates pushed the Union left flank plum to the Nansemond river and constructed a battery on Hill's Point, this closed off the garrison to Union shipping. The Union set up a battery to command the Confederate works at Norfleet House. Next day on April the 15th these cannon began to fire and drove the Confederates out of this important position.

Crockett was now baptized under fire, and on the 24th of April there would be more skirmishing on Edenton Road which was close to the Nansemond River. Here Federal Gunboats came and shelled the 29th. Thank God this had little effect, and not too many men were killed. The battle was inconclusive as far as history goes, but both sides claimed victory. The death count has never been established for either side.

Crockett had a long talk with the Lord that night and offered up a prayer of thanksgiving for His protection and watch care. Crockett also thanked Him for giving him the strength to be brave. Crockett told Jesus, that without your mighty power I would throw down my gun and run like a rabbit. He also told the Lord that his life was in His hands and only the Lord knew the day he would give up his life. So Crockett felt confident to march into battle with his brave friends.

Both sides faced each other off until May the 3rd when Longstreet received orders to bring the First Corps to Chesterfield County. The night of May 3rd, the 29th left with all of Pickett's Division on a forced march. They marched all night and on the morning of May 4th they crossed the Blackwater River and set up camp in Southhampton County. They had covered 28 miles in one night. Five men fell behind and the Yankee's captured them. General Corse was very stern with his stragglers because of this.

Crockett and his friends were worn out, but there was little chance of those people coming after them. Everyone was tired but there was few complaints. They all knew the ground between them and the Federals was like a great gate that had been closed. The men also sensed that they had bigger fish to fry.

On May 9th ,1863 the First Corps had reached Chesterfield County where it camped and rested for a week. This is where they received great news, and some sad news also. They heard of the great victory for the South at Chancellorsville. The battle was fought on May 1st through May 4th. General Lee was facing General Hooker with 133,868 men. General Lee was absent of Longstreet's First corps. This left the Army of Northern Virginia with only 60,892 men. General Jackson and General Lee came up with a mad idea. Lee would divide his Army in the face of overwhelming numbers. Jackson ordered a forced march as quiet as possible south, then west, then back north where they would come straight at those people's left flank. The Yankee's had no pickets out and were cooking supper around 4:00 PM. The Second Corps charged into the unsuspecting Yankee's and with their Rebel Yell scared their paints off. Those people threw down what ever they had and ran east toward the main army as fast as they could. The whole Northern Army was in Panic. Stonewall Jackson's First Corps chased until it got too dark to see. Jackson wanted to destroy the Northern Army once and for all, but ran out of daylight.

General Jackson being a Godly praying man most likely thought of Joshua 10: 12-13 in the Holy Bible. Joshua was chasing and killing the enemy of the Lord and the Sun was getting low in the sky. Joshua prayed, "O sun, stand still over Aijalon, so the sun stood still and the moon stopped, till the nation avenged itself on its enemies." It did not work this way for General Jackson, It got dark and even his army was starting to become confused.

General Jackson and his aid-decamp scouted out to find the enemy so he could plan for an early morning attack. They had wandered far beyond the safety of the Confederate lines. Once satisfied, and with the protest of his officers he turned back toward the safety of his lines. They took a different road back and came up on some of the Confederate Pickets in the twilight. The Confederates were unnerved and begin to fire on what they though to be Yankee cavalry.

General Jackson was shot in the left arm. He was removed under friendly fire and taken back to safety. His bone was shattered by the smooth bore mini ball so it had to be amputated. He should have recovered, but pneumonia set in and a few days later he passed on to Glory. His last words were, "Let us cross over the river and rest under the shade of the trees."

General Lee, hearing of his demise said, "General Jackson lost his left arm, I have lost my right."

Crockett and all the men cheered when they herd of the great Victory. One man said, "That is two great victories in a row, first Fredericksburg in December and now in Chancellorsville."

Then they were told of the great loss of General Thomas "Stonewall" Jackson. A hush came over the entire First Corps. Then some of the men began to cry out loud. All that herd the news, knew that this was a great loss to the southern cause.

Thousands and thousands of good rifled Muskets were captured at the two great victories by General Lee's Army. Many of the old converted .69 caliber flint locks were traded in for the more accurate .577 caliber rifled muskets. The 29th would not get any of the captured muskets at this time. Many other needed supplies were captured also.

Morale was extremely high in the Southern camps. The men knew that they had a great and proven commander in General Lee. And General Lee had a proven army, one that did everything he had asked of them.

The winter had taken a toll but now the Army was in pretty good shape. Both armies had lost many men to measles, mumps, chickenpox, cholera, and many other contagious diseases. Many of the men had body lice and even fleas. Still under supplied and under fed the Southern Army would march through Hell if General Lee asked them to!

A few letters had found their way to David Crockett Whitt. He had to turn his head every time he would get one because of the tears that would well up in his gray eyes. Arminda was fine according to her letters, and so was little Floyd that would be two years old on the 30th. He is quite active now that he walks and can even run. Arminda reflected that John Floyd looks just like his Paw David Crockett Whitt. Billy, Crockett's horse was doing fine and Arminda made sure she mentioned him in most of her letters. She always mentioned the ladies getting together for prayer meetings to lift up the brave men defending Virginia. She had a big garden out and even a field of corn planted. She and some other ladies worked together to put out a cash crop of tobacco. She expressed how greatly she missed him, and feared for his life. She always told him not to worry about them, but to keep his mind sharply focused on his soldiering. Arminda always closed her letters to Crockett with a, "I love you."

Crockett wrote letters when he could. He expressed his love for Arminda and little Floyd. He told her that he had been in battle, but did not go into details. He always expressed his faith in Gods protection. Some day all of this hell of war will pass, and we will be together again. Hopefully Billy Yank will get tired of his folly and go back home for good.

By June 3rd ,1863 General Lee was collecting his army at Culpeper. By the middle of May Pickett's Division had arrived in Hanover County north of Richmond.

General Pickett received orders to take three of his brigades under Generals Kemper, Garnett, and Armistead and march to Culpeper. From history we learn that they marched to Gettysburg, Pennsylvania. These three brigades were at the front of the famous "Pickett's Charge."

General Corse's Brigade was left behind at the insistence of President Jefferson Davis. He felt it was important for the protection of the Confederate Capital. For two weeks they remained in Hanover and Spotsylvania Counties, but on June 25th it marched 15 miles to the railway near Hanover Junction. The 29th Infantry boarded a train that night and were delivered to Gordonsville fifty miles away. For about two weeks the 29th camped and guarded the gap of Cherry Ridge.

The men in the 29th wondered about the rest of the Division. They did not know how to feel, cheated or saved by fate. They all were awaiting word back from the Army of Northern Virginia. Will they finally draw out those people and put such pressure on them that they will yield to the South's Independence? Also they considered that a Yankee Army may try to sneak in and try to capture Richmond.

At Gordonville on June 17th they turned in their old smoothbore weapons and were given Enfield rifled Muskets of .577 caliber. These Muskets were also muzzle loaded but much more accurate and durable. Crockett and his friends felt more powerful with these new weapons in their hands. They could shoot and hit targets of much further distance. The 29th mostly from the mountains of Virginia were great marksmen to say the least.

On July 3rd the rest of Pickett's division and others were aligned to march across a mile of open field in the famous "Pickett's Charge." Fifteen regiments took part and they marched magnificently as if in a great parade while under fire of cannon and small arms the whole long way. The Yankee's said, "we don't have to guess where the rebels are, we can see them."

This was a blunder on General Lee's part, costing the South about 28,000 souls in the three days of battle. General Lee made few mistakes during his command, and even General Longstreet tried his best to talk him out of it.

On July the 5th, the Confederates retreated from Pennsylvania, crossing into Maryland west of the Blue Ridge. The 29th Infantry was ordered to cross the Blue Ridge to meet Lee's retreating army. They left Gordonsville on July the 8th. They marched through Madison and Rappahannock Counties. On July 10th they marched 22 miles across the Blue Ridge to Luray, in Page County. This is a long march considering the sweltering July weather. They seemed to be marching on adrenaline because they sensed the need to protect the retreating army.

From there they marched northwesterly through Warren and Frederick Counties, and arrived in Winchester on July 13th. That night and the next day the retreating Army of Northern Virginia crossed the Potomac.

July 20th the 29th Infantry marched 15 miles south down the Shenandoah Valley to Cedarville in Warren County. The Army had learned that Federal Cavalry from the east was coming to seize the gaps in the Blue Ridge. These gaps would be used by the Southern Army to cross back into northeastern Virginia.

The next morning the 29th headed to Chester Gap about twelve miles away. This was a forced march in sweltering summer heat, and they reached the gap just before those people and skirmishing started as each side began to feel out the other. This back and forth skirmishing continued most of the day. The gaps were cleared out and in three easy marches the 29th Infantry arrived in to Culpeper on July the 24th.

Crockett felt relieved to be back with the main Army of Northern Virginia. They all talked about Gettysburg and felt sure they could overcome the setback.

August 1st, the 29th Infantry left Culpeper Court House and marched 15 miles to Rapidan Station. On the 3rd, the 29th marched to within eight miles of Orange Court House.

The 29th Infantry was detached and on the 8th of September 1863 marched to Henrico County. They marched through Richmond where they boarded a train to Petersburg. They arrived in Petersburg Sunday 13th of September and spent one night. Next morning they received orders that lifted their spirits to the heavens. The 29th Infantry was headed to western Virginia. No mater what they would face back there they were exhilarated to be heading into their home counties. All day long that was the talk and Crockett was right in the middle of it. He praised God for this wonderful news.

Crockett noticed that every man in the 29th had a smile on his face. The men looked like a bunch of vagabonds wearing their ragged dirty gray clothes, long hair and mostly bearded faces, but happy faces.

They had business to take care of near Bristol on the Tennessee and Virginia line, but all knew they would have a chance to go home for a visit with their families. Crockett could hardly wait to see his bride and baby Floyd, but there was no need to write a letter because he would most likely beat it home. He wondered if the baby and even Billy his big red horse would know him.

A Federal Army in east Tennessee was threatening Bristol. Major General Samuel Jones, commanding the little army in western Virginia did not have enough troops to oppose the threat, so this is why General Corse's Brigade was sent to reinforce him.

The night of September 14th they boarded a train of cattle cars, flat cars, and some sat on top of the cars. The train stopped in Lynchburg, Wytheville, and Glade Springs. They arrived in Zollicoffer Station, Sullivan County, Tennessee on the night of September 16th. The trip of 340 miles took a little over two days.

For two days Crockett and his friends stood picket duty. The Yankee's came up for a skirmish at Zollicoffer Station on September 20th. The 29th Infantry lost a few brave souls to the Yankee's, but those people left pretty quick.. The 29th marched about 10 miles to Carter County, to Watagua River. Some mutton was served up for the men to eat.

The fighting was over along the Tennessee-Virginia border for now. Many of the men were granted furlough due to the closeness of their homes. Part of the 29th boarded the train and headed out to Petersburg on October 1st, and arrived there October 5th. On October 8th & 10th, the Army gave out some tents, clothes and blankets.

The 29th was ordered back to East Tennessee. They boarded a train again on October 13th and arrived back in Tennessee, after spending ten days in Abington. November 1st they were in camp near Blountville,

Tennessee.David Crockett Whitt was one of the lucky men that got to go home, he borrowed one of the Army mules as did some of the other men. He left the Bristol area September 23rd and covered the 60 miles to Baptist Valley in two days. Crockett came riding up to the little Whitt cabin on the morning of the 25th of September.

Arminda was out gathering corn from the field. When she saw him she threw down the husks, grabbed Floyd off his blanket he was playing on, and ran like the wind. Crockett dismounted, turned the mule lose and ran to meet her. Oh what a reunion, Arminda sat Floyd down, and leaped into the air with her legs spread. Crockett caught her and she held him tight with her legs wrapped around him. After they held on to each other for a minute or two they heard little Floyd saying, "Paw, Paw."

Arminda slowly straightened her legs and let her feet touch the ground. Crockett turned Arminda loose long enough to reach down and pick up his little son. John Floyd knew his Paw and grabbed Crockett around the head for a tight hug. After Crockett got little Floyd to turn loose he got a better hold on the youngster. He took his other arm and wrapped up Arminda again.

"How long do you have?" Arminda asked after finally regaining her composer.

"I have to be back in Abington by the 15th of October," Crockett said.

"I have to catch up with the Company as soon as possible after that. Guess I will have to leave here no later than the morning of the 13th," Crockett continued.

Crockett did not know it but the train would be back in Abington, Virginia bringing the rest of the 29th Infantry back from Petersburg. It would stop in Abington on the 15th of October, just in time for him to rejoin the unit. New orders were issued and the 29th would march around the northwest end of Tennessee.

Crockett holding little John Floyd and a arm around Arminda headed toward the cabin.

"What about your mule sweetheart, shouldn't you get her unsaddled and in the barn?" Arminda asked.

"Yes I almost forgot the poor thing after she carried me here so quickly, I will go right back out and do that soon as I can put my gear in the cabin," Crockett answered.

"You know, I think Floyd does look like me," Crockett said.

Crockett headed for the door to go out and take care of the mule and Floyd was right after him. Crockett picked him up and took him to care for the mule. Crockett could hardly wait to see his horse Billy. He carried Floyd in one strong arm and led the tired mule to water and feed. Billy, Crockett's big red horse had heard the commotion and trotted through the pasture to the fence by the barn.

Billy saw Crockett, and recognized him at once. He shook his head from side to side, and shook with excitement.

"Hey Billy is that you, big boy?" Crockett asked the excited horse.

At the sound of Crockett's voice Billy reared up on his hind feet and hit the fence with his front hoofs.

"Whoa boy, just settle down, I will come in there and see you in just a minute," Crockett said to his anxious friend.

Crockett was thrilled that Billy and little Floyd both knew him. Crockett got the mule unsaddled, fed, and watered. Billy carried on the whole time Crockett was working with the mule, while he still held on to Floyd. Finally Crockett went over to the fence and petted Billy while talking to him as a good friend, which he was.

Floyd reached out his little arm and touched Billy on the nose saying, "Paw, Villy."

Crockett looked at Floyd and said, "Paw's horse Billy, say B-illy.

"B-illy, B-illy," said the little fellow.

"That's right Floyd," Crockett said to his little son.

Crockett went into the barn and found a few oats and corn and brought it out to Billy for a treat. He only gave him a little so as not to mess up Billy's stomach.

Finally Crockett got away from his beloved horse and got back into the cabin. Arminda had the fire burning big and was heating a big pot of water. She had brought in the big bathing tub and had some cool water in it. You could see that she had shaved some soap into the water.

"Looks like somebody is fix-in' to get a bath round here," Crockett said.

"Yes sweetheart I aim to wash that army dirt off you, and I might get cleaned up also before bed time," Arminda said.

"I bet you are famished, I got a chicken kilt and in a pan, we can dine on ol Rufus and some dumplings for supper," Arminda said.

"Rufus, did you name your rooster?" Crockett asked.

"I should have kilt him before now, he was a wicked ol bird, but I been saving him for hard times," Arminda said.

As soon as the water was hot she stripped Crockett down and put him in the tub to soak. She took his dirty clothes and put them in a pile to be washed. She laid him out some of his clothes from the wardrobe.

While Crockett soaked and little Floyd played walking round and round the big tub, Arminda plucked Rufus (rooster) and cut him up for the boiling pot.

Crockett was at peace once again sitting here in the tub, and watching Arminda. He played with Floyd until the little fellow got tired, and Arminda put him down for a nap. Next Arminda got the shaving mug and straight razor. She sit at the head of the tub, took scissors and cut Crockett's beard as short as possible, then she bobbed of the long hair on his head. She bent down and gave Crockett a long wanting kiss.

She came up for air and said, "Got to get the rest of them whiskers offen your face."

Crockett gave her a smile as she lathered up his face in preparation to give him a clean shave. She took the big leather strap and whetted up the straight razor to a fine edge. Next she gently lifted the whiskers off of Crockett's face and revealed the crease in his chin.

"There it is," she said.

"There what is?" Crockett asked.

"Your Whitt chin, silly," she answered.

That was a family trait of the David Crockett Whitt family. Most of the family from that line have the crease in the chin.

Arminda gave him another kiss, and took him by the hands and pulled him to his feet. Next she toweled him dry especially the lower portions. She admired his manly body as she helped him to dress. As she buttoned the last button on his shirt, she smiled one more time and turned toward the pot on the fire.

"I have to get the supper Crockett, will you empty the tub and put more water on to heat?" she asked.

"After supper is over and we get the baby back to bed, you can give me a bath," Arminda said.

Then gave him that special look that only a woman can give a man.

Arminda made the dumplings on the chicken, mashed some potatoes, and dipped some pickled beans from a crock. She fried some corn cakes and a dinner for a king and queen was ready.

Arminda set the table and then got the baby up. Little Floyd whimpered some but started waking up to eat supper.

"If he don't get up now he will want to be up all night," she explained.

Crockett smiled as he realized Arminda's plan to have him for her self tonight. Crockett and Arminda enjoyed their special supper as did little Floyd. They talked about many things but not much about the war. The South was just holding on now trying to buy time hoping that the next election in the North would elect a President that was against the war.

Crockett asked her all about her family and of course his. They could hardly believe that the two of them and Floyd were all together for a short time. There would be long moments that the two of them would just sit and gaze upon each other.

After supper Crockett took Floyd and played with him, while Arminda cleaned up after supper. There was little left of Rufus and the dumplings. Crockett nor Arminda had a meal like this for some time. Little Floyd played so much with his Paw that he was ready for bed about dark, and that was just the way Arminda planned it.

CHAPTER 33

NEVER-ENDING WAR

Finally Arminda got little Floyd down for the night and brought out the bathing tub again. The water in the big iron pot was scalding by now and Crockett poured it slowly into the tub and added cool water to just the right temperature. Arminda brought out the soap bar and shaved some into the awaiting water. She got a big towel and her night shirt and sit them on a chair beside of the awaiting bath.

She took off her shoes and socks and walked over to the tub. She stood there waiting for her loving husband to assist her. She stood by the tub and Crockett removed one piece of clothing at a time slowly and deliberately. Arminda stood completely naked before Crockett, and he wanted to do some touching and exploring, but she stepped into the warm water and sat down.

"Just you wait Mister Whitt, you have to give me a bath for now," Arminda scolded in a loving way.

"Soap up that wash rag and wash my back to start with," she directed.

Crockett gently washed her back, neck and shoulders. Then as he finished each part he moved around to wash her full breast. It had seemed like a hundred years since he had enjoyed such beauty. Arminda was a beautiful lady of only nineteen, at this time in the fall of 1863.

Crockett took his time and gave her a good bath, and he leaned over and gave her a long passionate kiss. Next he took her by her beautiful hands and gently raised her to her feet. He took the towel and wrapped it about her and helped her step out. Next he dried her back down and including her lovely buttocks. Then he moved to the front and dried under her chin and moved down to her breast. He took one breast at a time and dried it completely. Next he dried her lovely tummy. Finally he took the towel into her most secret treasure.

Arminda took Crockett and pulled him as close as she could and said, "Darling I love you, please take me to our bed."

Crockett picked her up into his arms and carried her to bed. They enjoyed the ecstasy of marital bliss most of the night until Crockett gave in to his exhaustion. There was a new son conceived that night and in about nine months little Jonas Lee Whitt would be born.

The next few days seemed like a blur, with the hands of the clock making formidable speed round and round. Crockett visited Rhoda and her fine family a few times, and aunt Nancy over at the old Hezekiah House. He went to church on the Lords day and had several friends and family come by for short visits. He tried to find time to ride Billy for a little while each day. He would hold Floyd, pull Arminda up behind him and his big red horse would take them for a ride around the little community. They did not want to think of it, but they both knew time was fleeing away to the day Crockett would leave again to serve Old Virginia. Crockett worked around the little farm doing what he could in the short time to help Arminda. He drug in some timber and sawed it up so Arminda could easily chop it into fire wood. He also helped her gather the corn and put it in the crib.

Crockett and Arminda had gone to Church on Sunday the 11th of October, and rested the evening away enjoying being with each other and little Floyd.

The 12th was a Monday and a gloomy looking day. The weather looked like it could present a cold rainy day for Crockett to travel on the morrow.

Crockett set out his gear by the door and his clean old gray and butternut Confederate Uniform on a chair by the bed. Arminda had packed some things in Crockett's haversack such as writing materials, some sewing thread and needles to do some mending with. She even wrote him a love note to find later. They made love again that last night which made it twenty nights straight, but who is counting?

The morning of the 13th came quickly and it was cool with drizzle rain. Crockett was up and saddled up the army mule. Arminda fried a piece of salt-pork and made some sawmill gravy on it. She baked several biscuits and had them ready in a short period of time. Crockett would take the left over biscuits when he left. Bless her heart she got up at least an hour before Crockett and had things going before she woke him up.

Soon as breakfast was over he got his gear, held baby Floyd and Arminda for a minute. Gave them a big kiss and mounted the mule. Crockett hid it but tears streamed down his face just as much as they did Arminda's. Even little Floyd hollered for his Paw. Crockett hurried across the field to the Kentucky Turnpike that followed Indian Creek to the Clinch. When he got close to the road he wheeled his mount and waved to his beloved family.

He was riding in the rain on his way back to Abington, to catch a train he thought. When he would get there he would be surprised that the 29th had been to Petersburg and would arrive back in Abington the 15th the same day Crockett would.

Crockett was stopped by a column of home guard near Lebanon. They wanted to know what he was doing here when his unit was off somewhere fighting.

"I am from the 29th Virginia Infantry and am on approved furlough, as a matter of fact I am on my way back to meet up with Company H," Crockett affirmed.

The home guard was bullish and was looking for an excuse to hurt Crockett.

"I have papers in my haversack, allow me to get them for you," Crockett said.

"Go ahead but don't try enny thing solder boy," the lead man said in a rough voice.

Crockett handed them the papers and his attitude changed.

"Go ahead Private Whitt, and be careful," The man answered.

Crockett received his papers and headed on out the road toward Abington. He thought what may have been, had he not had his furlough papers on him. The home guard was notorious about retrieving deserters, many were shot without a chance to comply and return to the war.

Just before noon on the 15th of October, Crockett rode into the Confederate military camp in Abington, Virginia. There was a train sitting at the station unloading troops and gear. What is this all about, Crockett thought.

Crockett rode closer and realized it was his regiment the 29th. How could they be here, they left for Petersburg at the end of September,

Crockett reasoned. He saw some of his friends so he dismounted and walked over to them and asked what happened.

"We just got back from Petersburg a little while ago, been gone about two weeks I reckon," answered Isaac Puckett.

"Well how come you fellers come back?" Crockett asked.

"Didn't need us too much in Petersburg, so we come back to rid out east Tennessee of the Yanks," Isaac said.

"Well I better check in with Lt. James Stephenson, I see him over there by the train," Crockett said.

"Yep, better muster in so's they know you are back, then you can come back and help us, we ain't working too hard, jest taking our time," Isaac Puckett said.

"By the way Crockett they gave out some new tents and stuff, back in Petersburg, and I got us one," Isaac added.

Crockett started to walk away, and Isaac spoke again, "Have a good furlough friend?"

"Sure did, seemed like I died and went to heaven," Crockett said.

"Bet you had an angel too, didn't you Crockett?" Isaac asked.

"Sure did, her name is Arminda," Crockett added.

"I thought so," said Isaac.

"When you come back I got some more stuff I drew for you back at Petersburg," Isaac said.

"Thanks Isaac, soon as I muster in and take this mule and take care of her, I will be back," Crockett said.

Crockett went over to Lt. James Stephenson and stood straight and saluted him.

"At ease Crockett, did you enjoy your leave?" ask Lt. Stephenson.

Crockett stood at ease, and said, "Yes I did and I saw my brother-in-law John Madden Stephenson while I was in the valley."

"How is my big brother and the family?" Lt. James Stephenson asked.

"Doing good, he and Emma are figuring on moving over to Kentucky in the spring, to be close to Paw," Crockett said.

"Don't surprise me none, they have been talking bout it for some time," said Lt. Stephenson.

"Crockett you go turn in that mule and tell them to take care of it, then you go over and help your comrades, if you ain't too frazzled from the trip," said Lt. James Stephenson.

"Yes sir, I am in decent shape, got a little sleep last night and only rode bout half a day today Sir," Crockett answered.

The Lieutenant nodded his head and gave Crockett a smile.

Crockett was back with his circle of friends from Baptist Valley, in a short time. Isaac dug down into a crate and pulled out a great coat, and held it up.

"Looks like this ort to fit ya, Crockett," Isaac said.

"We were drawing out some stuff that came in while we were in Petersburg, got me a coat and snatched this-un for you," Isaac said with a smile.

"Thanks a bunch, let me see if it will fit me," Crockett said.

He put the great coat on and buttoned it up.

"How does it look?" Crockett asked.

"Warm," answered Isaac.

"Thank you so much Isaac, you are a good friend to me," Crockett said.

"Hell, somebody has to look after you," Isaac said with a laugh.

Another private was with the circle of friends that Crockett had seen but had never got to know before. Crockett walked over to him.

"My name is Crockett Whitt, what's your name private?" Crockett asked.

Henry Plaster from Russell County, seems like I know you Crockett these fellers have talked a lot about you," Henry said.

"Good to meet you Henry Plaster," answered Crockett.

"I have seen you around but just never got to know you, seems like bout the time you get to know a feller something happens to um," Crockett said.

"Hope nothing happens this time," Henry said.

"Me too!" Crockett said with a smile.

Crockett and Henry Plaster became instant friends.

The 29th Infantry camped in Abington for about ten days, then began marching and counter marching all over northeastern Tennessee. On the 25th of November they marched 20 miles to Kingsport. They were in Bean Station on the 20th of December. On Christmas Day they were 4 miles east of Rogersville. December the 29th they crossed the Holston River on a ferryboat.

January 1st they were camping near Whitesburg, Tennessee. On the 8th they marched from Whitesburg to Bull's Gap, about 7 miles away. The 15th, they marched 17 miles to Morristown. Then they marched close to Dandridge where they came close to some Yankees, but there was not a scrap this time.They were back at Bull's Gap on January 20th. The 22nd of January the 29th Infantry left Bulls Gap in route to Bristol about 80 miles away. They arrived there on January 26th 1864 to meet a train and receive orders.

Crockett and his friends were headed back to Petersburg, then ride the rails into North Carolina. This was their last venture into western Virginia, until the veterans come home for good after the war. They got to Petersburg in the morning on January 28th and on that night they pulled out on a train going south to Kinston, North Carolina which was 190 miles away. On January 30th they arrived at Kinston and marched three miles to camp. Their entire trip from Bristol to Kinston was a ride of 450 miles.

"Seems like all we do is march and ride trains," said one soldier.

"You left out fighting Yankee's," another one added.

"Speaking of fighting Yankee's, we head out in the morning to New Bern," said one of the sergeant's.

"We are back in Pickett's Division and he intends to rid New Bern of those people," added the sergeant.

On January 31st they marched 25 miles through swampy grounds, on February 1st the 29th Infantry went 5 more miles to the Yankee outpost. They attacked those people and sent them on the run. They captured what ever the Yankee's left behind. They drove the Yankee's 10 miles into fortifications outside New Bern. On February 2nd the brigade took a blockhouse and prisoners. The Yankee's held the rest, and the attack gave out. General Corse withdrew on the 3rd day of February and marched back to Kinston. The men were all wondering what the next move would be.

February 7th 1864 the 29th Infantry marched with General Corse to Goldsboro, North Carolina where they spent a nice quiet three weeks. In early March they thought they were needed in Richmond so they marched to the railroad and boarded a train on March 3rd. The train traveled 90 miles to Weldon, North Carolina where they were turned back by orders. On March 4th they were returned south to Goldsboro, then on to Kinston again. We can just imagine what the soldiers had to say about this unnecessary train ride. Today we would say the left hand don't know what the right hand is doing. I never learned why they thought they were called to Richmond.

They had another quiet month camping in Kinston, then on April 16th the 29th Infantry marched 25 miles in two days, toward New Bern again. Once again they were called back. There was some dissension in the ranks, but nothing more than some complaining.

On April 30th the troops marched in grand review, had inspection of arms, then mustered for pay. On May 2nd the 29th Infantry was given orders to march to New Bern once again, beginning in the morning of May 3rd. This was their third expedition toward that place. They covered 25 miles, and on May the 5th the 29th Infantry marched 10 miles and attacked those people just south of New Bern. They drove the enemy into fortifications. The 29th pressed those people and captured two blockhouses, artillery pieces, and prisoners.

Federal gunboats came up the Neuse River and subjected them to a terrific shelling. It was the worst the 29th had ever experienced. One soldier stated that the Yanks were throwing scrap metal at them.

The night of May 5th was spent in a battle line. A Confederate Gunboat was supposed to come up and assist in the battle, but it never came. May the 6th General Corse ordered a withdrawal. They took three days to march back to Kinston. Before they had reached Kinston rumors ran through the ranks that the 29th was headed back to Virginia.

Some of the men expressed that they hoped someone had the right orders this time, so that they would not travel in another meaningless venture.

On Monday, May the 9th the order was given to break camp, pack up tents and pack the supplies. The 29th Infantry marched into the town of Kinston about three miles in distance and prepared to take the train north. They waited most of the day and finally pulled out of Kinston around 10:00 at night. The train was sluggish because of the bad condition of the railroad. The men hoped that there would not be a derailment. They got to Weldon, North Carolina on the 10th of May and got off the train to rest and eat. They boarded the train again that night and rode about 35 miles to Garrett's Station, Virginia. Here they encountered a problem with destroyed tracks. The Yankee Cavalry had sneaked in and tore up the railroad. The men had to detrain and a night march of 12 miles was required to reach Swift Creek, where once again they would get on another train north. They would ride for18 miles to Petersburg. It took the poor Confederate transport 48 hours to bring them 177 miles.

Crockett and the other tired troops detrained in Petersburg and heard the urgent news of why they were needed back in Virginia. This was about 10:00 am. The people of Petersburg was glad to see them . They learned that General Lee was trying to hold off Grant and those people at the Wilderness and Spotsylvania.

General B.F.Butler brought his 36,000 Yanks up the James River and landed them at Bermuda Hundred. He was poised to march east and take the railroad and turnpike which connected Petersburg to Richmond City.

The Confederate high command reasoned that the Yanks were really after Richmond, and toops were called in from everwhere within reason, to Drewry,s Bluff. This was a Confederate fort on the south side of the James River. Drewry's Bluff was south of Richmond and about 20 miles north of Petersburg.

There had been several little but sharp battles up and down the turnpike, but the Yankee's were held at bay except for a broken section of railroad. The 11,000 Confederate troops in Petersburg would have to march north to Drewry's Bluff.

Crockett and his friends realized that this was a really serious situation. They had to be strong and hold those people out of Richmond. Everyone was tired but somehow mustered renewed strength to rush to the defense.

Alexander Phillippi a Chaplin with the 29th Infantry had the men gather for a quick prayer service before they marched off. He was a good spiritual leader which preached every Lords Day that they were able. He even held revivals, especially after Gettysburg. Many men had accepted Jesus Christ as their Personal Savior. Crockett always looked forward to the meetings even though Alexander was a Lutheran not a Baptist.

The 29th Infantry formed up and started to march toward Richmond along with the 15th and 18th Virginia Infantry under Temporary

Division Commander General Robert Hoke. They left about 1:00 PM only three hours after getting off the train.. They marched carefully at first because they knew a Yankee Army three times their size was up the road.

Rain moved into the region and would last for several days. The 29th was used as flankers and the army moved about 10 miles and stopped for the night. The 29th was tired, wet and hungry by now. They were under arms all night.

May the 12th brought heavy rains and the 29th moved a short distance and formed a line for battle. They were at a place they called Half-way House near Drewry's Bluff. Skirmishing started about 11:00 am and went on heavily all day. Some cannon fire was encountered and the 29th Infantry skirmishers were driven back. Shooting stopped at dark.

Things were quiet and peaceful now in the pale light of campfires and lanterns and Crockett said, "Thank you Dear Lord."

After supper Crockett took time to write a letter to his beloved wife Arminda, because who knew what the next day would bring. He tried to give her encouragement and wrote some about Floyd and the new little Whitt that soon would arrive.

Crockett knew more fighting would most likely happen in the morning. He and his friends talked some, then Crockett got off to himself to read some scripture from his little Bible and do some talking with the Lord. He felt at peace and was ready to go if the Lord required his life.

On the 13th of May the Union Army came closer and with concentration but no major battle that day. A North Carolina Regiment got pushed back so the 29th hurried over to support their retreat. This worked out better for General Corse, because he had a smaller line to defend.

Saturday the 14th came with rain again. Crockett moved out of his trench along with his friends which they had held for thirty six hours to take up a new position. This was to be a hard day for the 29th Infantry, they were ordered to serve as pickets and skirmishers out in front of the rest of the Southern Army. They were exposed to pot shots and would be the first to greet the oncoming Yanks.

By midmorning the Federals were closing in on the Confederate line. The 29th was out in front buying time as they grudgingly gave small bits of ground, as they slowly backed toward their main army. The 29th gave up a number of lives and several wounded. For the 29th it was the bloodiest day of the war to this point. Worse days were just ahead.

May 16th was a foggy smoky morning. General Corse held the extreme right of the line. To the left the Confederate line extended almost two miles. Up the line the Confederates started to move toward the enemy as early as 5:00 AM. The fighting was heavy as Crockett and his friends listened, wondering just when they would have orders to advance. It was not long before those people's skirmishers began sending hot lead into the 29th. The attack on the left was well on the way when the 17th and 30th Virginia Infantry came up to reinforce Corse. They had been separated from the 29th since Kinston. They just arrived tired and hungry but ready for a fight. They lost several souls just marching up from behind the 29th. The 30th moved to the left of the 29th and the 17th to the right of the 29th. Soon seven Confederate Brigades were in action and were pushing the Union 18th Corps. Many of the Yanks were leaving the field in disorder. In front of Corse's and Clingman's Brigades those people were not backing up.Crockett and his unit had fought back several attacks but none had been an all out attack.

At just before 10:00 AM General Corse and General Clingman received orders to send the five Virginia and two North Carolina Regiments in an all out charge against those people.Around 10:00 PM the 29th Infantry along with their comrades climbed out of the trenches right into a blistering fire from the Yanks. The 29th gave their famous "Rebel Yell", and covered ground quickly. The Confederate cannons gave support as the boys charged into the mouth of hell. They had to travel between a quarter and a half of mile through tangled growth under smoky foggy conditions. The noise was horrendous. The Yankee fire slowed down because they began to move away from the yelling Rebels. Half a Federal Brigade seemed to be the target of the 29th. Much of the Federals gave ground, but were not routed. The 30th had to fall back some because of fire from other directions. Those people were retreating none the less. They headed back through the woods to their original camp at Bermuda Hundred. They left their dead and wounded. They also left much of their equipment behind as they hurried away from the Confederates.

Many of the Confederates enjoyed the food left behind. A lot of prisoners were captured. Many of the prisoners were fresh off the boats from Europe and many did not speak enough English to say, "I surrender."

President Lincoln was supplying the Northern Army with a never ending supply of men, but they were green compared to the Southern Vets.

The 29th gave up more souls in this latest fight, but some how Crockett never had a scratch. It was a great victory for the 29th Virginia Infantry.

General Corse and General Clingman were ordered to give chase to those people and did for awhile until a great thunder storm hit and the daylight slipped away. It took the Yankee's four days to move from Bermuda Hundred to the Confederate line, but only one half a day to get back as the hot lead flowed from the Confederates. By noon on May 17th the Confederates were regrouped and following the Yanks.

By Wednesday May 18th both sides were sizing up the situation and picking out good ground to fight on. Some high ground on the James River by the name of Howlett House, was just such a place. Both sides wanted it. It would serve as an anchor to the end of the battle line and also control the James River. Here the 29th faced bitter fighting again and gave up more souls and wounded. But now the Federals were whipped into the trenches and could be managed by a much smaller southern Contingent.

General Beauregard had arrived a few days before and took charge of the army south of Richmond City. Many of the solders didn't even know this until later. Crockett saw him ride by with his contingent of officers.

General Lee was in a struggle north of Richmond with General Grant and needed help. General Pickett's entire Division was reunited and the 29th headed north on the night of May 19th. They marched fifteen miles and camped on the Capitol Square in Richmond City.

They left Drewry's Bluff to a much smaller army to manage the entrenched Yanks.

Crockett, Isaac Puckett, his newest friend Henry Plaster and his circle of friends were fortunate to have come through the past six months. They camped together and talked about how the Lord had to have shielded them from the hail of minni balls.

Crockett got to see the Confederate Congress in session and the Honorable McMullen complimented the 29th Infantry. Many Richmond ladies walked by to look at the soldiers and of course be seen. Soon there would be a train coming on the Fredericksburg Railroad to carry the 29th Infantry north to support General Robert E. Lee.

Crockett wrote Arminda again today and told her how God had protected him in battle. He did not go into any of the details except that they pushed back the Yanks. He should be getting some of the backed up mail from home anytime. Arminda was great with child by now and Crockett eagerly awaited the news of his new child. If the baby was a boy Crockett wanted to name him for Jonas his father and add Lee for his middle name for General Robert E. Lee. Jonas Lee Whitt would be his name, If it was a girl, Susannah Lee would be her name, for Crockett's mother.

Sergeant Rufus Brittan had been commissioned much earlier and now was Lieutenant. He gave a report that 117 men were killed, wounded or missing. A lot of ranking officers were shot up just as bad, and low ranking officers were advanced in grade. By May 18th the 29th Infantry had lost one fourth of it's strength when you add the sick, captured, wounded and killed. Many of the wounded did not live very long, yet some lingered for weeks. The impact of the low velocity .58 caliber mini ball was harsh, usually crushing bones as it past through the body. That is why so many limbs were amputated during this grave war.

On May 21, 1864 the Regiment boarded the Richmond & Fredericksburg Train to Penola Station. Then the men marched five miles to Milfore in Carolina County. The 22nd of May Crockett marched twelve miles with his regiment to the North Anna River and joined General Lee and the Army of Northern Virginia. The 29th Infantry was temporarily attached to the Third Corps.

General Lee's army was tired and worn. They had fought Grant's people in the Battle of the Wilderness to a standstill while being out numbered six to ten. The fighting had shifted from the Wilderness to Spotsylvania County, where desperate actions had taken place. The Confederate's held a battle line along the North Anna River, now Pickett's division rejoined the Army of Northern Virginia. Crockett was familiar with this place because last summer the 29th marched through here and Hanover Junction. They only stayed four days then marched out on May 27th 1864. The line of defense moved to east of Richmond and just north of the Chickahominy River.

The 29th Infantry arrived on this new front on May 30th and lost some more dear souls.

On May 31st the 29th Infantry moved two miles on the Confererate right and arrived at Cold Harbor on June 1st 1864.

The Confederate Army had built a zig-zag breastwork which gave them a clear shot in a wide radius. The Confederates were out numbered a little less than two to one, but were well fortified. Actually General Lee hoped that Grant would send his boys that way. The heavest fighting took place on June 3rd when Grant sent in a large number of soldiers trying to win by shear numbers. It was an un-Godly slaughter as the Confederates mowed down seven thousand Union Boys in less than ten minutes. Neither side could believe their eyes as they saw a field of blue dead or wounded. The 29th was involved in this and were given the name of the "Bloody 29th".

The 29th did their duty but felt no honor this day as they saw the results of their action. Was General Grant this stupid, many of the men on both sides wondered?

It was reported that many of the Union boys wrote their name, address and a short testament as to their wishes after death, and pinned it inside their blouse before the charge.

Fighting went on in a lesser scale until June 13th, when the 29th Infantry was pulled out and marched to Melvin Hill near the James River.

Grant would not call a truce at Cold Harbor so that the wounded and dead could be removed. He thought it would declare a defeat for the North. It was sickening to see the bloated bodies that lay before them. Even wild hogs came out of the woods and dined on the dead. The

Confederates were not allowed to leave their breastworks for several days even to take care of bodily functions. It was a stinking mess in the trench and also in the field of view before them was horrifying.

Crockett was so shocked at this battle he would never forget it the rest of his life. The night of June 3rd many sounds came from the killing field as the wounded men begged for help. Crockett saw many spirits rising from the dead as they released their souls. He prayed most of the night. The Confederates lost fifteen hundred men in this conflict which was insignificant compared to the Union loss of seven thousand in a ten minute period.

The 29th Infantry along with two divisions marched to the James River and crossed on a pontoon bridge near Drewry's Bluff, where they had fought the big battle about a month earlier.

While General Lee's men stayed in their breastworks in Cold Harbor, Grant slipped away with the largest part of his army and crossed the James River ahead of Lee and forced the Confederates to back out of the Bermuda Hundred line. This is the line that the 29th had helped to acquire for the South back in May.

General Beauregard's little army was in tight spot so the 29th Infantry marched in haste to bolster them. The 29th made good time, covering nine miles to the Bluff and eight more to the Plank Road where the Yankee's started shooting at them.

The 29th got their dandruff up! Once again the 29th was driving those people with the same success they had in May. The Bermuda Hundred line was once again in the hands of the Southerners. The Southerners occupied the line from Fort Howlett on the James River southward to Fort Clifton on the north bank of the Appomattox River. Crockett's friend from Baptist Valley, Lieutenant John W. Stephenson, gave up his life on June 16th as a result of the actions of war. Crockett really hated to hear this news as he knew John and most of the Stephenson family.

Crockett could not help but think back to the good times before the war. He thought about Arminda and little Floyd. He used his stored up memories to escape the reality of war. Crockett would even go back to his childhood and relive fishing trips with the family on the beautiful Clinch River. He remembered catching the flopping Small Mouth Bass and strong little Red Eyes. Crockett could see himself playing on the old bearskin rug and pulling his ears while he laughed the day away. He didn't remember the day that his big brother John Bunyon Whitt killed that bear, but heard the story many times. Crockett would think of the little things that made him so happy growing up in Tazewell County, and even the trip to Kentucky. Then a boom of distant cannons would bring him back to this dreadful place called Burmuda Hundred line. As much as he hated this dreadful existence he knew he was much better off than his captured comrades rotting away in P.O.W. camps like Point Lookout. He wondered if Arminda had delivered their second child yet, which was due around the end of May. He thought, O God, how much longer will we have to fight, and give up so many good men to the "Damn Yankee's"? It seemed like every time they killed one of these northern intruders, ten more with new blue uniforms and equipment would come forth.

Mail should come again soon since they are in this more permanent protected place here at the Bermuda Hundred line. Crockett tries to stay busy gathering wood, cleaning his musket, mending his shoes and clothes, on the days he doesn't have picket duty. They enjoy prayer meetings as often as possible, and reading the scripture to themselves most everyday. He and his circle of friends spend time telling stories and laughing at jokes. They try to keep each other lifted up. The morale is much better than any one could imagine, because down deep they still thought they could win their Independence through sheer perseverance. They did this while under bombardment most every day by the Yanks cannons.

Crockett got four letters, one came all the way from Greenup County, Kentucky. He took his letters and headed off to be by himself so that he could consume every word without distraction. Before he could even open them his eyes welled up with tears. He looked at them and saw one from Kentucky and knew this one was bound to have had trouble getting here. It took four months to make the trip and yet it was a wonder that it got through the lines at all. He had three letters from Arminda and most likely had news of a new baby.

He carefully opened all the letters and started reading the one with the olders date. Crockett is a father again and his new son is named Jonas Lee Whitt. Crockett is elated at the news, and he also noted that Arminda was doing quite well back in Tazewell County despite the war. Arminda gave an account of the birth and mentioned Rhoda had been there and helped her through the whole birthing period. He whispered a prayer of thanksgiving to the Lord for this good news. Crockett read the other two letters and took comfort, knowing that Arminda and his two little sons were doing well.

Crockett opened the letter from Greenup County, Kentucky. It was from his father Jonas Whitt. It was just one of those letters letting Crockett know that the Whitt's in Kentucky were doing well. Jonas did complain some about getting old and having many aches and pains, but was still able to get about. Jonas knew Crockett was off in the war, but had no comments about it because he knew if it was read it may not make it to Crockett. It was good news just to know that Jonas was still alive and able to write.

Crockett would write a letter back to Jonas and tell him about little Jonas L. Whitt. He only used the letter L, instead of Lee, for the middle name in case the letter was read by the wrong people.

Crockett also wrote a long sweet letter to his bride and his two sons. And he also asked about his big red horse "Billy." Arminda usually included a little note about Crockett's horse, but had failed to mention him this time.Crockett could only hope his horse was not in trouble in any way. He would ask in his next letter.

CHAPTER 34

LIVING THE WAR

The Bermuda Hundred line had become a trench dug out and fortified by the Southern Army. It will be Crockett's new home for nearly nine months. This is the same ground taken by the 29th Infantry on May 18th and retaken on June 16th 1864. Now General Pickett's Division was dug in and not about to give up this ground to those people. This was a new type of warfare developed by the Army of Northern Virginia and copied by the Yankee Army.

The Yanks also dug in a distance east of the Confederate line, and the ground between the trenches became known as "No Man's Land". There was no mass charges during this time, the only shots from muskets came from sharp shooters. Of course both sides traded cannon fire. Before you stuck your head up for a peek you had to raise your hat up on a stick or musket to see if the snipers were awake.

Those troops on picket duty stayed in the trench, or sometimes sneaked out into "No Mans Land," while the other troops lived in fortified huts behind the line. Picket duty came every three to four days. The huts were not identical to each other, they were built to the taste of each group. They did have chimneys, to aid in cooking and also for heat. It did not take long to clear the immediate area of trees and bushes. After awhile the wood supply was nearly a mile away and the men stayed busy gathering and transporting it.

Food had become scarce because Sherman's Yanks had wreaked destruction on Georgia and cut off the supply lines from the south. Also the Shenandoah Valley was under Yankee rule. Most of their food came from the Carolina's and southern Virginia during this time. Once food could be gathered it had to be transported on the worn out and battered railroad. By winter the rations were reduced to a pint of cornmeal and an ounce of bacon, when they could get it. One three day period they lived on frozen turnip tops.

Some of the men on firewood duty started raiding nearby farms to steal chickens or anything edible. This brought protest and General Corse ordered that none of his men would take part in these depredations on the Virginia farms. He also started holding frequent roll calls to keep up with his men. He took further action by placing patrols behind the lines. I am sure the men felt trapped and hungry and had too much time to think of home and better times. Lee was trying to hold on to the Confederacy until the North had Presidenal elections. If Lincoln was defeated the North may elect a a man that was not pro war. There had been many demonstrations in the streets of northern cities demanding that the war be ended. This was the hope of the South, because they knew that Lincoln was not the most popular President.

Some of the men got packages from home, if their homes were in a Confederate controlled area. The men from the 29th did not get much because their homes were way to the west in western Virginia. The men of the 29th had not received pay for six months, and if they had been paid, the money would buy little because of the gigantic inflation of Confederate money. There was little complaining among the troops because they knew the state of their nation was on their backs.

Even though a terrible war was going on, a strange phenomenon occurred any time the pickets from both sides got close. The pickets would start a conversation with the opposing picketts. They would be quite friendly, trading coffee for tobacco, or news of kin. Some times they would give a newspaper to their enemy. These chance meetings sometimes led to desertion, from one side or the other.

When officers knew this was going on, they would send artillery over the heads of the pickets to break up the parlay. Most of the men were getting the idea that this war was a "Rich mans war, poor mans fight."

Many of the Northern men relayed the message that they were forced to be here and really had no hard feeling against Southern Independence. Likewise the Southern men told them they were only defending their homes and country.

"If that Damn Lincoln would only listen to both sides there could be peace tomorrow," said one of the Confederates.

It was getting way up in the fall of 1864 and the weather had been turning cold. The men on the Bermuda Hundred line prepared for winter getting in all the wood they could and mending up clothes and shoes as best they could.

The 29th got word that there had been an attack back in western Virgina with Saltville as the target. General Stephen G. Burbridge gathered troops from Ohio and Kentucky including the 5th United States Colored Cavalry at his station in Mount Sterling, Kentucky. They marched eastwardly to the Big Sandy River and headed up river toward Virginia.

The Confederates were well aware that the North was planning such a raid to shut down the salt works and lead mines around Smyth County, Virginia. They had been on the lookout for some time, because they would have to gather all the help they could from western Virginia to hold off the Yanks. Most of the soldiers were out in eastern Virginia with General Lee holding off Grant's Federals. Old men and mere boys answered the call, Home Guard, and a few Regular Army gathered in Saltville.

As the Yankee Army descended Road Ridge, part of the Kentucky Turnpike, a little Army of around 200 hit them near the little town of Raven, Virginia, in Tazewell County. They knew they could not stop an army of that size, but they could hold them up for a while. Finally after some delay the Yankee's marched up the Clinch Valley toward Indian (Now Cedar Bluff, VA). The little army of old men and boys followed the Yankee's, taking shots at the rear guard. When the Yankee's got to Indian, another little surprise awaited them. About 300 men and boys were waiting with their old Brown Betsys and squirrel guns. The Yankee's lost more time trying to rid themselves of the pesky Rebels. These little delays worked and a good makeshift Southern army gathered at Saltville and dug in to greet the intruders.

It was rumored that a young maiden, Molly Tynes, who was visiting Tazewell County from Smyth County left her elderly family and rode across the mountains at night to warn the people of Saltville that the Yankee's were coming.

Several of the ladies from Baptist Valley and around Indian gathered on a ridge above the marching Yankee Army to watch while the little

Home Guard took them on at Indian. Arminda and Rhoda brought a wagon load of children and watched from the safety of the heights. This would be something to write in a letter to Crockett.

"My Gawd, look at them Niggers marching with them Yankee's," said one of the older women.

"Our boys will give them a royal welcome, I bet," said another one from another wagon.

By the time the Yankee Army made it to Saltville the Southerners were almost ready. More men were still hurrying to enforce the little army awaiting the Yanks. General Alfred E. Jackson took charge of the makeshift Southern Army at Saltville. The Yankee's thought there would be little defense, but the Virginians were stubborn and hard to deal with. The Southern army was pushed back some, but when they saw armed black soldiers threatening their homeland the southern army got their dandruff up. As more Southern men joined the ranks during the day the tide of battle turned for the Virginians. Even though the Virginians were still outnumbered General Burbridge retreated and set up a camp for the night out of range of artillery. They build many camp fires and sneaked out during the night, without doing any harm to the salt works. There were unproven rumors that the Southern men murdered captured black troopers.

Next day the Confederate Calvary chased after the retreating Yankee Army and gave up the chase in the Clinch Valley near Richlands, Virginia.

The next letter Crockett would get from Arminda would be a long detailed letter about the Yankee Invasion through Tazewell County and their hasty retreat back through Indian toward Kentucky. It was the talk of the area.

This battle in Saltville happened on the 2nd and 3rd of October 1864. The Yankee's wanted to stop the production of salt and lead from Smyth County, because it was so important to the southern cause.

Crockett and his circle of friends got word on October 4th that an 8000 man Yankee Army had invaded western Virginia. They all wished they could be there defending their homes, instead of being stuck here at Bermuda Hundred line swapping artillery, with the Yanks. On the 5th of October good news came that the Yanks were being chased toward the Big Sandy River, from Saltville. Good letters should be coming from wives and friends, to the men of the 29th Infantry.

Crockett also heard a bit of good news that Colonel Mosby's Rangers had captured a Federal train near Kearneyville. He also captured almost two million dollars from a Yankee pay master on the train. Crockett felt his manic life in the trenches was not much help, but he was encouraged by news like this. The South needed to pray for Lincoln to be defeated so that a pro-peace President would be elected in the United States.

Around the 1st of November 1864 the 29th Infantry received it's last consignment of new troops from western Virginia. There were nearly forty of them, and they were either real young or much older than the average troops. These last soldiers proved to be a faithful lot. Among these troops were two young men which were Crockett's distant cousins. James Byrd Whitt, and William McGuire Whitt was their names. Their father was John Floyd Whitt the son of Archibald Whitt. Archibald was Crocketts Great Uncle, being a brother to Crockett's Grandfather, Hezekiak Whitt.

In early 1865 the remnant of men from the 45th Virginia Infantry were transferred to the 29th Infantry. These were not new recruits. The 45th Infantry was another outfit from western Virginia. It had been shot up from several battles in 1864. There was only about twenty of them and each had a good record with the 45th. These men had lost their fervor for the war. Here in a new unit, asigned to this strange place, with little food and poorly clothed, most of them crossed the line while on picket duty and took the amnesty, the North offered.

This amnesty was offered to any Confederate soldier, that would take the oath of allegiance to the United States, and would be allowed to sit out the last of the war in the north as free men. This caused some leakage of manpower to the North.

It was a simple thing to do, you only had to wait for your turn on picket duty. When you were in hollering distance of the Yankee's you could request to come over and take advantage of the amnesty.

During the winter of 1864-65 several of the 29th crossed over. It was mostly the troops of the 45th, and some of the new younger men. Some men that had served from as far back as 1861 also crossed. But the most of the men stayed true to the cause and suffered through this time of cold and hunger. Crockett could not understand why some would defect, considering all they had gone through.

Crockett and the 29th received word that Union General Stoneman had brought 5500 troops out of Knoxville and raided southwest Virginia in December of 1864. He destroyed several miles of the Virginia and Tennessee Railroad, and many iron furnaces. He pushed back the weak Confederate defenses all the way to Saltville. They took sledge hammers to the salt kettles and then headed back to Knoxville. The Yanks had missed two thirds of the sheds, and less than one third of the kettles. In a couple of weeks salt was flowing from Saltville again. Stoneman came again in the Spring of 1865 and destroyed more of the railroad and lead mines. By now all the salt and lead in the world would not help General Lee and his Army. He would surrender on April 9th 1865.

Alexander Phillippi, the regimental chaplain, was still on duty with the 29th. He held regular worship services which helped in a great way to keep good morale. Crockett especially enjoyed these times.

The 29th Virginia was the largest of the regiments in General Corse's Brigade having 418 men present at the end of November 1864. The quality of clothing was rated "poor" to "bad" in an inspection report. Winter was on them and they needed 159 coats, 155 pair of trousers, 56 hats, 38 blankets and 33 pairs of shoes. Over a third of the men lacked basic clothing. By the end of January 1865 the 29th had set up workshops to mend such shoes and clothes as the men had. Crockett looked about as tattered as the rest of the men.

It was an ordeal to keep firewood as the men had to carry it over a mile now. It did help to keep the men from thinking of worse things. The men felt safe back of the lines, even though it was a demanding chore. The men could keep reasonably warm in their little huts, but while on picket duty they had no heat, and I am sure some of the men loaned out their coats to their friends while they served on picket duty.

When the 29th recaptured the Bermuda Hundred line back in the summer the heat was an enemy. Now it was the winter cold that was taking a toll on the undersupplied men. There was a steady trickle to the field hospital at Chester Station.

On January 4th 1865 the 29th along with the rest of Corse's Brigade went across the James River where it was temporarily assigned to Kershaw's division of the First Corps. They returned to the Bermuda Hundred line sometime during February 1865.

On March the 5th Picketts Division marched out of Bermuda Hundred line which had been their home for the past eight months. And were relieved by Mahones Division of the Third Corps. The weather was terrible that day and they only traveled two miles. They stopped in a driving winter rain and set up a camp.

After two days of foul weather, General Pickett had his Division march in review. I think that the military does such stupid things to get the mens minds on other things. Marching in Review has a way of instilling pride in a military unit. After the review the men rested another day and dried out somewhat. A night march took them to Manchester on the southern bank of the James River, which is now part of Richmond.

The Division crossed the James and marched through the capitol city of Richmond again, but this time it was night. Crockett did not get to see much because of the darkness of night.

Pickett's Division was needed on the north side of Richmond because Sheridan's Union Cavalry was moving out of the Shenandoah Valley crossing on the north side of Richmond. He was going to join Grant for the final showdown in Virginia. Lee's Cavalry was too weak alone to keep the stronger Yankee's out of the city. The 29th was needed to protect the north end of Richmond while those people moved through.

Crockett along with his division marched along the Brook Turnpike almost daily, or counter marched from March 12th through March the 19th. They were basicly following the Yankee troopers eastward through Ashland and Hanover Court House, then along the Mechanicsville Turnpike. On March 15th there was a skirmish at Ashland but there was no record of the 29th losing any men.

The crisis passed, Crockett and his comrades rested for a day or two. On March 21st Pickett had his Division march in review for what would be the last time. The little but powerful army marched proudly.

On March 26th the brigade marched seven miles to the railroad in Richmond. The men boarded the train for a twenty mile ride to

Dunlop's Station, just north of Petersburg. They marched three miles to a factory where they camped for three nights.

The war was drawing to a close, but most of the men did not fully understand this. Crockett and his circle of friends did not dwell on the idea of losing the war. They tried to keep a postive mind on that matter. They knew that the Spring would bring a much stronger assault by those people. By now they knew Grant would use every man he had to subdue the South and he had an endless supply. The Confederates would mow down many young Yanks, but a steady toll would be taken on the shrinking Southern Army as well. Crockett could not help but think of Cold Harbor and the seven thousand slain in a matter of ten minutes. Crockett would be haunted the rest of his life by these horrific memories. Many a night after this great war would be over, Crockett would awaken and have Arminda hold him to sooth the great beast of horror in his mind.

For months now General Grant had been extending the Union lines to the south and even west. General Lee had to follow suit and spread his thin gray line. As the end of March approached, Grant was putting together a mobile force under General Sheridan to break the railroad in Dinwiddie County. This was one of the few supply lines still open to the Confederates. This would cut off the Southern Army from supplies and even a way to retreat.General Sheridan commenced the assult on March 28th which if successful would divide the two cities of Richmond and Petersburg.

General Lee knew what the Yanks were up to and on the 29th of March 1865 he committed Pickett's Division of infantry and three small divisions of cavalry to deal with the threat. General's Corse and Terry moved their Brigades and crossed the Appomattox River on pontoons above Petersburg to the southside railroad. The heavens opened up with a steady downpour. The roads became a sticky mess of mud.

Stuart's Brigade was there waiting and they boarded the train for the last regimental train trip. It was a short ten mile trip to Sutherland's Station, but it took hours to load and unload. Crockett and his circle of friends all talked about the movements and became concerned even more when they saw General Lee arrive at Sutherland's Station.

General Lee was most definitely concerned about the movements of Sheridan's people.

General Lee gave orders to General Pickett to take his three brigades along with two of Bushrod Johnson's Division to Five Forks, and meet Confederate cavalry waiting there. From there the force was to march to Dinwiddie Court House. General Lee expected Pickett to come upon the awaiting Union cavalry.

The night of March 29th 1865, the 29th Virginia made a small march, and on the 30th continued on to Five Forks. Five Forks was a vital crossroads which was a key to the entire area.

On March 31st , 1865 Crockett along with the division, set out for Dinwiddie Court House. In the early afternoon they came up on a ford on a small stream called the unusual name of Chamberlain's Bed. Dismounted Yankee Cavalry were dug in and guarding it. General Corse along with his 29th Infantry were out front and got the job of clearing out those people. The 29th had to go upstream alittle ways and flank the Yanks. This cleared them out and the force was able to move along for about thirty minute when they came upon a stronger force to reckon with. General Corse could not drive them out alone, so General Rooney Lee's Cavalry unit came into action on the left and Terry's Brigade on the right. This force chased the Yankee's away and cleared the way to Dinwiddie Court House. Now Pickett's troops were in line of battle with skirmishers to the front, all were advancing down the road. The Union cavalry was to their front and continued hitting the Division. The resistance caused casualties on both sides. The 29th along with the Division pushed the Yanks ahead, and into the village that served as the county seat. The Confederates tried twice to dislodge the Yanks from the village, but had little success as night time approached. Crockett and his circle of friends had been under constant stress the live long day fighting the Yanks back. Somehow they were uninjured, physically.

General Pickett ended the assault for the time being. The days fight on March 31, would be remembered as the battle of Dinwiddie Court House. The effect to this point stalled the Yankee offense. The 29th was involved all day in this battle, counting the continued struggle on the road.

Crockett was glad to see the darkness of night come to this place.

He remembered to thank God for His loving kindness, and safe keeping.

The battle on the 31st was not a great victory, but credit must be given to the southern boys. It threw a wrench into the gears of the Yankee strategy and slowed their plans. With confidence and courage the Southern Boys fought like they did in bygone battles in the past. The 29th took casualties along with the rest of the Division but it is not known how many.

Pickett's Division stayed on the battlefield the night of the 31st. General Pickett learned during the night that a large force of Yankee infantry was coming up to join Sheridan's Army.

By daylight on April 1st 1865 the 29th along with the Division were moving down the road toward Five Forks. They had carefully gathered their wounded and were moving down the muddy sticky road.

Yesterday the 29th along with the rest of Corse's Brigade were out in the front as the vanguard unit. They had spearheaded the the push on the Yankee's. Today on the road to Five Forks they were at the rear, along with a small cavalry unit to deal with any persuing Yanks.

Isaac Puckett was marching beside of his friend David Crockett Whitt and wanted to try and bring some humor to their situation.

"Hey Crockett, you got mud on your foot," said Isaac trying to get Crockett to look down.

"I know, I know it is fools day also," Crockett stated.

Crockett turned to Isaac and both of them formed a big smile.

The Division arrived at Five Forks around noon and set up a battle line of about a mile and three quarters long, along White Oak Road. They were facing the south where the Yanks were expected to come from. They gathered some fencing and timbers and fortified as best as they could. General Corse was assigned the westernmost part of the battle line. General Pickett told all of his officers that Five Forks must be held. Everything settled down and was quite peaceful. General Pickett and his higher ranking officers went to the rear to a fish fry. Some southerner's had seined out some fish out of Nottoway River and this would be a treat for the officers.

Late in the afternoon the long blue line of the Yanks appeared on the horizon. The Division checked their muskets and gear as they realized a fight was brewing. The Yankee's were concentrated on the Confederate left the opposite end to where Crockett and his friends stood ready. The Yanks attacked about 4:00 PM and General Pickett was still eating fish.

The three left brigades gave a good account of themselves, they gave little ground as they mowed down many of the young boys in blue. The South also lost several good men. General Pickett arrived on the field with information that another Union infantry was coming up from the rear and threating to take the road. General Pickett pulled out Mayo's Brigade from the line to hold up this new group of Infantry. When this was done General Corse's Brigade was isolated from the rest of the army.

At this point Crockett and the rest of the 29th had not been in the thick of it. General Pickett ordered General Corse to change positions to face the east and and hold back those people so the Southern Army could withdraw. Crockett along with the Brigade came under sharp attack from the west. The Mini Balls whizzed past Crockett like a swarm of mad hornets. The Brigade was in danger and a dismounted cavalry unit stepped in to reinforce Corse. This stabilized the situation for a time. Next the determined Yanks reformed and made another charge. The Southern boys sent them a withering fire but they kept coming.

The stronger Yankee Army overwhelmed the weary Confederates and it was time to run. The 29th had been pushed before but never this hard. It was every man for himself and Crockett ran with the rest northwardly toward the southside railroad. They ran through the woods and fields wading the Hatcher's Run stream. Somehow Crockett and Isaac Puckett found each other and ran together. In the darkness of night the headlong mob of a Brigade reached the vicinity of the railroad. The officers took control and in a little time had the men under their discipline.

The 29th lost several men the last two days, some seventy captured, some killed and many wounded. Even Colonel Giles of the 29th was captured. General Pickett had been considering replacing Giles with a better man but never got around to it. Somehow Crockett was unhurt except plenty hungry and worn.

The loss at Five Forks, the lost rail line and a breach in the line at Petersburg on April 2nd prompted General Lee to evacuate Richmond and Petersburg that night. April 3rd the Yankee's moved into the Capital City of the Confederacy. Richmond had fallen but the government was safely on the move toward Danville, Virginia.

General Lee led the rest of his army west toward Pickett's broken Division. They were reunited and would move toward the west. General Lee was cut off fron taking a route toward the south by the Yankee's. He headed his Army to the west where he hoped to meet a supply wagon train and then head to the mountains of North Carolina where he could join with more of his army under General Joseph E. Johnston. General Johnston commanded over thirty one thousand troops.General Lee had plans to have a united force to deal with Sherman, then have another face off with Grant.

Crockett and his circle of friends still survived and were heading west with the main body of Lee's Army of Northern Virginia. They would see another battle on April 6th at Sayler's Creek.

Lee's Army was spread out along the road heading west. It began to look like they may escape the blue coated Yankees again. On April 6th 1865 Phil Sheridan's mobile force were waiting at Saylor's Creek. They plotted out a battle plan to hit Lee's Army. As I have studied this battle I think it was only to slow the Confederates down and have a chance later to force Lee into a battle or surrender. The attack went just right for the Yanks, as they divided the Army of Northern Virginia and captured thousands of Lee's troops. The 29th was right in the middle of this fight.

General Corse and seventeen other men from the 29th fell into the hands of those people. Not only General Corse but other high ranking Generals were taken. Richard S. Ewell, Barton, Simms, Kershaw, Curtis Lee, Dubose, and Hunter. Curtis Lee was the elder son of Robert E. Lee. General Lee saw some of this action and exclaimed, "My God has the army dissolved?"

Crockett and his five friends broke free and ran after the main body after emptying their muskets on the mounted devils. They got a little way down the road and jumped into the cover of honey suckle vines.They thought if they could go undetected they would be able to catch up with the main army in a day ot two. There was so much confusion during this action, the Confederates were stunned. Along with Crockett, somehow his friends Burdell Brewster, J. W. Birchem, D.C. Lewis, Ias Colston, and Isaac Puckett were still free from the Yanks. They were really hungry and tired, yet they had an adrenalin fed strength. They huddled together in the thicket listening to the Yanks rounding up the unfortunate men that could not escape. Finally about an hour after darkness fell the five talked out a plan to scramble westward toward Farmville. They reasoned that they would stay close to the edge of the road and hopefully leap to freedom if they heard the Yanks coming. They also had a great hunger because their rations ran out on the 5th of April. They would be on the lookout for something to eat as they traveled toward the main body of the army. Crockett ask God for food and help.

General Pickett along with a remnant of the 29th some how escaped and were with General Lee's Army heading on toward Appomattox, Virginia. Most of the Division and a vast number of the 29th Virginia Infantry were scattered over the byroads of Amella County. They were all hungry, exhausted and left behind by the main Army just like Crockett and his circle of friends. Most of these men would be captured or just plain give up to get something to eat.

The circle of friends traveled along the road on the night of the 6th. They had several false alarms and jumped off the road each time. Just before daylight they spotted a flicker of fire off in the woods. They decided to investigate and sneaked through the woods like a band of Indians.

They were surprised to find a group of run a way slaves cooking a wild hog they had trapped. They told them that they meant them no harm, but desired to eat with them. The blacks were alarmed but agreed to share their food with Crockett and the other five.

It was the best pork they had ever tasted. After the meal the blacks gave each of them a small portion of the cooked hog to take with them. The beaten down Confederates thanked the black people and left them alone.

They moved about a mile west on the road to Farmville and found another thicket to hide in. Having a meal in their belly, they all fell into sleep. This was the morning of April 7th 1865. After hiding out most of the day and traveling the thickets beside the road they were close to Farmville. Crockett thanked God for his loving kindness and the meal of pork they had received.

They traveled the night of of the 7th and had to jump and hide again. This time a band of lost Confederates were captured less than one hundred yards from Crockett and the five. Yankee Cavalry swooped out of nowhere on the unsuspecting gray backs, and marched them toward Farmville.

Crockett and the five talked about their situation and wondered about the wisdom of heading to Farmville. The reasoned that they should skirt around the town and try to catch up with the main body at a later date. They were close enough to Farmville to hear many Yankee's talking, and realized they should avoid the town.

The morning of April 8th was coming with the rising sun. and it was time to find a suitable hiding place. They were fortunate to find another thicket large enough to hide all of them. Crockett and his circle of friends quietly eat their last morsel of pig bacon and laid down to sleep. They did not sleep too much this day as the Yanks kept the road hot, they were rounding up more poor Rebels. Also more and more army was on the chase to catch up with General Lee.

Crockett and the circle of friends reasoned together as to what course of action they should take. Some wanted to follow the main body of Lee's Army, while others thought they should just strike out to the south and get away from this place.

"If we stay around here we will just be captured and taken to one of those awful prisons," said one of the six.

Crockett was one of the first to say out loud what they all were thinking.

"I am true to our country, but I am afraid we have a lost cause and must get away from the Yanks before we are carried off," Crockett said.

"I agree with Crockett, we should strike out for home, if we run into our army we can join back up," said Isaac Puckett.

They all agreed and tried to get some rest before the night came again. Just in the twilight, on the evening of April the 8th 1865 the six Confederates eased out on the road and crossed over to the other side. They had gone less than a mile when two groups of mounted men merged on them from both the east and the west. It was too late to run. The Yankee's captured Crockett and the other five. They were held with shotguns, and .44 caliber revolvers.

A mouthy Yankee Sergeant did the talking.

"Well hello Johnny Reb, just where are you off to?" he asked.

Isaac spoke up and said, "We are heading home Sergeant, we have had enough of this war," trying to convince the Captors to let them go.

"Well not today, you ain't going nowhere," answered the sergeant.

They were marched about a mile into Farmville and each were questioned for about an hour each. Finally an Officer told them to lock up the six in a big barn along with some more of the captured Southerners. Water, a piece of pork and bread was brought out and given to each man. Crockett took time to thank God for the food and for sparing the lifes of his friends.

Chapter 35

Out of the Pan, Into the Fire

When Crockett was being questioned, he answered truly and frankly. The young Union Officer was not the overbearing man Crockett expected. He made Crockett feel at ease as he questioned him. Crockett sat and the young man paced.

"Private what is your name?" he asked.

"David Crockett Whitt, sir," Crockett answered.

"Well private, how did you get a name like that?" he asked.

"Well sir, I was born in 1836 the year of the Alamo, David Crockett was famous, so my Maw named me after him," Crockett answered.

"Well David how many Darkies do you have on your place?" he continued.

"None sir, I don't own no slaves," Crockett answered.

"None, well how come you are fighting against the United States?" asked the young officer.

"Cause you all are down here attacking our country," Crockett answered.

"Well, David what makes you think you can secede from the union?" he asked.

"Well not to be testy sir, if you would go back in history to March 4th 1789 the Union was formed. Each State had to decide if they wanted to join or not. There was nothing written down about not letting a state out, and that was on purpose you see," said Crockett.

"When New York, Rhode Island, and Virginia ratified the Constitution, they specifically stated that they have the right to go back and govern themselves. The right of secession was understood and agreed to, even George Washington who presided over the Constitutional Convention was a delegate from Virginia. You see Sir, the Constitution was an experiment, and the folks here in Virginia wanted their Independence." continued Crockett.

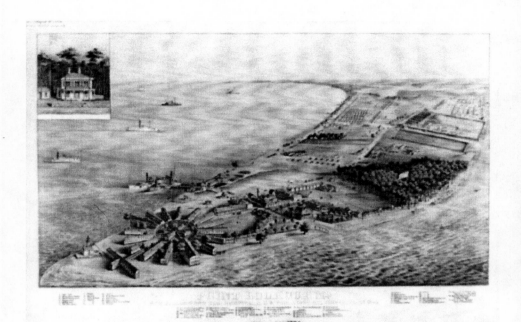

Point Lookout, 1904. Almost 40 years after the war.

"Are you saying that if we had not crossed over into Virginia there would be no war?" asked the officer.

"That is purty much right, I reckon," replied Crockett.

"Well how come you fellers invaded Gettysburg?" the officer asked.

"Well I reckon after almost three years of fighting here, General Lee decided to give the North some of the same," Crockett answered.

"David, do you know where Bob Lee is heading for?" asked the officer.

"West I reckon, that is about all I know not to be smart, we privates are not privy to all the information," Crockett answered.

"Did you know that General Lee and General Grant are talking surrender terms?" he asked.

"No sir, all I know is that you alls cavalry cut us all apart back at Sayler's Creek and we have been trying to get out of this place," Crockett answered.

"Me and my friends had decided to strike out for home when you fellers caught us," continued Crockett.

"You mean desert, David?" the officer asked.

"Well in a way that would be right, but the way we looked at it is the army deserted us, and we just wanted to get away from you fellers," Crockett answered.

"You boys sure look poor and ragged, are you ready to get something to eat Private?" the young officer asked.

"I reckon I could eat something Sir'" Crockett replied.

"Well you go with the private and he will see you fellers get some food," ordered the officer.

"Thanks sir, could you tell me Sir, what are you going to do with me and my five friends?" Crockett asked.

"You will be transported tomorrow to Point Lookout Prison, then I reckon after the war you can go back home, thank you David, for talking with me, and I hope we will all be countrymen sometime down the road," the young officer said.

Crockett was not pleased to hear Point Lookout, all he ever heard of that place was bad. Folks called the unlucky people that ended up there, "Lee's Miserables,"

Well I guess I better try to explain one thing at this time. All of my research stated that David Crockett Whitt was captured on April 6th 1865 near Farmville Virginia. I went with April the 8th 1865, because Crockett personally stated on his war disability application to Virginia on May 15th 1906, that he was captured near Farmville, Virginia the evening before Lee surrendered. He plainly wrote April 8th 1865. Well I guess some folks may disagree with me, but if he was at Cold Harbor, Drewry's Bluff, and many other encounters, including shivering in the trenches of Bermuda Hundred line, and about three months in the hell of Point Lookout, an old man should know when he was captured. Crockett was sixty nine when he applied for disability from Virginia. By the way the Northern Troops got their Veteran Benefits shortly after the war from the United States. I guess it mattered which side you were on.

Next day General Lee and General Grant would meet at the McLean's House in Appomattox, Virginia. This place was picked because it lay between the two Generals. The Northern Army had surrounded the Confederates on three sides, and left Lee with little choice. The Confederates lost time at Sayler's Creek and more time when Lee sent out men to forage for food around the country side.

General Lee sent out flags of truce and ask Grant to meet with him and talk on the matter of conditions he previously offered. Grant was traveling from Farmville toward Appomattox Court House to set up a new headquarters. Grant looked improperly dressed for such an occasion, but the traveling on muddy roads and fording the Appomattox river left him mud spattered and in an unmilitary look. He was most anxious to meet with General Lee, and maybe end this awful war.

General Robert E. Lee donned his new gray uniform on the evening of April 8th. I don't know why he dug it out and put it on that evening unless he was pretty sure of meeting Grant. The next day he rode about two miles to meet at the McLean House. After negotiating the conditions of surrender, Lee surrendered the Army of Northern Virginia, not the whole Army. Lee surrendered 28,231 men.

After the fighting at Sayler's Creek, General William Nelson Pendleton was nominated by other high ranking officers to speak to General Lee about a surrender. Pendleton and Lee sat under a pine tree and talked about the subject on the morning of April 7th 1865.

When the talk was over Lee thanked him for his and the other officers input. General Lee said, "I trust it has not come to that. We certainly have too many brave men to think of laying down our arms, Indeed, we must all determine to die at our post."

On the evening of April 7th, General lee received a dispatch from General Grant.

General R. E. Lee.
Commanding C. S. Army:

General: The result of the last week must convince you of the hopelessness of further resistance on the part of the Army of Northern Virginia in this struggle. I feel that it is so, and regard it as my duty to shift from myself the responsibility of any further effusion of blood, by asking of you to surrender of that portion of the C. S. Army known as the Army of Northern Virginia.

Very respectfully, your obedient servant,
U. S. Grant
Lieutenant-General
Commanding Armies of the United States

General Lee read the dispatch carefully and turned to General Longstreet his trusted subordinate, and let him read the dispatch.

"Not yet," answered General Longstreet.

With the meeting this morning with General Pendleton, now the dispatch from Grant, it was weighting heavily on General Lee's mind. Lee chewed on it for two more days, before coming to a decision.

After the surrender General Lee issued General Order, No. 9. April 10, 1865.

General Lee told his Adjutant-General Lieutenant Colonel Charles Marshall to compose a document. He expressed to Marshall his feelings toward the men of the Army of Northern Virginia.

After Marshall finished the rough draft he gave it to General Lee to read. Lee made minor changes and completely omitted one paragraph that Lee thought would insight bitterness between the Union and the defeated Confederates. Copies were made in ink and given to the Corps Commanders to read to their men.:

> *After four years of arduous service, marked by unsurpassed courage and fortitude, the Army of Northern Virginia has been compelled to yield to overwhelmingnumbers and resources.*
>
> *I need not tell the brave survivors of so many hard fought battles, who have remained steadfast to the last, that I have consented to this result from no distrustof them. But feeling that valor and devotion could accomplish nothing that would compensate for the loss that must have attended the continuance of the contest, I determined to avoid the useless sacrifice of those past services have endeared them to their countrymen.*
>
> *By the terms of the agreement officers and men can return to their homes and remain until exchanged. You will take with you the satisfaction that proceeds from the consciousness of duty faithfully performed, and I earnestly pray that a Merciful God will extend to you His blessing and protection.*
>
> *With an increasing admiration of your constancy and devotion to your country, and a grateful remembrance of your kind and generous consideration for myself, I bid you all an affectionate farewell.*
>
> *R. E. Lee*
> *General*

Crockett along with his five friends and many more captured men began to trudge toward Point Lookout on the morning of April 9th 1865. They were a poor defeated lot. As they marched along in the early afternoon the Union guards and officers began to celebrate and cheer. Before any of the prisoners could even ask, the Yankee's started shouting, "Lee has surrendered."

Crockett's heart leaped, could this be true and does this mean they will let us go home? It wasn't long before he got the answer, as the overbearing guards goaded them on. One of the prisoners ask why they couldn't turn them loose, and a guard went over and slapped him on top of the head with rein of his horse.

"You Damn Rebels have killed my friends and even my brother, now by God you are going to pay," said the belligerent Yankee.

"Besides that, you stupid Reb's would go and join up with Johnston and we would have to fight you again," continued the guard.

An officer rode up and pulled the guard to the side and spoke to him in a low tone.

Crockett heard the guard say, "yes I understand , Sir."

Crockett figured that the men had orders not to physically abuse them unless provoked. Crockett hoped that the officers would stay close.

Some of the guards kept saying over and over, "Lee has surrendered, and we have a grand General, Grant is the best in the land."

The defeated Rebels held their tongues, as they marched along. They all felt like they would be turned loose before long since General Lee surrendered. Crockett and his five friends stuck together like glue and all were thankful to be alive. Crockett thanked God for his protection and prayed for freedom to go home to his little family.

The prisoners heard that all the Confederate Soldiers that were at Appomattox were given food and some were able to take a mule or horse and head for home. Why are we still marching on to Point Lookout? It became evident that the solders had a vendetta against the captured Southerner's. Crockett would just have to bide his time and stay out of trouble with these angry Yanks. Crockett was now one of, "Lee's Miserables," since he was on his way to Point Lookout Prison Pen.

I had mentioned earlier that the 29th Infantry was the largest in Corse's Brigade. On April 9th 1865, Lee surrendered only 30 men of the 29th. The rest were either killed, captured, hospitalized, or wandering the countryside. The ranking officer of the now small 29th Infantry was First Lieutenant John Alexander Coulson of Company C, and this made him the commanding officer, at the time of surrender.

Crockett arrived across the bay from Point Lookout at City Point on April 13th 1865 along with hundreds of Confederate Prisoners of war. Steamers were waiting to transport the defeated southern men. The march from Farmville had not been too hard, and all the men had received crackers and meat. The Yankee soldiers were not friendly to the troop of gray clad men of the Army of Northern Virginia.

Most every Yankee harbored resentment for what they called the Rebels. Any chance they had they abused the poor undernourished, and worn "Sons of the South."

Crockett and his friends said little as they journeyed overland, but stayed close to each other. Now they saw the steamers waiting to take them across the Potomac River, the upper part of the bay to Point Lookout.

The six friends from southwest Virginia stuck together like glue as the Yankee's crowded the southerners on the steamers. They put so many men on each boat, it was standing room only. The Captain complained to the Federal officer that the boat was at risk of going down in the bigger than usual waves caused by the Spring winds.

"Hell, that wouldn't be no loss, cept for the boat and one fussy captain," said the officer.

"That ain't one bit funny," replied the captain.

"Go on and take this worthless load cross the bay, and get back we got to get it done," continued the officer.

The boat captain shook his head from side to side as he hollered, "cast off."

Crockett and his friends were on the front of the boat. They looked in the direction the boat was traveling and saw the hazy form of land and some buildings. They all talked quietly together about their fate and the need to stay together. A guard saw them talking and hollered at them.

"Hey you stupid Rebels, close them traps," said the young guard with both hands on his musket.

Crockett and Isaac Puckett both nodded their heads at the guard and quit talking.

As the boat pulled into the dock at Point Lookout, they were greeted by two lines of insolent Negro Yankee guards.

"Yaw com on in, welcome to Point Lookout," said one of the black soldiers.

"The worm has turned, now your asses belong to us," another one hollered.

"How you boys like being the slaves?" another one asked.

A white Union Major, the Provost Marshall, A.G. Brady rode up on his horse, and the Negro guards became quiet. He addressed the boat load of ragged Confederate's.

"I am Major Brady, the Provost Marshall here at this institution. I am the law here, you will obey every order you receive or die. Try to escape and you will die. Behave and someday you will go home. Welcome to the Federal camp, Point Lookout," said Major Brady as he wheeled his steed around and rode off.

The following statement was given by Charles T. Loehr, October 11, 1890. He was one of the captured Confederates housed in Point Lookout, captured during the battle of Five Forks, Virginia.

"He wrote in his little New Testament on June 3rd 1865, ("If it were not for Hope, how could we live in a place like this? Point Lookout, June 3rd, 1865.")

"In turning back to those dark days of our country's history, I do so simply to present these facts and incidents in which I was a participant. I want to show how the Confederate soldier suffered even after General Lee had bid his farewell to his army at Appomattox. The "surrender at Appomattox," so often quoted by our Southern orators to denote "the soldier who has done his duty," is but partly true.

General Lee surrendered about 26,000 men, of whom only 7,892 were armed. A greater part of them were men that were on detail duty, or held some position which kept them safely in the rear. It is a fact that few, very few, indeed, of Ewell's and Pickett's men escaped from those that stood in battle line doing their duty on the evening of April 6, 1865.

At the bloody ridge of Sailor's Creek: the men left there as a forlorn hope of fighting, with few exceptions, were captured or killed; and I assert without fear of contradiction that there were more fighting men at the close of the war in Point Lookout Prison alone, not to mention Fort Delaware, Hart's Island, Johnson's Island, Newport's News, and other questionable places of amusement, than there were in Lee's whole army at the surrender, I make the remarks necessary in justice to the Confederate soldiers who suffered and starved in the fearful prison-pens of the North, but did not "Surrender at Appomattox."

At City Point several transport steamers were lying, and we were ordered on board of them, each boat being packed with human freight to it's full capacity.

Some of the boats landed their unwilling passengers at Newport's News, while most of them, and the one I was on, reached Point Lookout on the morning of the 5th. (Crockett arrived on the 14th.) Landing at the wharf, we were formed in open line for inspection; that is, we had to empty our pockets and lay our baggage on the ground before us, while the Federal sergeants amused themselves by kicking overcoats, blankets, oilcloths, canteens and everything that had a U.S. on it, into the bay. This left us in a sad condition, for there was little in our possession that had not been the property of the United States, at one time or another, and became ours by the many victories and captures we had helped to gain.

After putting us in light marching order, we were marched into the prison-pen, or "bull-pen," as it was called. The prison consisted of a space of about twenty acres, surrounded by a high board fence, on the outside of which was the top, a platform for the guard to walk upon. The guards consisted of Negroes of the worst sort. Inside the grounds, about fifteen feet of the fence, was a ditch called the "dead line." The sentry fired upon anyone who crossed it.

The camp was laid in regular rows of small tents, each double row being a division, of which there were ten. These were again sub-divided into ten companies of about two hundred men each. Through these streets or rows there ran small ditches; but the land being very shallow, the drainage was very imperfect. Point Lookout being a tongue of land where the Potomac and Chesapeake Bay, barely five feet at it's highest point; and herein was the worst feature of the prison. There was no good drinking water to be had; the water was impregnated with copperas, and tasted quiet brackish. To this source was a great deal of the fearful mortality that occurred there traceable.

When we came there the prison was already full, and the small tents were totally insufficient to accommodate us. Many were without shelter of any kind, and exposed to the bad weather which prevailed for the greater part of our stay. We had but few blankets, and most had to lie on the bare ground; so when it rained our situation became truly deplorable. Our rations were just such as kept us perpetually on the point of starvation, causing a painful feeling of hunger to us helpless-starved prisoners. Four small crackers, or a small loaf of bread per day, and a cup full of dish-water, called pea-soup, horrible to taste, and a small piece of rancid salt meat, was our daily fare. So hungry were the men that they would eat almost anything they could pick up outside from the sewers; potato peelings, cabbage stalks, or most any refuse that hardly the cattle would eat, was greedily devoured. The scurvy, brought on by this wretched diet, was prevalent in its most awful form.

It was not unusual to hear it stated that sixty or sixty-five deaths had occurred in a single day; and it was said that eight thousand six hundred dead Confederates were buried near the prison pen. (14,000 were accounted for by letters, and other sources)

It is wonderful how much a human being can stand. I myself (Charles T. Loehr), who was never sick during the whole war, was taken down with erysipelas. It was a bad case, so said the Federal surgeon said who examined me. "Entirely too late to do anything for him; neck and face swollen black and green." Those who did the packing up, that is placing the dead bodies in rough boxes, seeing me, one of them said, "there goes a fellow we will have to box up tomorrow." I was removed to the hospital pen, and with two of my company Alexander Moss and John Harris, both of whom I saw stretched out in the dead house on the following day. The hospital could only accommodate about twelve hundred sick, and there were no less than six thousand sick and dying men within the main building and tents surrounding it. Being assigned to a tent there was room for about sixteen, but which had no less than forty in it, I was placed on the damp ground, only one thin blanket being given me. The two nights I spent there were simply horrible. The praying, crying and the fearful struggles of the dying during the dark night, lit up by a single small lantern, was awful. The first night about five or six died, and the next morning found me lying next to two dead comrades. The second night was a repetition of the first; and that day, though just in the same condition, I asked the Federal surgeon to return to camp, which was granted, thinking I might just as well die there as anywhere else. But I got better, how I cannot explain; perhaps it was my determination not to die there in spite of them, that kept me alive.

Great as the sufferings of the men were from want of sufficient food and medicines, they were much increased from want of clothing.

Some were nearly naked, only one ragged shirt to wear, and this covered with vermin. On an occasion of Major A. J. Brady's (Provost Marshall) visit to the camp, which happened on an unusually bright day, the men were seated in the ditch in front of their tents, busy hunting for the tormentors, having their only garment off, using it for the field to hunt in. (Lice and Insects were the prey), Brady smilingly remarked to some who through modesty attempted to hide, "Don't stop, I like to see you busy."

Talking of Major Brady, no one can say that he was not always polite, and he appeared to be friendly towards the prisoners, (other accounts paint a different picture of him) yet it is said that he made more than $1,000,000. outside his pay, from his position. Having charge of all the sutler establishments, and all the money, boxes, letters and presents passing through or in his hands, his position must have made him a rich man.

Next our guards. As already stated, they were Negroes who took particular delight in showing their former masters that "The bottom of rail was the top." On one occasion one of the North Carolina men, who have a habit, which is shared by our Virginia Country cousins, in whittling every wooden object they come across, was enjoying this sport on the prison gate, when one of the colored soldiers shot him down, nearly blowing his head off. This created some little excitement, but what the result was I never learned. During the day we had access to the sink built on piles in the bay, but at night the gates were closed, and boxes were placed in the lower part of the camp, to which the men were allowed to go at all hours of the night. There were hundreds of sick in camp, cases of violent diarrhea, reducing the men to skeletons.

As these men were compelled to frequent these boxes, the Negroes would often compel them at the point of the bayonet to march around in double quick time, to carry them on their backs, to kneel and pray for Abe Lincoln, and forced them to submit to a variety of their brutal jokes, some of which decency would not permit me to mention.

The white sergeants in charge were hardly of a better class than their colored brother. They belonged to that class of mean cowards who dare not face the foe on the battle field, whose bravery consisted in insulting and maltreating a defenseless prisoner. Often I have seen them kick a poor, sick, broken-down prisoner, because he was physically unable to take his place in line at roll-call as quickly as the sergeant demanded. Prisoners were sometimes punished by them too horribly to relate. Men were tied, hand and feet, and had to stand on a barrel for hours; others were bound and dipped head foremost in a urine barrel-all this for some trifling offence, such as getting water from a prohibited well, stealing perhaps something eatable, or some other small affair.

But most things, whether good or bad, will come to an end. More than two months had passed since Lee's surrender. The Confederacy was no more, and the Federal Government took courage. About the middle of June it commenced to release those that were still living, but, in consequence of the inhuman treatment they had received, too feeble to fight again. Then we were duly sworn not to fight them again, to support the Constitution and amendments. Also registering our good looks, weight, height, &c., and getting our signatures made as free men again."

The above report by Charles T. Loehr, has been proven out by other accounts by prisoners locked away in the damp mire of Point Lookout Prison Pen.

On the 14th of April, 1865 Crockett and his five friends stepped off the boat and fell into lines as directed by Yankee sergeants and the Negro guards. They were instructed to empty their pockets and lay all of their gear on the ground for inspection.

"Johnny Reb, you ain't in the United States Army so anything got U.S. on it take it off and lay it with the rest of the baggage on the ground," yelled the belligerent sergeant.

Most of the Southern soldiers had mostly U.S. things that had been captured in many big battles. Coats, blankets, canteens, and many other items were cast on the ground. The Negro's made a game of kicking the piles of clothing and supplies into the bay. Crockett along with the rest of the captives stood there in disbelief. Most of the men had only ragged paints and shirts, very few blankets made it through this so called inspection. The men were to bear the elements in thin ragged clothes.

Next the men were marched through the gate of Point Lookout Pen where Crockett saw thousands of countrymen wasting away in this small plot of about twenty acres. There were row after row of small weathered tents. Crockett had heard stories of this place, but nothing compared to the reality he saw.

Crockett and his five friends were marched to a place in the pen and halted. One of the sergeants yelled out, "You six are now in Company D, 7th Division, Point Lookout Prisoner of War Camp, remember it."

The six said nothing, but stood there at attention.

"Can't you Johnny's speak, say yes Sir," when you hear an order.

"Yes Sir," replied all the men in this line.

"This here tent is yours, least when it gets vacated," grunted the sergeant.

"Dismissed," yelled the sergeant.

Crockett and the others looked in the ragged decaying tent and saw two sickly men laying on the bare ground. Crockett stood up and scanned the surroundings. He saw the wall with the black guards looking menacing at the thousands of Southern men. They were just itching to shoot into the crowds. Crockett also saw the ditch that ran around the pen about fifteen feet from the stockade, this was the "Dead Line." It was explained by the sergeant earlier that any prisoner crossing it would be shot down.

Some of the healthier prisoners came up and introduced themselves to the new arrivals. After talking some and asking questions Crockett decided to sit down and rest as did the other men. Something dreadful happened, their bodies began to burn and sting. Crockett lifted his shirt and found he was covered with body lice.

"My God, I am being eaten alive," said Burdell Brewster one of the circle of friends.

The men that had been there for some time began to laugh!

"Ain't really funny, son," said one of the older prisoners.

"But we got to find something to laugh about in this hell hole," he added.

"What do you do about them?" Crockett asked in a serious tone.

"Don't worry they won't eat you up, jest pick um off," replied the older man.

"Hell I got me a fat one I keep under my arm, he's the biggest bastard in the bunch," replied another man.

"What for?" asked Crockett.

"I can produce him for winning a bet, since nobodies got nothing, I jest yank him out for show," he said as he reached under his left arm pit and brought out a whopper of a louse.

The six new arrivals found one thing to laugh about.

Isaac Puckett spoke up, "Hold on to your faith men, nothing last forever, the war is over, surely the Yanks will let us go home any day."

Crockett looked at him and smiled.

"With what we been through in the past few years, we can survive this," Crockett said.

Back in Tazewell County Arminda has learned that General Lee has surrendered and Crockett should be coming home any day. She cleaned the house, got all the clothes washed, and readied for her beloved husband.

Everyone in Baptist Valley was saddened by the news that General Lee surrendered, but was glad their men would be coming home. A few made their way back home in their ragged clothes. They were for the most part skinny and worn. Crockett and his five friends did not show up!

"My God, where is my husband," declared Arminda.

Rhoda and her family had Arminda and the babies over for supper and held a prayer meeting for Crockett and others that had not made it home. John Bunyon Lowe and Rhoda tried to console Arminda.

"Crockett is not dead, the Yankee's must have him in one of those prisons," said Rhoda.

"The war is bout over, so they will be letting our boys come home," declared John Bunyon Lowe.

Arminda took hope, she did not have a feeling reflecting that Crockett was dead. After talking to the Lord and hearing others lifting up Crockett in prayer, and hearing the families words of encouragement, Arminda felt sure he would return.

After spending a terrible night at Point Lookout, the morning of April 15th 1865 brought reality to David Crockett Whitt. Yes this is real, not a nightmare. A nightmare that is here and now. After going through the morning hours, and learning the ways of the prison, all hell broke loose.

Major Brady (Provost Marshall) come riding his big footed horse up and down the rows or streets of the entire compound. The poor

Confederates scattered to keep from being trampled. Brady was shouting, "Lincoln is dead, you damn Rebs will pay for this."

The Black guards went berserk and many of them fired into the compound. Crockett and his five friends hit the ground getting behind any cover available.

Major Brady had learned this morning, that last night at the Ford Theater in Washington, President Abraham Lincoln had been assassinated by John Wilkes Booth. All of the Union soldiers were saddened, and were wanting revenge. The poor underfed, half-naked Confederate soldiers in the prisons were at their mercy.

Crockett and others discussed this in whispering tones, and decided the only course was to stay out of the Yankee's way and stay humble. Each one also prayed for the loving God of heaven to protect them. One of the men had a little book of the Psalms, he opened it to his favorite, the 91st . He read it aloud to Crockett and the men that were gathered around him.

After the reading Crockett said, "This Psalm is all about God giving protection to those that love Him."

"Amen," said Issac Puckett.

Some how no one was injured by the horse or the shots that were fired into the pen. All day long the Negroes yelled slurs at the prisoners and pronounced vengeance on them. They pointed their muskets and made gestures at the men. The men were quiet and hardly moved all day long. No rations were given to them this day.

CHAPTER 36

TO EVERYTHING THERE IS A SEASON

Crockett borrowed a Bible and was led to the 3rd chapter of Ecclesiastes. He read it over and thought it over. He went to his friends to share the message. Crockett told them he wanted them to hear this word of God that proved, nothing is permanent and that all things are temporary, even this hell hole they now lived in would end.

Crockett turned to the marked page in the little Bible, and read.

Ecclesiastes 3: 1-8
1. To every thing there is a season, and a time to every purpose under the heaven:
2. A time to be born, and a time to die; a time to plant, and a time to pluck up that which is planted:
3. A time to kill, and a time to heal; a time to break down, and a time to build up;
4. A time to weep, and a time to laugh; a time to mourn, and a time to dance;
5. A time to cast away stones, and a time to gather; a time to embrace, and a time to refrain from embracing;
6. A time to get, and a time to lose; a time to keep, and a time to cast away;
7. A time to rend, and a time to sow; a time to keep silence, and a time to speak;
8. A time to love, and a time to hate; a time of war and a time of peace.

After the reading, the men all had comments, reflecting that if they could just stay alive, a new season would come and they all could go home. All of the men listening took hope and thanked Crockett for reading the word to them.

Point Lookout. May 30" 65

Dear Father

You will no doubt be surprised to receive a letter from me from this place. I arrived here 14" april, was captured on the 6", near Farmville Va. — I have signified my willingness to take the oath of allegiance. I wish you to go to work, and try to get me released as soon as possible. I think if you make an effort you will be successful. I belonged to Co "H" 29" Va regt. If you can do nothing, get my brother in law Thompson to do what he can. I have five comrades in here. if you can get them released by vouching for them I would like to have you do so. Their names are Burdell Brewster, J. W. Birchem, D. C. Lewis, Isaac Puckett, & Jas Colston all of my regt. Do what you can for me & write

your aff. son, David C. Whitt
Co "D" 7" Div. Pt Lookout md

Prisoner of war

Letter from Crockett to Jonas Whitt

Taking oath at Point Lookout, Maryland. June 1865. It is thought that the picture is staged, and the men were cleaned up and even had gear in front of them.

ROCKETTS LANDING, RICHMOND, VIRGINIA.—[SKETCHED BY J. R. HAMILTON.]

Rocketts Landing, Richmond, Virginia. Crockett landed here from Point Lookout, Maryland, June 22, 1865.

It was a good thing Spring was here, but on this slab of beach the pen was located on was surrounded by water. April nights and some days were really chilly because of the constant wind, and the men had thin ragged clothes. About one blanket per 16 men was the average. The highest ground of the camp was only about five feet above the water. Little fire wood was available.

Crockett and his five friends had been in the pen for about a week, when one night a strong wind came up. The extra high tide came into the camp, even into the tents, and the men had to get up from their sleep and stand up until the waves subsided. Many of the sick and weak had to be held up as best they could. Many days sixty to sixty five Confederates died, but after this night over 300 died because of exposure.

It took every ounce of hope to survive there with the lack of food, and the lack of the simple necessities of life. The men were so hungry, they would eat most anything. Dead fish washed up and were consumed, or an occasional rat would make the misfortune and wander into the camp. The men found that rat meat was quite good.

In its living conditions and treatment of prisoners, Point Lookout has often been compared to Andersonville, the Confederate prison for Union troops in Georgia. The mortality rate at Point Lookout was greater than that of the Confederate prison at Andersonville. Moreover, the fatalities at Point Lookout were due to unnecessary neglect, while those at Andersonville were due to a real want in the Confederacy as a whole. The United States War Department's official statistics showed that more Southern prisoners died in Northern Camps than did Northern soldiers did in Southern camps. The death rate in Northern camps was 12%, while the rate in Southern camps was about 9%. The people in the South were starving by the end of the war and couldn't feed their own troops, but the North had no such excuse.

It was on purpose, the treatment prisoners received in Northern prisons, to weaken and destroy the enemy of the United States. Both houses of the U.S. Congress passed HR 97 which was designed to slowly eliminate the Southern prisoners. If anything qualifies an outrage, surely this does.

Crockett leaned heavily on the Lord, and his five earthly friends to get by each day. As bad as the war was, this was even worse.

Finally, toward the end of May 1865, some good people brought paper, pens, ink and postage stamps and gave it to the prisoners. Major Brady let the men have them, he figured it would keep them busy and it didn't come out of his funds. He did lay down the law to each prisoner, that nothing could be written derogatory of the Point Lookout Prison. Each letter had to be delivered to the officers unopened. The officers would read through and censor any thing they thought should not be in it. They would destroy the whole letter if they thought it made the North look bad.. Only one page was allowed to be mailed.

Crockett was thrilled to be able to write home. He composed a one page letter to Arminda, telling how he loved her and that he would come home as soon as possible. He also wrote a letter to his father Jonas Whitt in Greenup County, Ky. He asked Jonas to help expedite his release. Many of the prisoners were not well educated and had bad penmanship, so Crockett helped a number of them write a letter home. He remembered how Samuel Truitt made him practice writing each letter over and over in the little school house at Truittville, Kentucky. Crockett felt fortunate and glad to be able to do something for his comrades, his education paid off. Now if these pesky lice would leave him alone, he thought as he scratched at the little tormentors.

Below is a bona-fide letter written by David Crockett Whitt.

Point-Lookout, May 30 '65

Dear Father,

You will no doubt be surprised to receive a letter from me from this place. I arrived here 14" April was captured on the 8" near Farmville, Va. I have signified my willingness to take the oath of allegiance. I wish you to go to work and try to get me released as soon as possible. I think if you make an effort you will be successful. I belonged to Co "H" 29" Va. Regt. If you can do nothing, get my brother in law Thompson (Alfred) to do what he can. I have 5 comrades in here if you can get them released by vouching for them, I would like to have it done so. Their names are Burdell Brester, J. W. Birchem, D. C.

Lewis, Isaac Puckett, and Ias Colston all of my regt. Do what ever you can for me I write.

Your Aff. Son David C. Whitt
Prisoner of war; Co" D, 7" Div. Point Lookout Maryland

The letter was of excellent penmanship and well written all on one small sheet of paper. Here it was the 30th of May and the Yankee's were still holding them. Lee had surrendered way back on the 9th of April 1865 and they were still living a hell on earth at Point Lookout.

It is likely that Jonas Whitt never saw this letter as he passed away on July 2nd 1865. I don't know if Jonas had time or if Alfred Thompson took steps to have Crockett released.

Finally in June 1865 the United States started releasing the Confederate Prisoners of war. In the month of April 1865 12,110 men joined the ranks of POW's in Point Lookout. On hand at Point Lookout, on May 31st 1865 were 18,365 men. Released in June were 18,536. Some of the men were released and died, not being able to leave the God forsaken place.

Crockett survived the rancid food, the ill-treatment, the exposure to weather, and all the evil Negro guards could deal out. He was finally selected for parole, and released on June 22nd 1865.

The selected prisoners having lived through the season of hate now were coming into the season of "Going home." Things good or bad all come to a conclusion in time. The Confederacy was no more, and the Federal Government took courage. It started to release those that were still living, but, in consequence of the inhuman treatment they had received, were too feeble to fight again. Then they were duly sworn not to fight them again, to support the Constitution and amendments. Charles T. Loehr said, " registering our good looks, weight, height, and getting our signatures made us free men again. Crockett was listed as fair complexion, brown hair, eyes were gray, height 5 feet 11 ½ inches tall. No weight was listed.

A new season has come to Point Lookout, and Crockett is glad! The Federal Government is finally letting the Confederate prisoners out, and just in time, another month or so and many more would die. Crockett with the last name of Whitt, beginning with "W" was let out later than his five friends. His friend Isaac Puckett headed to Russell on the 16th of June. Crockett felt lost without his close friends, but all the men were friends because they were all in the same situation.

Finally a Yankee sergeant came and got Crockett on the 21st of June and took him to another holding pen for paroled prisoners. By now the prison looked bare, yet it still housed hundreds. In the new pen they were properly whitewashed to kill the lice. This was an enclosed space adjoining the hospital on the east, where in nothing but sand and some rank weeds could be found. Here the released prisoners were stored until a sufficient number were on hand to make up a boat load.

On the 22nd of June 1865 the paroled men were ushered into a big tent where they stood in front of Major Brady. He had them place hands on Bibles, as many as six to a Bible, and say the oath that they had already signed.

The following oath is what they signed, now they took it together:

I David Crockett Whitt of the County of Tazewell, State of Virginia, do solemnly swear that I will support, protect, and defend the Constitution and Government of the United States against all enemies, whether domestic or foreign; that I will bear true faith, allegiance, and loyalty to the same, any ordinance, resolution, or laws of any State, Convention, or Legislature, to the contrary notwithstanding; and further, that I will faithfully perform all the duties which may be required of me by the laws of the United States; and I take this oath freely and voluntarily, without any mental reservation or evasion whatever.

Signed: David Crockett Whitt Subscribed and sworn to before me, this 22nd day of June, 1865.

He (Major Brady) spoke a few words of thanks for their becoming United States Citizens again. Crockett and the men were jubilant, knowing that they were really going home. The sad thing was that some of the men were so sick and weak that they may not make it home. The night of the 21st one of the men died. The more healthy veterans helped the weaker men, and some would be helped all the way home by personal friends. After spending a day there without rations, there were enough men to make the trip on the 22nd of June, 1865.

Crockett and the others in the holding pen were ordered out, finally they would embark on the journey home as free men. They were loaded on one of those secondhand New York ferry boats. The men still had not been fed, but what was new about this place.

After arriving in Richmond, (Rocketts Landing) the men were met by some more Union soldiers. Here they were asked their destination and given a train passage from Richmond to the nearest train station to their home.

They complained that they had not been fed in two days, so the sergeant said he would see that they got a meal. They brought out crackers, a small portion of salt pork, and water. The men eat it savagely, and were glad to get it. Crockett took time to thank God for the food and for his new found freedom. He also asked God to go with each man, and get them home safely.

Crockett was given a passage voucher from Richmond to Petersburg on the train, where he would board the Virginia and Tennessee railroad train to Abington, Virginia. He was tired and worn, but he remembered all the fighting as he went up the James River to Richmond. He saw the fort and the Bermuda line, he also remembered the times of going through Richmond to hold back the Northern Armies.

Could a picture have been taken of the men who arrived in Richmond from prison pens during those days, it would not be believed that the men who walked from the boat at Rocketts Landing (Part of Richmond) in June, 1865, were the proud soldier boys that left here in April, 1861. Silent, friendless, and sorrowful each one went his own way. No welcome, no cheer awaited their return to the city and to their homes. Oh how few could boast of having homes! Nothing but ruins everywhere; but the man who was a good soldier generally proved himself to be a good citizen.

Crockett traveled with a few men he new by face only, he had seen some of them in the prison, but with thousands of faces, they all seemed the same. Crockett got to Petersburg as quick as the train could take him. He remembered the old railroad from the many trips he made on troop trains back and forth during the war. The track was back in place this time and he did not have to do any walking to Petersburg.

Arriving in Petersburg he went to the ticket window to check departure on the Virginia & Tennessee line. He would have a lay over until the next morning, and he also found out that the track was still out in spots from Wytheville to Abington from the last raid by the Yankees.

Crockett decided to get out and see if he could find something to eat. He came to a church and saw a line of men waiting for something. He reasoned it must be food they were giving out.

"Hello", he said to the last fellow in the line.

"Hello to you, hope the beans hold out," he said.

"Beans, what a great sound," Crockett said.

"You must be one of the men just let out of prison," the man said.

"Yes sir, and I am so hungry," Crockett said.

Crockett received a big bowl of soup and a piece corn bread. He bowed his head and thanked God for the food, and for his freedom. He also asked the Lord to take him home safely.

The soup was mostly water but it did have some chewy meat in it. Crockett didn't mind one bit to take the extra time to chew this tasty meat. There was real beans as well. Crockett's body was in dire need of good nourishment, because the diet, or lack there of, in Point Lookout lacked the vitamins and minerals he needed. Crockett had lost a lot of weight from a mostly lean body to start with. He was always tall and slim, but very strong.

Some of the men at the church told Crockett about a barn he could sleep in for the night. They said the owner did not mind, and actually provided some blankets and fresh straw. During this time there were many homeless folks and transients including many freed Negro's. The owner had been a soldier in the lost cause of the Confederacy and wanted to help the needy. Crockett followed the men to the barn, and slept there that night. He slept lightly and made sure he was up in time to get to the train station. He went by the church that he had eaten at the night before. Some ladies were out there handing out some fresh baked biscuits. Crockett took one and told the lady thanks, and "God bless you."

Crockett hurried along to the station eating his biscuit and thanking God for providing for him. When he got to the station the train was sitting there making the familiar noise of hissing and blowing, as the live steam prepared to expel energy. The engine and even the cars had a look of dilapidation and even forlorn. There were no bright Confederate National flags flying on the engine as Crockett reminisced.

Crockett hurried to the conductor and presented his travel voucher.

"Go ahead and get on board soldier, today you ride to freedom not to war," the old conductor said.

"But you are only riding to Wytheville, the road is still out towards Abington," he continued.

"Yes sir, the ticket master told me about it yesterday, reckon I will get to walk some," Crockett replied.

"Reckon you have done some of that, ain't you soldier?" asked the conductor.

"Yes sir, I figure I marched a few miles, but not lately, been in the Point for about three months," Crockett committed.

"Well soldier, you are lucky, I hear that not many of you fellers get out of there alive," replied the conductor.

"I owe it to the Lord, he is so good," replied Crockett.

"Alright soldier, go find you a seat, I got to check tickets," said the busy conductor.

Crockett took a seat and before long the engine came to life and the old train lunged forward with a jerk. The train moved toward the west picking up speed, but not too fast. The railroad was in dire need of maintenance, as it had been used heavily during the war years with little repair.

Crockett sat back and watched the countryside go by. There were no large herds of cattle or other farm animals to see. It seemed that every house along the railroad had been burned. One good thing that Crockett saw was that people were out doing farm chores. Also he noticed some new buildings were going up, but mostly little modest cabins, not the big Antebellum Mansions that once flourished in the Southland.

Before long Crockett drifted off to sleep, as the rickety rattling train moved along. He fell into a dream of dread. He thought he was back on a battle line and thousands were dieing in front of him and also on each side. He could see the most dreadful sights of war. He was scared beyond measure as he saw the long lines of blue clad faceless men coming at him. He was loading and firing like clockwork, but they just kept coming. He looked around for his friends, but could not find any of them. Crockett woke up with a scream as the conductor shook him gently.

"You are alright son, You just had a bad dream," said the conductor.

"Thank you," Crockett said as he looked about, and wiped great drops of sweat draining down his forehead.

Crockett sat up straight and focused on reality, knowing that he was alive and well. He would have many dreams and dreadful thoughts the rest of his life, but time would start to erase some of them.He should get to Wytheville some time in the evening and spend the night there before starting his walking journey towards Tazewell County.

"My goodness, I will be back with Arminda and the babies in a few more days," Crockett said to himself.

Back in Baptist Valley, more soldiers were arriving from Northern Prisons, and Arminda watched each day for her beloved Crockett. Rhoda helped her keep her faith, he will be coming any day now, she would say.

Arriving in Wytheville, Virginia late in the day on the 23rd of June 1865, Crockett was amazed at the condition of the town. He saw the results of the last Union influx. Buildings were burned and crops had been burned. There were little sign of livestock. Some reconstruction had began but it was progressing slowly.

Wytheville had been a prime target because of it's location on the New River and it's being at a crossroads. It was close to lead mines, pig iron foundries and also close to the salt works in Saltville. There had been battles in Saltville, Marion, and Wytheville, and the last ones had been defeats for the South. Earlier in the war the area was able to turn back the Union invaders.

Crockett got some much needed rest on the train and had some food here and there. He needed a real meal and hoped some how he would get one here, but the pickings were scarce. Crockett talked to a few towns folks and found he could stay in the hay loft at the livery stable. All so he was directed to the parsonage where he might get a meal.

The people were not being stingy, they just didn't have much to give. Most of them would have been glad to help a man that had defended them and served a time in the prison pen at Point Lookout, if they could. Food and shelter were in a real shortage in the summer of 1865. There would be some food in the fall after the harvest was reaped.

Crockett was in luck, the minister and his wife got paid mostly in food and produce, and he had on hand a big chicken, sweet potatoes, and some early June apples. Crockett was invited to have supper with the Parsonage family. The wife had baked the big chicken, sweet potatoes, and prepared lettuce and onions with hot grease poured on them. Crockett had the best meal this evening that he had had in at least two years.

The minister and his wife enjoyed Crockett so much, even though he ate most of their food. After a good long heart felt prayer of thanks, and good eating, Crockett and the couple had a good conservation.

They talked of the good times before the war, and of their hopes to come. The minister pointed out that things don't look good now, but the killing and destruction is over. Now the people in the south have to stay strong and rebuild their lives and homes.

They talked about Crockett's little family and even Crockett's horse, "Billy." Crockett told them how smart and loyal Billy was, and he added, "I wish he was here right now, I wouldn't have to walk home!"

"I sure hope he is alright and has not been carried off," Crockett continued.

The minister and his wife talked as positive as possible to reinforce Crockett.

The evening was passing fast and Crockett was getting sleepy with the full stomach, and time of contentment. The minister had a prayer with Crockett before he left to go and sleep in the hay loft. The minister told Crockett to come by in the morning before he headed out on the trail. He said he would.

Crockett did not have hunger pangs, but he did have a slight belly ache from eating a full meal, his stomach was shrunk due to the lack of eating the last six months. His last three months and more while serving in the army Crockett was not fed too well, and then the time in the prison pen he was on a starvation diet. His skin tone was gray and pale, but a few good meals with good vitamins, would restore his rosy face.

Crockett retired into the new straw and warmed by the blanket, he slept like a baby. He could not remember having any dreams, but he still felt sluggish and slow to awaken. He did have an urge to get to the outhouse, this was a good sign that things were beginning to work right, once again.

Crockett returned the blanket to the man that ran the livery stable and thanked him whole-heartedly. Then he went over to the parsonage as requested. The minister's wife had fixed him a bag with apples, a couple of sweet potatoes, biscuits, and a little dried beef. Also she gave him an old worn blanket to knock off the chill when he slept on the trail. Crockett was overjoyed at the gifts he knew came from God through these kind servants. The minister prayed for Crockett and all the soldiers trying to get home, and thanked God for the opportunity to help folks.

Crockett bid them fair well, and headed out on the road toward Rocky Gap. As he went up the road he couldn't help but think back to the stories he was told about the trip the family made from Montgomery County to Tazewell County way back in 1837. He remembered the story of three outlaws that were sent away by Jonas and the family with the old muskets. He had heard the story so many times it seemed like he remembered the actual account.

Heck, I was just a little baby in Maw's arms when we crossed through the gap, I bet things sure looked different way back then, Crockett thought. Crockett thought what a relief, not thinking of all the depressing things I have been in for so long.

Crockett walked along looking at the beautiful mountains and nature around him. As he looked way up the little road he saw a man and a horse. The man was off his horse, and bent down on the ground doing something. What's this all about, wondered Crockett? There seemed to be nothing to fear so Crockett continued up the road. By the time Crockett came close, the man was standing and waved his hand. Crockett waved back.

Crockett moved into speaking distance, and the man dressed mostly in black said, "Hello there and God bless you."

"Hello to you and may God bless you," Crockett replied.

"I am Robert Sheffey, but you can call me Brother Sheffey," the man said.

"I am David Crockett Whitt, you can call me Crockett," Crockett answered.

Sheffey stuck out his hand and greeted Crockett. Crockett took his hand and gave him a good firm shake. Brother Sheffey told Crockett that he was a traveling preacher heading out on his circuit for the summer. Crockett told Brother Sheffey that he was on his way home from the Pen at Point Lookout.

"Bless your heart Crockett, I have heard of that terrible place, I am so glad you survived it," said Brother Sheffey.

"Me too, a lot of good men died there, I owe my well being all to my Lord," Said Crockett.

"I am so glad to know that you are a praying man," Replied Brother Sheffey.

"Can I ask what you were doing there on the ground, just before I got here?" asked Crockett.

"Oh! I was riding along on Gideon and noticed this bug laying on it's back and couldn't get up, so I got down and turned the little creature over," explained Brother Sheffey.

"You got off your horse to turn over a bug?" Crockett asked in amazement.

"Why sure, when I see any of God's creation in trouble I try to help," answered Brother Sheffey.

"Well Crockett, tell me where you are heading and about your family," said Brother Sheffey.

"I'm bound for Baptist Valley over in Tazewell County where my wife Arminda and two little sons are waiting for me. John Floyd and Jonas Lee are my babies names," Crockett answered.

"It has been nigh on to two years since I been back home, and I am anxious to get there," continued Crockett.

"Well bless your heart, Crockett," Brother Sheffey said.

"How bout you Brother Sheffey, you got a family?" asked Crockett.

"Sure do, I just left them two days ago, my wife Eliza just delivered me a new baby boy, Edward Fleming Sheffey," answered Sheffey.

"I got the fields planted and her Maw and Paw are watching over them and I am off on the Lords work till harvest time," continued Sheffey.

"Heck, Brother Sheffey, how on earth do you just ride out and leave your little family?" Crockett asked before he thought.

"Well it ain't easy, but the good Lord has called me and I am on a mission to help the poor defeated people. Some are defeated by the devil and the rest are defeated by the North," replied Sheffey.

"My dear wife Eliza just said the other day, "what kind of world was our baby born into, we are a defeated people in a torn land!"

"I told her little Edward Fleming would live in a world with hardships, it is always that way. Maybe some good will come of the defeat our Lord has allowed us to suffer," said Sheffey.

"I can't believe God has not used the folly of men for His grand purpose," continued Sheffey.

"Thank you Brother Sheffey, I needed to hear that," Crockett said.

"Well Crockett we better get moving or you ain't never gonna get home, we can talk as we travel, if you don't mind me traveling with you," Sheffey said while turning toward Tazewell County.

"Not one bit, long as you are heading towards Baptist Valley," replied Crockett.

"I am, and if you like good eating, we can stop for supper at brother Alex St.Clair's place. They are expecting me and I plan to have Bible study with them tonight. They will not mind one bit if you come with me," explained Brother Sheffey.

Sheffey led Gideon along as he and Crockett talked. Brother Sheffey stopped abruptly, and turned to Crockett.

"The Lord just reminded me of something, you are tired and weary Crockett, get up here and let Gideon carry you up this mountain, he don't mind one bit," said Brother Sheffey.

"I can't ride your horse while you walk, Brother Sheffey," declared Crockett.

"Sure you can, I ain't tired and I know you could use a ride, now get up there and let Gideon feel good too!" answered Sheffey.

Crockett hesitantly put his foot into the stirrup and pulled himself up on the nice saddle horse. Gideon turned his head way around and gave Crockett a look over. Crockett petted Gideon on his strong neck.

"See I told you Crockett, Gideon is glad to do the Lords work by carrying a worn out feller like you," said Brother Sheffey.

Sheffey headed up the mountain road leading Gideon, and Crockett relaxed into the saddle.

"Now ain't that better Crockett?" asked Sheffey.

"Sure is, but I feel kinda bad riding your horse," replied Crockett.

"Just enjoy the ride and we will be there fore you know it," said Brother Sheffey,

It was after the supper hour when they got to the St. Clair residence, followed by a group of youthful followers to whom he called out a greeting as he they entered their neighborhood. Sheffey embraced them all with a strong arm and a "Bless your little heart," or a handshake and a "It's a Lords blessing to see you again. Crockett was amazed as the children embraced him with such a greeting. He had never seen anything like it.

One of the bigger boys took Gideon and headed to the barn. Free of Gideon, Sheffey wrapped his arms around as many of the children as he could. The joyful entourage brought Brother Alex St. Clair to the front porch.

"Brother Sheffey! Bless the Lord you got back to us safely. Come in, Come in!" exclaimed Alex St.Clair.

"And I see you brought someone with you, Welcome stranger," continued St. Clair.

Crockett stuck out his hand and the strong hand of Alex St.Clair gave him a good shake.

Alex St.Clair looked back at Brother Robert Sheffey and asked, "have you had your supper yet?"

"No but let us have family devotions first and thank our dear Lord that He has brought us back together again."

Brother Sheffey sent a boy out to get his Bible from his saddle bag, and when he returned he gathered the neighborhood children about him and opened the Bible. Crockett was amazed as Brother Sheffey turned to the Psalms, and read, "O come, let us sing unto the Lord: let us make a joyful noise to the rock of our salvation."

When he had finished his devotion he blessed all the children by name and asked them to go back to their homes, fore it was beginning to get dark.

After a long passionate prayer for the household, the country, and many named petitions including Arminda, Crockett's babies, Eliza and little Edward Fleming Sheffey, Mrs. St.Clair brought out a plate of biscuits, butter, honey and a jar of huckleberry jam and set it before Sheffey and Crockett.

"Crockett, just look what the Lord has provided for us, through his dear servants, the St. Clair's.

"God is truly good to his children," Crockett said in a low voice.

The St.Clair's set down at the table to be with Brother Sheffey and Crockett. As they ate, the conversation turned to Crockett.

"Crockett, tell us about yourself, I see you still wear the uniform of a soldier" said the man of the house.

Between bites of the great biscuits and jam, Crockett said, "I am on my way home from the Pen at Point Lookout, heading to Baptist Valley over in Tazewell County.

"My wife and babies are waiting for me to come home from the war," Crockett exclaimed.

"God bless you Crockett," said Mrs. St.Clair.

CHAPTER 37

HOME AT LAST!

I am so glad you have overcome that place, so many young men died there, Mister St.Clair.

"I hate to judge but, if some folks don't seek the redemption of Christ they will bust Hell wide open for being a part of such places," said Mrs. St.Clair.

"Let's talk on more pleasant things interrupted Alex St.Clair.

"Yes, lets talk about Crockett getting home to his family and friends," said Mrs. St.Clair.

Crockett smiled and said, "The sooner the better."

"How long will it be, before you get there?" asked Alex.

"I guess bout three days, if I don't dilly dally too much," replied Crockett.

"Well you can head out in the morning, or wait till services is over and me and Gideon will escort you as far as Abbs Valley," said Brother Sheffey.

"How long will that be?" asked Crockett.

"After preaching and praising the Lord, we can eat our dinner and travel on over to another brother's house for the night and then I want to travel on to Tazewell County," answered Brother Sheffey.

I want to stop and visit every war widow and bereaved mother there and all the way back to Bland County, exclaimed Sheffey.

"I am beholding to you for helping me get home, but don't let me interfere with the Lord's work," replied Crockett.

"The sweet Lord has put it in my head to help you all I can, you are the Lord's work," answered Brother Sheffey.

Next morning after a good breakfast provided by God, through the St. Clair's, they all went to the Ebenezer Church for services. Sheffey led the way carrying his fleece that he always had with him. He used it whereever and whenever he prayed. He would throw it down on the ground or on the floor of a church and kneel on it while talking to God.

Brother Robert Sheffey was well known for his praying, and his faith. His prayers were answered, mostly instantaneously. Some say he was a poor orator, but people knew when he prayed things happened.

After a spirit filled service, the jubilant Sheffey led the way back to the St. Clair's home for dinner. Sheffey blessed the food, the house, and the people, and after eating they did not tarry there. As promised Sheffey saddled up Gideon and headed out towards Abb's Valley with Crockett riding and Sheffey leading. Brother Sheffey had a special glow about him as he walked along the mountain road.

Crockett felt bad for riding, but he was weak from the ordeals of the war and the pen at Point Lookout. Crockett prayed a special prayer of thanks for putting Brother Sheffey here to help him. He prayed for Brother Sheffey and his work.

As promised Brother Sheffey escorted Crockett all the way into Abb's valley, where Crockett would leave him. Crockett was so amazed at the reception Brother Sheffey got everywhere he went. The children would be the first to reach him when he came into a little community.

He was well loved by Gods people and feared by sinners. Even un-churched folks would seek him out in times of trouble, but the bootleggers and such gave him a wide berth. Folks relayed to Crockett by testimony, of the miraculous answers received after Brother Sheffey prayed. He walked with God and believed God and God answered his prayers.

It was related to Crockett in a story by Allen Newberry one of Brother Sheffey's flock, about a bootlegger Sheffey had confronted. Sheffey had gone to the bootlegger to try to get him to stop making the devil's drink that poisoned some husbands that were otherwise good men. The bootlegger took offence and knocked Sheffey to the ground. Sheffey was on his knees before the brute, and blood flowed from his nose. Sheffey lifted his hands toward heaven and prayed for a big oak tree to fall on the mans still. There were no oak trees close to the still. A few days later Sheffey met the bootlegger on the road with a wagon filled with his belongings.

Front: Rachel and Rhoda Whitt (sisters to Crockett), Jonas Whitt.
Back: Mildred Trutt. The boy is thought to be David Crockett Whitt.

The man pointed at Brother Sheffey and said, "Preacher you have put me out of business."

"What do you mean?" asked Brother Sheffey.

"You prayed for a big oak tree to fall on my still, and the wind blew one down, way up on the ridge, it rolled all the way down into the holler and crushed my still," he said in a humble voice.

"Praise God," said brother Sheffey as he watched the man travel down the road.

Then Brother Sheffey took time to pray for the bootlegger to come under conviction and accept Christ as his personal savior.

There were hundreds of stories and testimony about God working miracles through his servant Brother Robert Sheffey.

As Brother Sheffey and Crockett parted in Abb's valley they embraced and had a prayer. Brother Sheffey told Crockett that he would come through Tazewell County from time to time and hoped to see him again.

"If I hear of you being round about we will come and hear your preaching, you are always welcome at my house," Crockett said sincerely.

"Thank you Crockett, I go where the Lord leads me, and I hope he leads me your way again." answered Brother Sheffey.

Crockett headed down the valley towards home and Sheffey went about doing the Lords work. Crockett was a stronger Christian for knowing Brother Robert Sheffey.

The next day Crockett walked into his little farm with his unkept beard and hair, still wearing the ragged dirty gray uniform of the Confederacy. His looks did not matter to Arminda and his little sons. He was home safe and alive. Crockett could be cleaned up and nourished now that he was in the loving arms of his little family. Crockett had not been home for more than ten minutes when he asked about his horse.

"Yes Billy is safe and sound, he is a little thin like the rest of us, John Luther Lowe, (nephew) ran and told me that the Yankee's were coming and I took Billy and what food I could carry to the woods," exclaimed Arminda.

"Bless your heart, I wish I could have been here for you," Crockett stated.

The grave of Jonas Whitt. Big White Oak Creek. Greenup County, Kentucky.

"John, is that Rhoda's little boy?" asked Crockett.

"Yes, but he is getting to be a purty big boy now," replied Arminda.

I just had got back to the house when three of them stealing devils showed up wanting to carry off anything they could, One came through the house while the others collected the mules, cow, and whatever else they could get," Arminda explained.

"The one in the house got fresh with me, I slapped the hell out of him and he went out laughing trying to hide the pain," she said. "Dammed Yankee, I wish I would have been here for you," replied Crockett.

"I'm not, they would have killed you," answered Arminda

"Sorry I flaired up like that, but I love you and the boys so deeply, I am glad you are alright, we can survive without some things," Crockett said in a humble voice.

"Let's get you cleaned up," Arminda said as she went out and got the bathing tub and set it by the fire place. Next she put water in the big pot on the fireplace to heat up. She also brought in some water and poured it into the tub, and shaved off some soap to dissolve.

Crockett set there holding both of his boys, John Floyd four, and Jonas Lee two. Lee had never seen his Paw. The boys held on to their Paw with both hands, as they were afraid he would leave again.

"Don't worry boys, your Paw is home to stay!" exclaimed Crockett.

Arminda got the boys to turn loose of their Paw, so she could do some grooming on him. She sat him in a chair and put a cloth around is neck and went to work with her scissors and comb.

As the long hair and beard fell away she said, "I know my Crockett is hidden in this hair, somewhere."

Crockett laughed!

"Thank God, you are home safe and sound, when you didn't show up I got really worried," said Arminda.

"Isaac Puckett sent word by a man traveling with him that you should be let loose soon, as they went by the alphabet, the W's should come soon. At that point and time all I had was hope that you were still alive and would come home some day. I felt so relieved when he come and told me the news, so I have been looking every day," explained Arminda.

"Who was the man?" asked Crockett.

"Don't remember, he could have been an Angel of God," she said seriously.

Arminda continued her clipping and talked in between. She cut the beard as close as possible to make it easier to shave, and the hair on his head was also cut quite short.

Crockett looked at the hair on the floor and said, "I had a plenty didn't I sweetheart."

"You had a plenty," Arminda replied.

"Speaking of Angels, I met one on the road and he helped me plumb to Abb's Valley," Crockett said.

Arminda stopped cutting and looked at Crockett expectantly!

"His name was Brother Robert Sheffey, he provided for me and even insisted I ride his horse while he walked," exclaimed Crockett.

"Sheffey, I have heard of him, he has come through these parts a time or two. I heard he preached at the Pisgah Church," said Arminda.

Brother Sheffey was sent by God to help me home, I feel sure," exclaimed Crockett.

"I was weak as a kitten when I saw that dear saint helping a bug turn over," Crockett continued.

"What do you mean, turning a bug over?" asked Arminda.

"He even helps bugs, he says they are Gods creation and it is our job to help even bugs that need us," Crockett answered with a smile.

"Everywhere he went he was welcomed with open arms, even the little children ran to meet him," continued Crockett.

"I am sure God sent him to help you back to me, I love you so much Mister Whitt," exclaimed Arminda.

"Me too! And I love you and the boys, It was God's will for me to survive the war and also that hell hole, Point Lookout," answered Crockett.

"The boys, Crockett!" Arminda said reminding him of the young ears.

Crockett nodded his head in acknowledgement.

"That is exactly what it is!" Crockett affirmed.

"We have about three years to catch up on, I can't hardly believe I am actually home," said Crockett.

After the hair cut, Arminda put Crockett in the tub of warm water and the boys kept walking around holding the rim of the tub. They were not about to let their Paw too far from them. Arminda started fixing some supper, while Crockett soaked and entertained the boys. Arminda fried up some corncakes to serve with new honey. She also had a little salt back bacon for meat. That was about all she could give Crockett for his home coming meal.

After a clean shave, and bath Crockett put some of his old clothes on. He enjoyed the meal like it was a banquet. After eating Arminda put the old ragged dirty uniform in the fire, and Crockett smiled in agreement.

With supper over Crockett, the boys, and Arminda walked out to the fence to see Billy. Billy came running up to the fence and gave Crockett a good looking over. Crockett laughed as he saw Billy trying to figure him out. Billy was not sure of him, but he trusted Crockett to pet his face.

Crockett pulled a big handfull of red clover and feed his horse.

"I wish it were oats big boy, but this will have to do for now," exclaimed Crockett.

"I hope you wouldn't mind, but you will have to help the family by pulling the plow, we will all have to pull our weight to get this place agoing again," explained Crockett.

Billy didn't understand, but he soon would. Crockett would have to teach Billy the facts of life on a one horse farm, as much as both would hate it.

After the family went back to the house, Arminda had to give Crockett some bad news. She had put it off until now not wanting to upset the homecoming. She went to the Bible and pulled out a letter from Emma Stephenson, Crockett's sister in Greenup County Kentucky.

"Sweetheart, I hate to give you more bad news, but here is a letter you need to read," said Arminda.

Crockett looked at the envelope and immediately knew the hand writing and saw that it was from Kentucky. He took the letter and sit down to read it. He read it at least twice, and looked at Arminda with tears in his eyes.

"My Paw, passed away on July 2nd, this letter come in a hurry," Crockett exclaimed.

"I just got it today just about an hour before you got here," explained Arminda.

Emma said that he died suddenly, thought it was a stroke, and Jonas did not suffer other than his rheumatism and old age.

"She was also inquiring of me," Crockett said.

"I am so sorry you didn't get to see your father again, you will have to write Emma soon," replied Arminda.

"I will write her tomorrow, after I get some things done," answered Crockett.

As the shadows grew long in Tazewell County, Crockett was content, but exhausted. He was ready to sleep in his bed with his wife, both of the boys wanted to sleep with their Paw. Crockett and Arminda let them lay on the bed with them for awhile and then put them to bed in their own bed. Arminda curled up in the arms of her husband for the first time in over two years, but there was no love making that night. In time Crockett would be himself after nourishment and rest.

Crockett fell into slumber still holding Arminda. After a few hours of sleep the demons of war paid Crockett a visit. He began to jerk and speak un-audiable sentences, and Arminda held him tightly. He dreamed that he was on a battle line and the enemy was bearing down on him. He seemed to be alone, yet among a multitude of soldiers. There was nothing he could do to stop the blue line of devils trying to kill him. Finally Crockett fired his last shot and ran as fast as he could screaming for someone to help.

Arminda shook him gently, and said in a soothing voice, "you are alright, you are alright, you are home and nothing can hurt you anymore."

Crockett became coherent as Arminda spoke. He was bathed in great drops of perspiration and trembling. Arminda held him tightly and continued to reassure Crockett that he was safe and sound.

"Sweetheart, you are home," she kept telling him.

"Oh thank God, I am so thankful to be here at home and have such a loving wife," Crockett answered.

"Now just relax and go back to sleep, I will hold you all night," answered Arminda.

"Thank you my loving wife, pray that I don't dream anymore tonight," pleaded Crockett.

"I will, you just get some rest now, you will be alright now," answered Arminda.

As Crockett drifted off to sleep, Arminda lay awake awhile wondering how she could help her husband resolve his post traumatic stress syndrome. Of course they never called it that back then, it was shell shock or war demons. It would take prayer, time, and tender love for Crockett to get over this. He would always have reoccurrences from time to time even into his senior years, but the worst would pass away.

The next morning Crockett awakens in his own bed in his own home. He looks around and smiles. He shuts his eyes and opens them again, and smiles again at what he beholds. I am truly home is his first thought. He whispered a prayer of Thanksgiving!

"Arminda, wake up, I am really home!" exclaims Crockett.

"I know dear," she answered sluggishly.

"Did you get any rest?" Crockett asked.

"Got some after I finally went to sleep," she answered.

"How about you, did you get some rest sweetheart?" Arminda asked.

"I must have, after I had that terrible dream, I feel purty good this morning," Crockett answered.

The boys came into the room about half asleep, little Lee dragged his blanket along behind.

"Paw we are up," said the older son Floyd.

"Good morning boys, jump up here in bed with your Maw and Paw," Crockett said.

The smiling boys climbed up into the bed and Crockett hugged them both with his long loving arms. Then He reached back and included Arminda in the family hug. The little boys laughed and frolicked in the bed until Crockett said, "Everybody get up!"

Arminda cooked up some porridge for breakfast, while Crockett walked around the little cabin looking at every detail. He wanted to soak it all in little by little, and the boys followed him about looking around too. Crockett noticed them imitating every move, then he made a game of it. He would scratch his head, then he would bend way back and look at an object. Both boys did the same thing, just like their Paw.

He reached around and scratched his behind, turned quickly and asked? "Is your tail itching boys?"

All four laughed out loud, in amusement, as he caught them scratching their behinds.

After breakfast was over Crockett went out and saddled up Billy. He was going to take a little ride around the place and see what improvements could be done. He also wanted to ride over to the cemetery where his Maw Susannah, Grand Maw Rachel, and Grand Paw Hezekiah were buried. He also rode by the John Bunyon Lowe place to see Rhoda and all the family. He also stopped at the old Hezekiah house to see Aunt Nancy, the widow of Uncle James Whitt. He didn't spend too much time, but he wanted them to all know he was home safe.

Billy performed well, being as he had not been rode much in the past two years. Crockett rode back to the house and saw Arminda getting her wash tub out to do some washing. He rode Billy up close and talked for a minute while sitting in the saddle.

"Think I will take a little ride into Indian and over by the mill, might be I can get some work doing some milling," Crockett said.

"Do you feel up to it?" asked a concerned Arminda.

"I feel purty good this morning, might ort to do it now fore I run out of steam," Crockett answered.

"Steam, what does that mean?" asked Arminda.

"Oh, that was a term I learned in the war, when the engine got low on coal, it would run out of steam and could not pull the cars," Crockett explained.

"This morning I seem to have energy, but later in the day I may run short of energy," Crockett continued.

"I understand, the boys run me out of steam most every day," Arminda confessed.

"You go on and take your ride, might be that you can find some work," said Arminda.

"Just be careful and don't tire yourself out," she continued.

Crockett headed down Indian Creek to the Clinch River, then turned Billy upstream through the village toward the McGuire grist mill. Crockett spoke to several folks around Indian, but most didn't recognize him.

Crockett felt free as a bird as he and Billy made their way up the narrow road by the wonderful Clinch. Billy even picked up on Crockett's grand spirit. Billy seemed to have a little extra bounce in his gait.

"Billy, this is the day that the Lord hath made, let us rejoice and be glad in it," Crockett said.

Billy didn't know what he said but he loved the tone and he loved having Crockett back on his back. Crockett petted his big red horse as they rounded the big bend in the river. There it was, McGuire's Mill and Mercantile just ahead. There were no wagons or horses tied by the mill, which was very unusual. Crockett steered Billy right up to the hitching rail and dismounted.

"Billy you stay here and wait for me," Crockett said as he tied a quick half hitch.

Billy acknowledge the command with a little head shaking. Then Crockett went into the mill. Mister Elijah McGuire was standing there scratching his head as Crockett walked up. Elijah McGuire turned and saw Crockett. He stuck out his hand as he instantly recognized Crockett. Crockett took his hand and gave him a good shake.

"My God, you are an answer to prayer, I don't have anybody that can dress and grove the mill stones and she has been out of alignment for a year or, maybe two," said the excited Elijah McGuire.

"Well here I am, believe it or not I just come to see if you might need a miller," Crockett said.

"Praise the Lord them Damn Yankee's didn't kill you Crockett," continued Elijah McGuire.

"Well it ain't cause they didn't try," said Crockett thinking out loud.

"Glad you made it home son, how did you find your family?" asked Elijah McGuire.

"Oh I knew right where I left them," said Crockett with a wide grin.

Elijah McGuire looked puzzled for a moment, then burst out with a chuckle.

"Well Crockett you still have that wit about you, must be how your folks got their name," he said.

"Crockett I can't pay much, but if you will get the old mill up and running, I will keep you in corn meal and flour all winter, and a little cash too," said McGuire.

"Let me take a look at her, I didn't think about working today," Crockett said.

"Well son you get me a list of tools and such and then you can come back tomorrow!" said the anxious Elijah McGuire.

Crockett looked over everything and gave Elijah McGuire the list and also told him he would need some help every now and then as he worked the stones. Elijah McGuire told him he would be there to help, and if needed he could get another man.

"Alright then, you get the block and tackle, grease, and other tools together and I will be here about eight in the morning, if that is alright with you," Crockett said.

"That is fine, by the way could you use some flour and mill to take with you today?" asked Elijah McGuire.

"Sure could, Arminda will welcome it," replied Crockett.

"Crockett how is your Paw Jonas a doing? Asked Elijah McGuire.

"He passed on to glory, just got the letter yesterday," Crockett said in a somber tone.

"Sorry to hear that Crockett, He was a fine man and a good mill right too," replied Elijah McGuire.

"You know he helped build this mill for my Grand Paw William McGuire didn't you?" asked Elijah.

"Yes sir, I remember Paw talking of your Grand Paw and all the McGuire Family, all good I will add," explained Crockett.

"Wait right here, I will get you some flour and good old yellow meal," continued Elijah McGuire.

He handed Crockett a five pound turn each of flour and meal and patted Crockett on the back.

"My God Crockett, you ain't got no meat on them bones, Arminda will have to fatten you up!" he exclaimed.

"You wait one more minute out by your horse, I got something else for you Crockett," Elijah McGuire said as he walked away.

Crockett tied on the mill and flower and was waiting patiently when Elijah McGuire came around the corner with about a peck of sweet potatoes and a sack containing two cabbage heads and some early green beans from the garden.

Elijah McGuire helped Crockett tie everything in place and told him, "I will see you in the morning friend,"

"Thank you so much Mister McGuire," Crockett responded.

"Just glad to help, besides that I expect to get some good work out of you just like before the war," declared Elijah McGuire.

"You know I will do my best, see you around eight in the morning," Crockett said as he and the loaded Billy headed back down the Clinch.

Crockett reached home tired but jubilant. He showed Arminda all the food he brought home. He explained that Mister McGuire was needing someone to fix up the old mill. He said that I was a Godsend.

"Oh my, I will let you and Billy go out riding everyday," said Arminda with a chuckle.

"Are you able to do the work?" asked the concerned Arminda.

"Yes I think so, I will have to be, I will just ease into it" replied Crockett.

"I think I will sit in the shade the rest of the evening, why don't you and the boys join me?" asked Crockett.

"That will be a good idea, you need to store up some steam for your work, promise me you will pace yourself," answered Arminda.

Crockett unsaddled Billy and turned him out into the pasture. He got his writing paper, ink, and pen and sit down under their shade tree on an old blanket. Arminda brought out a pitcher of cool water and some cups, and joined Crockett with the boys. They talked for awhile and enjoyed the breeze coming down the valley. They enjoyed about an hour of family time while Arminda stringed and snapped the beans she would cook tomorrow. After Arminda finished the beans she went to the kitchen to get something prepared for supper.

The boys played about in the yard until little Lee conked out on the blanket for a nap. And little Floyd entertained himself with some sticks he had gathered up. Crockett watched him between writing his letter to Emma and the folks in Truittville, Kentucky.

Crockett wrote a nice long letter asking many questions about all the family in Kentucky, and told them about being in the war and the tour in the pen at Point Lookout. He did not go into detail as to how bad it had been, but expressed his joy of being home. He also expressed his grief of Jonas passing, before he could see him again.

After supper, Crockett and his family walked around looking over the garden and what Arminda had been able to plant. He was amazed at how well she had been able to keep things going while he was gone. The garden had few weeds, and was well hoed. The big cornfield was also coming along even though it was not as big, or well tended as Crockett would have kept it if he could have been home.

"Sweetheart, you have done wonders, with no one here to help you," replied Crockett.

"I had to, we had no one to help, except John Luther helped me do the early plowing before the Yankees carried off the mules," Arminda answered.

"I am so sorry you had to go through that, there are so many people that used the war for an excuse to commit all kinds of atrocities," Crockett said.

"I worry about Virginia, the Republican Congress is bent on revenge, I don't think President Johnson can hold them down," exclaimed Crockett.

"I heard that Lincoln was going to welcome all the states back in the union, he wanted liberty for all and malice toward none," Arminda said.

"President Johnson is trying to follow that plan, but the trouble makers will get their way, I am afraid," said a somber Crockett.

"We just have to pray and do our part to heal the land," answered Arminda.

"Things are going to work out for us, I already have some work, and you have kept things together while I was gone," Crockett said.

"We never gave up, and now you are home again," said Arminda.

"I have had many close calls, but it was the sweet Lord's desire that I live," said Crockett.

"He has a plan for us, but I know not what," said Arminda.

"We better get in and get ready for bed," said Arminda as she squeezed Crockett's hand.

After the couple expressed their love they drifted off to sleep, and there were no war demons this night. Crockett woke up more refreshed than he had in months. Today he would go and get started on the mill repairs for Elijah McGuire. Everything sure looked better in the mountains of Tazewell County along the beautiful Clinch River.

Crockett was up early and ready for the new day. He ate a little breakfast, saddled Billy and headed down Indian Creek.He had packed a few favorite tools and was looking forward to the job. Crockett only hoped he would be physically able to do the work, another month in Point Lookout may have caused his demise. Thank God he was free and back home, was Crockett's thinking.

David Crockett Whitt gradually regained strength and was able to enjoy work and living. He would never be the strong young man he once was. The war and the stay at Point Lookout sucked his vitality away and left him a weaker man for the rest of his life.

He would be able to do a days work but it would tire him as much as a middle aged man. Crockett was not yet twenty nine, but he would deal with arthritis and low stamina to his dieing day. Of course Crockett would adapt and he and Arminda would have a good life, and raise eight children. He would be considered poor by most, but he was rich in many ways. He was able to provide for the needs of his family. He was also a man that would live by the instruction of God's Word.

Tazewell County was isolated somewhat because of the mountains, which brought folks out of North Carolina and Eastern Virginia to shed themselves of the Northern Carpetbaggers & Scalawags. After President Johnson was quenched by the vengeful Republican Congress, the North ruled the Southerners with an iron hand. Many folks moved deep into the Mountains to seek a more serene life.

CHAPTER 38

HOW IT WAS

The years of reconstruction were hard and seemed forever. Everything was scarce in the South, including money. Jobs were rare, and if you found work it paid little. Most folks got paid by barter. You do this for me, and I will do that for you, or take pay in food or goods.

Crockett was fortunate to have many abilities. He had learned building and mill work from his father Jonas Whitt. He was quite literate, compared to most folks in southwest Virginia. His family had made him learn, and while he lived in Kentucky, Mister Samuel Truitt taught him the art of hand writing. He also understood how the Government works and knew a lot of history of this new country. Even with all of his skills and talents, making a living after the war was a great challenge. The price of commodities were quite cheap, yet people could not get the money to buy them.

Here is some true examples of the barter system used by the folks in the post war era:

Crockett Whitt to Lue Kinorick;

To 15 ½ lbs Bacon at 12 ½ per lb $1.93 ¾
To 1 pk. Of seed corn   .12 ½
To Plowing horse one day   .25
To grazing one horse 2 months $3.00
To Bacon 13 lbs $1.62 ½

Total $6.93 ¾
Credit Total $2.85
Total owed   4.08 ¾

By 2 ½ days work	$1.25	
fixing fence and gate	.25	
making sled	.75	
cutting wood	.40	
threasing wheat	+ .20	
total	$2.85	

Amount Due Dec. 29, 1880 = $4.08 ¾

Some other items priced in Cedar Bluff in the year of 1881.

3 ½ yds. of Calico	.25
½ doz. Buttons	.05
Ammunition	.15
1 Halter	.75
1 Bill & Cury Comb	.40
2 Pair of shoes	$3.00
2 spools ?	.15

The above was taken from actual postings on a ledger for David Crockett Whitt. Did you take note of the wages for working 2 ½ days? Paid only $1.25. Making a Sled paid only .75 cents. Fixing fence and gate paid only .20 cents.

Now we can understand why it was so hard to buy things in the South during the post war era! But with all that Crockett had been through, he could deal with the pains of reconstruction. He had Arminda and she had him to lean on. They looked for the day to day pleasures of simple living!

Another Ledger from September 20th 1892.

Mr. D. C. Whitt bought of E. McGuire and Son.

Cedar Bluff, Virginia	Debit	Credit
Aug 5 To 2 shirts for W. Johnson	$1.10	
Aug 5 To Tobacco W. Johnson	.10	
Aug 5 To (?) W. Johnson	.18	
Aug 25 To 1 suit of clothes	$7.75	
Sep 20 To 2 coats for boys	$3.00	
Sep 20 To Cash		$5.00
Oct 3 To Bal on pr of boots	$2.75	

David Crockett Whitt and Arminda Robinett Whitt

About 1910, Crockett's children and grandchildren.
Charles Henry Whitt took the photo.

McGuire Mill in Cedar Bluff, Virginia. Crockett worked here.

McGuire Mill in Cedar Bluff, Virginia.

Oct 11 To 2 pr Boy Boots	$3.12	
Dec 21 To Bacon & Coffee	.50	
Jan 6 Crushed corn for R.H McGraw	.33 $^{1/3}$	
Feb 11 Ground Corn		.45
April 1 Ground Wheat		.50

Total Over$ 18.50   6.28

I don't have the other page of this ledger. You will have to draw your own conclusion about William Johnson. The E. McGuire And Son refers to the Mill and Mercantile owned by Elijah McGuire mentioned earlier.

Crockett was in the trap created by the circumstance of war and reconstruction! He was unable to get enough money together to purchase his own land, yet the Federal Government subdivided plantations and gave forty acres and a mule to many Freedmen. It took Crockett thirty four years after the war to get money together so he could finally purchase land. He bought 20 ½ acres from his brother in law for the sum of $216.05. Below is a detailed description of this transaction.

This deed made this 2nd day of September 1899 between Silas H. Robinett and Elizabeth his wife of the first part, and David C. Whitt of the second part. Witnesseth that for and in consideration of the sum of $216.05 in hand paid by the party of the second part, to parties of the first part, the receipt whereof is hereby acknowledged by the parties of the first part. The parties of the first part have granted, bargained, and sold, and by these presents do grant, bargain, sell and convey to the party of the second part, a certain tract, piece, or parcel of land, situate lying and being in the County of Russell, on the waters of Swords Creek, and bound as follows.

Beginning at a dogwood on the side of Stone Mountain and come to the lands of said Whitt, and with two of his times S57 E33 poles to two hickories corner to said Whitt's land S73/4W60 poles to a locust on top of Stone Mountain and along the top of said mountain 57 9/10 poles to a locust and

*red oak, then leaving the top of said mountain N8 E 26 poles
and 6 feet to a locust, S 79 1/2 E 17 poles to a point of a cliff
N21 ½ E 57 poles passing over and through the head of a
spring (so as to divide the water) to the beginning containing
20.52 acres.*

*And the parties of the first part covenant with party of the
second part that they will forever warrant and defend the title
to the lands hereby conveyed, against the claims of all persons
whomsoever. Witness the following signatures and seals.*

   Elizabeth Robinett
    Silas H. Robinett
    County of Russell to wit:

*I Jonathan Boyd, a justice of the peace for the county
aforesaid in the State of Virginia do certify that Silas H.
Robinett and Elizabeth his wife whose names are signed to
the writing above bearing date on the 2nd day of September,
1899, have acknowledged the same before me in my county
aforesaid. Given under my hand this 3rd day of October
1899.*

Jonathan Boyd JP

So at the age of 62, almost 63, Crockett and Arminda now own
their own land bought and paid to Arminda's brother Silas. What a
freedom this was for the couple. Only 20 ½ acres but it was theirs to
do with as they chose.

Crockett always dreamed of having his own place so he could have
an apple orchard and grape vines. He could have more permanent
things and make changes without asking some land owner. Now he
is the landowner, even though he is getting old and not in the best of
health.

Silas Robinett, Arminda's brother, knew that Crockett and Arminda
needed a place of their own so he cut off a piece of his land and sold
it to them.

Crockett and Arminda both deserved to have a little farm after going through all that they had to endure. They were always there to lean on each other. The hard years of reconstruction was difficult to say the least. I will not delve into the details of this in this account, but will later if there is a latter days book for Crockett and Arminda.

As I reflect back on all the times and happenings of David Crockett Whitt, it is a wonder that I am here writing this book. It was the sweet Lord's desire for Crockett to survive the many battles, hardships, and cruelty of Point Lookout. Now I look at all of his descendents, and think of Father Abraham in the Bible. Crockett don't have as many as Abraham, but he has a lot that would not be here if he had not lived.

As I said earlier the Northern Troops received pensions from the United States, not that many years after the war. Crockett was a Confederate and his only pension or disability pay would have to come from his country, the defeated State of Virginia. By an act of the General Assembly of Virginia , approved April 2nd 1902, The Confederate Soldiers that are totally disabled because of service to Virginia in the war are able to gain a monthly payment to sustain them. All of which must be proven and backed up by witnesses and doctors.

David Crockett Whitt applied for his disability May 6th 1906. Doctor W. R. Williams gave him a physical and stated that Crockett was unable to earn a living by his usual vocation of manual labor. He had suffered Pneumonia and Typhoid during the war, due to exposure. Doctor Williams expressed that Crockett was almost totally disabled.

Crockett had to give names of men that served with him and still lived in the area. W. O. Lowe, Andrew Gross of Swords Creek, Joe Whitt of Lebanon, Va. were given by Crockett. Names of two witnesses of residence was H. L. Plaster and P. S. Robinett both of Russell County, Virginia where Crockett resided.

Crockett was described, in May 1906, as an old man of 69 and disabled from exposure. Crockett stated that he had Rheumatism and Catarrh. (inflammation of nose and throat) Crockett was awarded his disability shortly after the 8th of September 1908, and drew a few checks of $18.00 per month before he passed away on 28 November 1909.

I believe David Crockett Whitt to be a great man by the life he lived. He did no great acts alone, but his life and enduring, has left a Legacy that will live on through the blood of his many offspring.

The Descendants of David Crockett and Arminda Robinett Whitt are listed below and is not a complete list. I have searched for all of them but some have not surfaced at the printing of this book. (1. first generation, 2. second generation, 3. third generation and so on.)

1. John Floyd Whitt married Mary M. Honaker.
 2. William Floyd Whitt married Dora Ethel Day.
  3. Hazel M. Whitt
  3. Helen Delcie Whitt married Winfred Elmer Justice.
   4. Phyllis Justice married Gary Miller.
   4. Joan Justice married Herbie Ball.
   4. Joyce Justice married Tom Harmon.
   4. Earl Justice married Peggy.
   4. Carl Justice married Marlys
   4. Mike Justice married Ann.
   4. Larry Justice married Mary.
  3. Olaf L. Whitt married Clarence Boyd.
  3. Dorothy Pearl Whitt married Stevens.
  3. William F. Whitt married Loretta.
  3. George Harold Whitt married Maxine.
  3. Jack Herbert Whitt married Dorris Wells.
   4. Scott Whitt
   4. Dane Whitt
   4. Bruce Whitt
  3. Glen Whitt
  3. Guy Whitt
  3. Ronald Whitt married Loretta
 2. Mary Belle Whitt married Grover Rakes.
  3. Stella May Rakes married Clarence R. Hicks.
 2. Jonas C. Whitt married Gladys.
  3. Douglas Whitt
  3. Garland Whitt
  3. Frazier Whitt
 2. Albert Jesse Whitt married Ava Elizabeth White.
  He second married Florence Euna Whitt.

      3. Ralph W. Whitt

      3. Willard R. Whitt married Laura.

      3. Donald J. Whitt married Rowena Howlett

          4. Rebecca Whitt married Conrad Brown.

              5. Amy Brown married Matthew Proctor

                6. Elias Proctor

      3. Thomas Whitt married Carol.

      3. Dean Whitt

2. Rosa Arminda Whitt married Charlie "Will" Byrd.

      3. William Herbert Byrd

      3. Mary Magaline Byrd

      3. John Harvey Byrd

      3. Robert Cornus Byrd

      3. Delora Mae Byrd

      3. Maude Byrd

      3. Grace Byrd

      3. Floyd Curtis Byrd married Bonnie Ellen Salyers.

      3. Clarence Byrd

      3. Emily Byrd

      3. Thelma Betty Jane Byrd

2. George Washington Whitt married Winnie Yates.

      3. Lucy B. Whitt married Shannon Webb.

          4. Garnet Webb

          4. Gaines Webb

          4. Betty Webb

      3. Waneta B. Whitt

      3. William Buford Whitt married Goldie Marie Peck.

          4. Connie Marie Whitt married
Kerry E. McGloghlin

              5. Ken Edward McGloghlin married
Marlene Beth Sparks

              5. Tina McGloghlin married
Brian Keit Keen

                6. Kerry Keen (Twin)

                6. Keith Keen (Twin)

      3. Hershel L. Whitt

2. Florence E. Whitt

1. Jonas Lee Whitt married Mary Virginia Robinson.
   2. George Dewey Whitt married Annie Marilyn Steele
      3. Kermit Leo Whitt married Mary Lou Johnson.
         4. John Bryan Whitt married Tamela Denise Cook.
            5. Bryan Austin Whitt
         4. Timothy Leo Whitt married Cynthia Sue Shrader.
            5. Lindsay Michelle Whitt
            5. Derek Troy Whitt
         4. Sherry Lynn Whitt married David Mark Harrill.
            5. Housan Gene Harrill
      3. Arville Phillip Whitt
      3. Geneva Largey Whitt
      3. Dortha June Whitt
      3. Edna Iris Whitt
      3. Edith Estelle Whitt
      3. Margaret Evelyn Whitt married unknown.
         4. Wayne
   2. Joseph E. Whitt married Eula.
   2. James (Jim) Whitt
   2. Walter Whitt married Elsie.
   2. Ada Samantha Whitt married Marvin Wade.
1. Margaret E. S. (Maggie) Whitt married Charlie Boston Steele.
   2. Walter Steele married unknown.
      3. Frank Steele
   2. Pearl Steele
   2. Ethel Steele
   2. Fred Steele
1. James Crockett Whitt married Maude B. Bishop.
   2. Clarence Whitt
   2. Florence Euna Whitt married Albert Jesse Whitt.
   2. Della Margaret (Mae) Whitt married Samuel Jackson Christian.
      3. Ruby Christian married Giles Sims, second married Frank Brewer.
      3. Harold Edward Christian married Nellie Lane.
      3. James Loyd Christian married Audrey Keith.
      3. Phyllis Lee Christian married James Floyd Gibson.
      3. Bobby Dean Christian married Patricia Ann Lambert.

4. Deanna Lynn Christian married Michael Faulk.
    5. Christopher Allen Faulk married
    Betty Joy White.
        6. Christopher Roland Faulk
        6. Melody Ann McKenzie
4. Deanna second married Ronald Walton.
    5. Bobby Jo Walton married Jason Cross.
        6. Ashley Nicole Cross
    5. Angela Margaret Walton
4. Deana third married Richard Russell.
4. Deana fourth married William Cross.
4. Deana fifth married William Baker.
3. Bobby Dean Christian second married
Elizabeth Dillon Barrett.
3. Bobby Dean Christian third married
Elizabeth Dillon Barrett.
3. Bobby Dean Christian fourth married
Charolyn Elaine Lowe
3. Dennis Ray Christian married Nancy Shafferman.
2. Thomas Albert (Abb) Whitt married Alice Gray White.
  3. Billy Eugene Whitt married Rose Marie Shannaberry.
    4. James Albert Whitt
3. Doyl Garrnett Whitt married Ruth Ann Bales.
    4. Connie Lynn married Claude Dotson.
        5. Joshua Alexander Dotson married
        Rebecca Griffith.
           6. Alexia Brooklyn Dotson
        5. Shannon Marie Dotson.
    4. Tamara G. Whitt
    4. Mark Dolye Whitt
    4. Christy Beth Whitt married Jimmy
Keith Absher.
        5. Ambern Nicole Absher
        5. Kelli Denise Absher
        5. Kristen Danielle Absher
3. Doyl Garnett Whitt second married
Norma Jean Goodie.

    2. Claudy W. Whitt

1. Mary F. (Mollie) Whitt married Rosco Statten Hall.

    2. Ocie Kathryn Hall

    2. Stanley L. Hall

    2. Paul B. Hall

    2. Hazel E. Hall

    2. Ethel C. Hall

    2. Lawrence C. Hall

    2. Virginia Ruth Hall

    2. Gertrude E. Hall

1. William J. (Bill) Whitt married Addie Richmond.

    2. Fred H. Whitt married Asia.

        3. Virginia Whitt

    2. Effie G. Whitt

    2. James C. Whitt

    2. William Frank Whitt

    2. Robert Whitt married Evelyn.

    2. Arthur Whitt

    2. Ralph Whitt

1. Milburn Robert Whitt married Mollie Alice Puckett.

    2. Rosania Armind Whitt married Albert Price.

        3. Joe Price

        3. Fred Price

    2. Rosania second married Jess Schrader.

        3. Betty Lou Schrader

        3. Norma Jean Schrader

        3. Shirley Schrader

        3. Lois Schrader

        3. Monk Schrader

        3. Vernon Schrader

        3. Fred Schrader

    2. Leara Magdalene Whitt married John Stinson.

        3. James Stinson married Wanda.

        3. Jean Stinson

        3. Robert Stinson

        3. Glen Stinson

        3. David Stinson

3. Hansford Stinson

2. Leary second married Tom Cook.

2. Raleigh Graham (Grim) Whitt married Euva Lorene Sparks.

    3. Janice Whitt married Rudy Wright.

    3. Alice June Whitt married Arthur W. Dailey.

        4. Kristena Elizabeth had a relationship with Pedro.

            5. Sophie Bryana Dailey

    3. Alice June second married Jacce Rush.

    3. Linda Whitt married Glenn Bremer.

        4. Brian Bremer

        4. Scott Bremer married Becky.

            5. Brett Bremer

            5. Bailey Bremer

            5. Bentley Bremer

            5. Bella Bremer

    3. Mary Whitt married Daniel Lawrence.

        4. Jarrod Lawrence

    3. Bobbie Whitt married Ann.

        4. Debra (Debbie) Whitt married Rick Zimmerman.

            5. Tiffany Zimmerman

            5. Lisa Zimmerman

            5. Blake Zimmerman

        4. Linda Whitt married David McCarthy.

            5. Becky McCarthy

            5. Katy McCarthy

            5. Sarah McCarthy

    3. Bill Whitt married Georgia.

        4. Tim Whitt

        4. Danny Whitt

        4. Michael Whitt

        4. Patty Whitt

    3. Richard (Rick) Whitt married Caroline.

    3. Jackie Ezra Whitt

    3. Pamela (Pam) Whitt married Alltop.

        4. Matthew Alltop

2. Robert Pascal Whitt
2. Leatha Martha Whitt married Otis Andrew Stinson.
 3. Jimmy Stinson married Patricia.
  4. Ira Stinson
 3. Steve Stinson
 3. Geraldine F. Stinson married Kenneth Nichols.
  4. Joyce Nichols married Howard.
  4. Charlene Nichols married Hueston.
 3. Margaret Stinson married John Anechiarico.
 3. Helen Stinson married Eugene Schrader.
 3. Mollie Stinson married Gifford Odom.
 3. Robert Daniel Stinson married Mary.
 3. Andy J. Stinson married Mary.
2. James Alderson (Fuzz) (Josh) Whitt married
Mary Sue Harmon.
 3. Mollie Alberta Whitt married James L. Scott.
  4. Barbara Scott married Don McCammack
  4. Lora A Scott married Brian Martin.
  4. Karen Scott married Jones.
  4. Jeffrey D. (JD) Scott married Patricia.
 3. James Garland Whitt married Peggy.
  4. Wayne Whitt
  4. Debbie Whitt
  4. Angela Whitt
 3. Janice Sue Whitt married Darwyn Nelson
 3. Judy Gail Whitt married Morphew.
 3. Gerald Ray Whitt twin
 3. Carol Gay Whitt married Edward H. Jones.
2. Wyniferd Francis Whitt married Edgar E. Bryant.
 3. Freeda Bryant married Kenneth Spencer.
 3. Rita Carol Bryant married Tom Pierce.
 3. Kenneth Bryant married Phyllis.
 3. Lonnie Ray married unknown.
  4. Christy Bryant married unknown.
   5. Jackie
2. Carol Lou Ellen Whitt married Frank L. Baxter.
 3. Brenda Baxter

3. Larry E. Baxter married Sue.

3. Sheila Baxter married Phil Altmeyer.

3. Frankie Darrel Baxter

2. Alice Whitt married Ralph Sparks.

    3. Sandra Sparks

    3. Connie Sparks

    3. Randall Sparks

    3. Paula Sparks

    3. Alisa Sparks

    3. Rejeania Sparks

2. Thomas Thurman Whitt married Alma Jean Cook.

    3. Alma Louise Whitt married Martin Koslucher.

    3. Harold Thomas Whitt married Shirley Koepke.

        4. Jennifer Whitt

        4. Kristian Whitt

        4. Kinsey Whitt

    3. Deloris Ann Whitt married Hill.

        4. Ericka Hill

        4. Lee Hill

    3. Leonard Thurman (Tiny) Whitt married Rhonda Gail Rhoads

        4. Jackson Thurman Whitt

        4. Tomas Leonard Whitt

    3. Marty Whitt married unknown.

        4. Ashlyn Whitt

        4. Amber Whitt

        4. Alexandrea Whitt

        4. Angelica Whitt

2. Isaac H. Whitt married Dolly.

    3. Juanita Whitt

    3. Milburn R. Whitt

    3. Elizabeth Whitt

    3. Isaac H. Whitt Jr.

    3. Paul William Whitt

    3. Amanda Grace Whitt

    3. Leara Jean Whitt

1. Charles Henry Whitt married Amanda (Mandy) Elizabeth Puckett.

2. William Henry Whitt married Annie M
    3. Alice F. Whitt
    3. Pauline Whitt
2. Ular Exie Whitt married William (Willie) Jesse Hess.
    3. Margery Jean Hess married Jack.
    3.Oma Exie Hess married Silas Miller.
    3. Roseann Hess married Leon Jennings Hale.
    3. Daphne Hess married Glen Stinson.
    3. Daphne second married Caroll Slate.
    3. William Harrison Hess married Betty Honaker.
    3. Arnold Wayne Hess married Betty Lou Belcher.
    3. Charles Ellis Hess married Lucy Ann Turner.
2. Pearlie May Whitt married Charles H. Jones.
    3. Daniel C. Jones
    3. Robert H. Jones
2. Marvin Bertran Whitt married Edith Lyle Fleming.
    3. Jerry Bertram Whitt married Etta Sue Gillespie.
        4. Melony Whitt married Michael Haun.
        4. Hollis Lyn Whitt
    3. Larry Paxton Whitt married Joan Greer.
        4. Rhonda Joann Whitt married Jason
        Van (Jake) Pittman.
            5. Jacob Paxton Pittman
        4. Marvin Larry Whitt married Geneva Mullins.
            5. Tyler Duvall Whitt twin
            5. Cassie Marie Whitt twin
        4. Kenneth Russell Whitt
        4. Teresa Carmen Whitt married
        Sean Michael(McCready) Jarrell.
            5. Sean Ryan Whitt-Jarrell
    3. Joseph Edward Whitt
    3. CHARLES DAHNMON WHITT Sr.
married Judy Ann Lawson.
        4. Charles Dahnmon Whitt Jr. married
        Carol Marie Ward.
            5. Denne' Lavonne Whitt
            5. Derek Tyler Whitt

        4. Charles Jr. second married Sarah Ford Hite.

        4. Jeffrey Kent Whitt married Susan.

            5. Jeffrey Claude Whitt

            5. Joshua Michael Whitt

    3. CHARLES DAHNMON WHITT Sr.
second married Sharon Cogan.

        4. Matthew Christopher Whitt

  2. Charles Robert Whitt

1. Charles Henry Whitt second married Liller Lee Simmons.

  2. Edward Franklin Whitt

  2. Billy James Whitt married Leah Osbourn.

      3. Deloris Whitt married Short.

      3. Leon Whitt

      3. Jeanie Whitt married Hamilton.

      3. Susie Whitt

      3. Keith Whitt

  2. David Eugene Whitt married Myrtle Lee Brown.

      3. Mike Whitt

      3. Mitzi Whitt

  2. David second married Betty.

  2. Ellis Ralph Whitt married unknown.

      3. Eddie Whitt

      3. Cloyd (Linda) Whitt married Lester.

  2. Madge Lois Whitt married Warren G. Mabe.

      3. Barbara Mabe married Thomas Busch.

        4. Aaron Busch

        4. Katie Busch

        4. Justin Busch

Grave of David Crockett Whitt. McGraw Cemetery. Russell County, Virginia (near Raven, Virginia).

ACKNOWLEDGEMENTS

Holy Bible, King James Version
Tazewell County, Virginia Court House
Russell County Virginia Court House
Greenup County, Kentucky Court House
Carter County, Kentucky Court House
The book, "Gray Ghost" the memoirs of Colonel John S. Mosby, edited by
    Charles Wells Russell.
The book, "Sheffey", The Saint of the wilderness, by Jess Carr
The book, "29th Virginia Infantry, by John Perry Alderman
The book, "The Frontiersman", by Allen W. Eckert
The book "The Hogs of Cold Harbor", by Richard Lee Fulgham, MA.
The book, "The Army of Robert E. Lee", by Philip Katcher
The book, "Thirty Myths about Lee's Surrender", by Patrick A. Schroeder
The book, "More Myths about Lee's surrender", by Patrick A. Schroeder
The Tazewell County Histotorical Society
The Greenup County, Kentucky Library
The Boyd County Kentucky Library
The Library of Virginia ,on line.
The Russell County Virginia Web Site, on line.
The United States Department of the Interior, National Park
Service, National Register of Historic Places.
Presidential History on line.
Point Lookout Southern Historical Society Pages, Vol. XVIII, Richmond,
Virginia. Jan.- Dec. 1890, Pages 114-120, on line.
The writing, "Outrage at Point Lookout", by Professor David Alan Black,
    June 18, 2003, on line.
The wikipedia free encyclopedia on line.
http://dahnmonwhittfamily.com on line.
Many other surfings on the free net.
Stories by word of mouth.
    Charles Henry Whitt
    Marvin Bertran Whitt
    David Eugene Whitt
    Jerry Bertram Whitt
    Larry Paxton Whitt
    Jesse Whitt
Articles and artifacts provided by Bobby Dean Christian.
Articles and artifacts provided by June Whitt.(Truitt Line)

Printed in the United States
152363LV00005B/3/P